Operations Research
in Production and
Inventory Control

Operations Research in Production and Inventory Control

by Fred Hanssmann

Technical Advisor in Operations Research

International Business Machines Corporation

Formerly Assistant Professor of Operations Research

Case Institute of Technology

John Wiley and Sons, Inc.

New York · London

Library of Congress Catalog Card Number: 62-10922

Printed in the United States of America

In thankfulness dedicated to my parents

WILHELM and EMMA HANSSMANN

Who through hard work made my education possible

Preface

This book developed from a graduate course "Production and Inventory Control" which is an integral part of the graduate program in operations research at Case Institute of Technology. I developed this course and taught it several times during the years of 1957–1960. The field of scientific production and inventory control has seen an enormous growth and evolution during these years and the entire decade. Only recently the growth of significant new concepts seems to have tapered off. I am indebted to Professor R. L. Ackoff, who first suggested that the field might be ripe for a systematic treatment; it was through his encouragement that I became interested in writing this book.

I have endeavored to write a *technical* book, but from the viewpoint of an *applied science*. Undoubtedly, the atmosphere at the Case Operations Research Group with its happy blending of technical competence and actual problem solving in empirical situations has contributed much toward the philosophy of this book. The purpose of operations research as viewed here is the solution of real problems, not the application of one's pet theory or technique. The use of mathematical theory and tools is justified only to the extent that it yields improved solutions of real problems. As long as over-all economics is a criterion, the cost of using sophisticated tools is as real as any other cost and must be considered in appraising the merits of such tools. For this reason alone, mathematical complexity often forbids itself, even when it is realistic; much more so complexity for complexity's sake. More will be said about this in the "Introduction." In any event, there are limits to the practical usefulness of a mathematical theory of production and inventory processes. In selecting the material for this book I have tried to stay within the limits of practical usefulness but, at the same time, to give a technically solid treatment of the selected material. I hope that I have succeeded in avoiding the two extremes of "cookbooking" and of irrelevant mathematical theory—irrelevant from the viewpoint of an applied science. Very little emphasis is placed on the mathematical solution of *formulated* mathematical problems. In all fields of applied science, the scientist rightly considers the mathematical formulation of his problems the major and more difficult part of his effort. The solution is, relatively speaking, routine. If necessary, it can be handled by mathematicians who need not be familiar with the particular field of application. For the reader who is interested in more detail about the mathematical aspects of the solution, numerous references are given. The book attempts to give a *systematic* coverage of the important concepts and problems in scientific production and inventory control, not a treatment of selected topics. The reader will also find a number of original developments which, to my knowledge, have not been published before. Of course, *errare humanum est*, especially in new areas.

The book is intended to serve both as a text and as an aid to the practitioner of operations research. The exposition is usually brief. When the material is supplemented by some numerical illustrations and exercises, it can easily be spread over two semesters. The major mathematical prerequisites of the course are calculus, algebra, and the elements of probability and statistics. Knowledge of queuing and linear programming techniques is also helpful. However, to make the book somewhat self-contained, the major mathematical concepts and techniques used in the text have been compiled without proof in a mathematical appendix.

I am indebted to Dr. Russel L. Ackoff, Director of the Operations Research Group at Case Institute of Technology, and Dr. Tibor Fabian, Director of the Management Sciences and Operations Research Division at Lybrand, Ross Bros., and Montgomery, for constructive criticism of the manuscript. Mrs. Grace White supervised most of the typing work with her usual competence and conscientiousness. Mrs. Juanita Robinson at the National Cash Register Company also typed parts of the manuscript.

FRED HANSSMANN

Dayton, Ohio
March, 1961

Contents

part IV: SERIES OF STATIONS

part V: APPENDICES

part I

INTRODUCTION

chapter 1
Principles of Approach

   This book gives an exposition of production and inventory control from the operations research viewpoint.   A key concept of operations research is the use of mathematical models for decision making. Therefore, mathematical models of production and inventory processes play a central part in this exposition.   On the other hand, somewhat paradoxically, the model performs only an auxiliary function in operations research.   Point of departure is the real world with its decision problems.   The goal is to arrive at a decision, and implement it in the real world.   What lies in between is a process of mapping the real world into a simplified model (conceptualization) and deriving solutions from it.   These steps are schematically illustrated by the closed loop in Fig. 1-1.   As a *research* activity, operations research does not comprise the actual execution of implementation; however, the *planning and control* of implementation are integral parts of operations research.   Furthermore, the research must always be conducted with a view to the feasibility of implementing research results.   In this sense, conceptualization, solution, and implementation are here viewed as necessary components of operations research.   If one of them is neglected, we are not longer dealing with operations research by our definition.   It is this concept of operations research which has guided the author in the selection of material and the distribution of emphasis in this book.

SELECTION OF MATERIAL

   The past decade has seen the growth of a vast literature occupied with a more or less mathematical treatment of production and inventory processes.   Many contributors to these publications use as their point of departure a mathematical model, and then proceed to derive mathematical solutions and study their properties in great detail.   In terms of Fig. 1-1, this is the solution phase.   The two other phases are quickly passed over or are lacking altogether.   As a well-known British

3

operations research leader has observed, "a verification of the model is a rarity"; he refers to this truncated activity as "sophisticated crystal-ball gazing" while another leader in the field condemns much of the operations research literature as "simply unscientific," for the same reason. The literature tends to give the impression that the relative weights of conceptualization and solution are 5% and 95%, whereas just the reverse allocation of effort is experienced in actual operations research work.

It is interesting to note a parallel in physics. Einstein, in his *Evolution of Physics*, makes this statement: "The formulation of a problem is often more essential than its solution which may merely be a matter of mathematics or experimental skill." The isolation of the solution phase in the literature has led to the production—one is tempted to say overproduction—of a large number of unverified mathematical "models," complex algorithms for optimal solutions, and existence proofs. It is clear that not all of this material is of interest from the operations research viewpoint. In this book, the following criteria for the selection of models have been used.

Realism

Emphasis is placed on models which have been verified by practitioners or—in the opinion of the author—have a fair chance of being verified. The concept of verification is rather wide. Direct verification may employ such means as statistical tests of goodness of fit

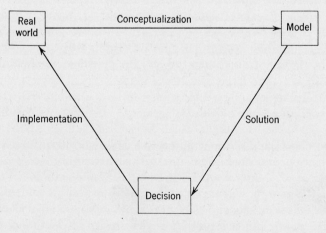

Fig. 1-1.

between the model and the real world; or it may secure executive agreement that the problem posed by the model is a fair image of the real problem. Indirect verification proceeds by proving that the solution derived from the model produces improved performance of the real system.

Possibilities of Implementation

Even relatively simple mathematical results usually pose great problems of implementation. Complex and involved algorithms for the solution of routine problems hold little promise of being implemented. Furthermore, the often substantial cost of using an involved procedure is ignored in work of this kind, whereas it is an important consideration in over-all optimization. The practitioner often solves this problem—somewhat intuitively—by using a simpler approximate solution. Unfortunately, we do not yet have a theory dealing with the seriousness of deviating from optimal solutions. However, practical experience has shown in many cases that the losses are extremely slight so that simple approximate solutions can be justified on economic grounds. Furthermore, the notion of an exact optimum does not appear to be very meaningful anyway in light of the crudeness of data and concepts. Finally, the time element and the smoothness of operations are essential considerations in practice to the extent that accuracy of the solution is sacrificed for them. For these reasons, preference is here given to simple solutions. Existence proofs are not dealt with at all. The researcher in applied science knows that his problems have solutions.

In summary, the author believes that some of the work published under the title of production and inventory control belongs into pure (not applied) mathematics. The fact that a topologist has a lot to say about trees does not mean that any of it is pertinent to landscaping.

In addition to the large number of mathematical models and solutions, the literature offers some contributions dealing with the conceptualization and implementation phases. It is far more difficult to give a systematic treatment of these topics than of mathematical models. The author has attempted to extract certain principles from the applications reported in the literature and from his own experience. A number of cases are discussed in order to show—however briefly— how practitioners have conceptualized real situations and problems into mathematical models. By and large, very little is known (or reported) about implementation. This material is found in the various chapters entitled "Applications."

DEFINITION OF THE PRODUCTION AND INVENTORY CONTROL PROBLEM

An inventory may be defined as an *idle resource* of any kind, provided that such resource has economic value. This implies that there is a *demand* for the resource. Demand is satisfied by *outputs* from the inventory. The inventory is replenished by *inputs*. Production may be defined as the process of input and/or output. We shall describe input and output by their respective rates $a(t)$ and $b(t)$ as functions of time t. If the inventory level at time zero is I_0, the inventory level at time t is given by the fundamental inventory equation

$$I(t) = I_0 + \int_0^t [a(\tau) - b(\tau)]\, d\tau \tag{1.1}$$

The rates $a(t)$ and $b(t)$ are not restricted to be finite but their time integrals are. Quite often, but not always, the output rate $b(t)$ is identified with the demand rate $r(t)$. Usually, the inventory function $I(t)$ gives rise to a so-called inventory-connected cost which by Eq. 1.1 is a functional of the production functions $a(t)$ and $b(t)$; the production functions themselves give rise to a production cost; and the mutual relationship of the demand function $r(t)$ on one hand and the output function $b(t)$ on the other hand determine the sales revenue and, perhaps, a penalty cost for failure to synchronize output and demand. In most general terms, the effectiveness of a production-inventory system during a certain time span is measured by a functional

$$E = E(a(t), b(t), r(t)) \tag{1.2}$$

of the input-output functions and the demand function. The functions $a(t)$ and $b(t)$ are under the control of the decision maker; less frequently, he may be able to manipulate the demand function $r(t)$, too, for example by price changes. Broadly speaking, the production and inventory control problem is concerned with finding functions $a(t)$, $b(t)$, $r(t)$ which maximize the measure E of system effectiveness, or some generalization of it. One of the most important generalizations is the replacement of E by its statistical expectation in the case of uncertainties in the system. The optimal functions must usually be found subject to certain restrictions. These may include the specification of classes of functions from which the optimal functions must be chosen.

By our definition of the problem, we have restricted ourselves to production-inventory systems. Pure production problems—such as production sequencing without any consideration of inventories—are not considered in this book.

CLASSIFICATION OF PRODUCTION-INVENTORY SYSTEMS

In order to give a systematic exposition, we shall classify production-inventory systems with respect to the following characteristics:

1. Topology.
2. Time behaviour.
3. Determinacy.

Beginning with characteristic 1, a production-inventory system can be conveniently illustrated by a network in which the nodes represent inventory stations and the links represent input and output channels (Fig. 1-2). The topology of the network could be further complicated by introducing alternative channels between nodes (e.g., different modes of production) and by permitting fusions of channels (e.g., combination of different raw materials into one finished product). The simplest possible system is a single station with single input and output channels. Most of the work to date is concerned with the

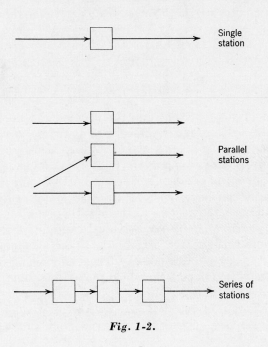

Fig. 1-2.

single station which is discussed in Part II of this book. If the output from one inventory station becomes the input to another, we speak of a series of stations. The individual stations determine the various levels of the series. If there are several stations on the same level, these are referred to as parallel stations. Parallel stations have received the most attention next to the single station. These are discussed in Part III while Part IV is devoted to series of stations. It appears that the topology of the system determines the basic mathematical structure of the control problem. Within a given topology we classify with respect to time behavior. A system will be called *static* if its parameters do not change in time, otherwise it is called *dynamic*. We further distinguish *deterministic* systems which contain no uncertainties from *probabilistic* systems whose indeterminacies can be described in terms of probability distributions.

MATHEMATICAL PREREQUISITES

Since relatively little emphasis is placed on the solution phase, routine applications of standard mathematical techniques have been omitted from the book. The reader will, therefore, find frequent instances where the discussion ends with a mathematical formulation of the problem or proceeds directly to the solution. To be able to verify the solutions, the reader should be familiar with elementary algebra and the differential and integral calculus for one and for several variables. Familiarity with the standard techniques for solution of assignment problems, transportation problems, and general linear programming problems will be helpful. It is felt that linear programming has become a standard tool over the years. Hence, there is no need here to add to the considerable introductory material already available in the literature. The most basic notions of probability theory and mathematical statistics, especially the notion of statistical expectations, are used throughout. Occasionally, more advanced mathematical results are given without proof, and the reader is referred to the literature. This is in accordance with the principal approach taken in this book which emphasizes the development of the model (conceptualization) and the discussion of the solution with a view to implementation. A short summary of the most frequently used mathematical facts and tools is given in the "Mathematical Appendix." This should make the book reasonably self-contained. The bibliography at the end of this chapter gives books and articles which deal with the inventory problem in some generality. The student may find these of interest as supplementary reading.

BIBLIOGRAPHY A

General

1. Arrow, K. J., Karlin, S., Scarf, H., *Studies in the Mathematical Theory of Inventory and Production*, Stanford, California: Stanford University Press, 1958.
2. Atwater, T. V. V., Jr., "The Theory of Inventory Management—A Review," *Naval Research Logistics Quarterly*, **1**, No. 4 (Dec. 1954), 295–300.
3. Barber, J. H., *Economic Control of Inventory*, New York: Cordex Book Company, 1925.
4. Bellman, R., *Dynamic Programming*, Princeton, New Jersey: Princeton University Press, 1957.
5. Bowman, E. H., Fetter, R. B., *Analysis for Production Management*, Homewood, Illinois: Richard D. Irwin, Inc., 1957.
6. Brown, Robert G., *Statistical Forecasting for Inventory Control*, New York: McGraw Hill Book Company, 1959.
7. Case Institute of Technology, *Proceedings of the Conference on Operations Research in Production and Inventory Control*, (Jan. 1954).
8. Churchman, C. W., Ackoff, R. L., Arnoff, E. L., *Introduction to Operations Research*, New York: John Wiley & Sons, 1957.
9. Dvoretzky, A., Kiefer, J., Wolfowitz, J., "The Inventory Problem," *Econometrica*, **20**, No. 2 (Apr. 1952), 187–222; *ibid.*, No. 3 (July 1952), 450–466.
10. Gourary, M., Lewis, R., Neeland, F., "An Inventory Control Bibliography," *Naval Research Logistics Quarterly*, **3**, No. 4 (Dec. 1956), 295–304.
11. Holt, C. C., Modigliani, F., Muth, J. F., Simon, H. A., *Planning Production, Inventories, and Work Force*, Englewood, New Jersey: Prentice-Hall, Inc., 1960.
12. Magee, J. F., *Production Planning and Inventory Control*, New York: McGraw Hill Book Company, 1958.
13. Moran, P. A. P., *The Theory of Storage*, New York: John Wiley & Sons, 1960.
14. Morse, P. M., *Queues, Inventories, and Maintenance*, New York: John Wiley & Sons, 1958.
15. Simon, H. A., Holt, C. C., "The Control of Inventory and Production Rates— A Survey," *Operations Research*, **2**, No. 3 (Aug. 1954), 289–301.
16. Vazsonyi, A., "Operations Research in Production Control—A Progress Report," *Operations Research*, **4**, No. 1 (Feb. 1956), 19–32.
17. Vazsonyi, A., *Scientific Programming in Business and Industry*, New York: John Wiley & Sons, 1958.
18. Whitin, T. M., "Inventory Control Research: A Survey," *Management Science*, **1**, No. 1 (Oct. 1954), 32–40.
19. Whitin, T. M., *The Theory of Inventory Management*, Princeton, New Jersey: Princeton University Press, 1953.

part II

THE SINGLE STATION

chapter 2
Static Deterministic Models

In the literature of recent years, a large number of elementary models for static, deterministic inventory processes has been considered (see Bibliography B). Quite often, these models are minor variations of each other, and their principal aspects are few. The great majority falls within the following framework of typical assumptions.

GENERAL FRAMEWORK OF
CONTINUOUS-DEMAND MODELS

1. Assumptions concerning the input-output mechanism:
   a. Demand is continuous at a constant rate r. As long as the inventory level is positive, the output rate is held equal to the demand rate.
   b. Inputs occur at discrete points or during discrete intervals in time and must be ordered L time units ahead of time. L is the lead time.
   c. Ordering time is to be signaled by a critical inventory level P, the reorder point.
   d. Input occurs at a constant rate p for a time span determined by the ordered quantity q. The possibility $p = \infty$ (instantaneous input) is admitted.
   e. Reorder point, input quantity, and time intervals between inputs are held constant in time.
   f. The process continues infinitely.
2. Assumptions concerning the measure of effectiveness (cost):
   a. There is a fixed charge s for each input (setup cost).
   b. There is a charge c per unit of input which may depend on the total input quantity q (quantity discounts, etc.).
   c. There is an inventory holding charge proportional to the time integral of the positive inventory level. The proportionality factor will be designated h. Less frequently, the inventory charge may be a more complex functional of the inventory

13

level and may depend on other parameters of the problem, such as the total input quantity q.

d. There is a shortage charge proportional to the absolute value of the time integral of the negative inventory level. The proportionality factor will be designated d. Here, too, more complex relationships have been considered. No demand is lost because of shortages (unfilled demand can be backlogged).

For such simple models, the inventory control problem becomes one of determining optimal values for the reorder point and reorder quantity.

THE SETTING OF REORDER POINTS

Let us assume that we plan for an inventory level I_0 immediately before inputs. Then we shall not reorder if the actual inventory A on the ground satisfies the relationship

$$A > R_L + R_t - Q_L + I_0 \qquad (2.1)$$

where

R_L = total demand during lead time L

Q_L = total input quantity during lead time L resulting from earlier orders

R_t = total demand during the "checking interval" t

The significance of the checking interval t is that orders can be placed only at equidistant points in time which are t time units apart. Equation 2.1 read at time zero says the following: If no additional order is placed now, the inventory level (before input) at time $L + t$ will still be greater than I_0. Hence, no order should be placed.

The quantity $S = A + Q_L$ may be viewed as a generalized stock level. In summary, the reorder point for the generalized stock level S is given by

$$P = I_0 + R_L + R_t \qquad (2.1a)$$

THE CLASSICAL ECONOMIC-LOT-SIZE MODEL

Turning to the determination of optimal reorder quantities, the classical economic-lot-size model offers the simplest example [59]. It assumes the simplest possible cost structure involving only set-up cost and inventory holding cost, and excludes the occurrence of negative inventory levels. Consequently, the inventory level immediately before inputs is $I_0 = 0$. This fixes the reorder point by Eq. 2.1a.

From the general assumptions 1a–1f, it follows that the inventory level $I(t)$ is a piecewise linear, periodic function of time (Fig. 2-1). For a full inventory cycle beginning at time $t = 0$, it can be written in the form

$$I(t) = \begin{cases} (p - r)t & \text{for } 0 \le t \le \dfrac{q}{p} \\[2mm] q - rt & \text{for } \dfrac{q}{p} \le t \le \dfrac{q}{r} \end{cases} \tag{2.2}$$

It follows that the inventory cost per cycle is

$$h \int_0^{-q/r} I(t)\, dt = \frac{h}{2} \frac{q^2}{r} \left(1 - \frac{r}{p}\right) \tag{2.3}$$

Consequently, the total cost of inventory and setups per unit time becomes

$$C = \frac{hq}{2} \left(1 - \frac{r}{p}\right) + s \frac{r}{q} \tag{2.4}$$

Differentiating with respect to q and setting the derivative equal to zero leads to the optimal reorder quantity (economic-lot size)

$$\hat{q} = \sqrt{\frac{2rs}{h[1 - (r/p)]}} \tag{2.5}$$

Of course, it is always assumed that $r < p$. Quite frequently it is permissible to set $r/p \approx 0$. Then, the inventory term in Eq. 2.4 takes the simple form $hq/2$. For the following models we shall make this simplifying assumption.

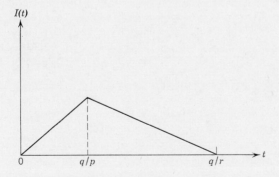

Fig. 2-1.

When the economic lot size, Eq. 2.5, is substituted back into the cost equation, Eq. 2.4, it is easily seen that the total cost per unit time associated with the optimal policy is

$$\hat{C} = \sqrt{2rsh(1 - r/p)} \qquad (2.6)$$

Fortunately, the cost is not very sensitive to deviations from the optimal ordering quantity [16,58]. The effect of incorrect data on cost is considered in [23,36,37].

THE CLASSICAL MODEL WITH SHORTAGES

If we allow the occurrence of shortages but otherwise maintain all features of the classical model, an additional degree of freedom is introduced [11]. After deciding on the period T between runs, we are still free to decide on the amount of shortage to be tolerated. At the same time, a cost of shortage has to be introduced since, otherwise, there would be no incentive for production. Let S be the stock level at the beginning of the inventory cycle (Fig. 2-2). The cost per cycle is composed of the cost of carrying an average inventory $S/2$ for t' time units, the cost of tolerating an average shortage $(q - S)/2$ for t'' time units, and the cost of one setup. Consequently, the cost per unit time can be expressed as follows:

$$C = \frac{1}{T}\left(s + h\frac{S}{2}t' + d\frac{q - S}{2}t''\right) \qquad (2.7)$$

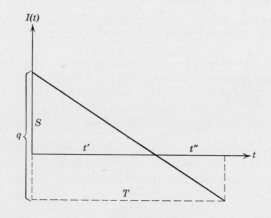

Fig. 2-2.

Substituting

$$t' = \frac{S}{r} \tag{2.8}$$

$$t'' = T - \frac{S}{r} = \frac{Tr - S}{r} \tag{2.9}$$

into Eq. 2.7 we obtain the cost function

$$C(S, T) = \frac{s}{T} + \frac{hS^2}{2rT} + \frac{d(rT - S)^2}{2rT} \tag{2.10}$$

The minimum can be determined by taking the partial derivatives with respect to the two control variables S and T. This yields the following results:

$$\hat{T} = \sqrt{\frac{2s}{rh}} \sqrt{\frac{h + d}{d}} \tag{2.11}$$

$$\hat{S} = \sqrt{\frac{2rs}{h}} \sqrt{\frac{d}{h + d}} \tag{2.12}$$

$$\hat{C} = \sqrt{2rsh} \sqrt{\frac{d}{h + d}} \tag{2.13}$$

It will be noticed that the cost of the optimum policy is smaller by the factor

$$\sqrt{\frac{d}{h + d}} \tag{2.14}$$

in comparison with the optimum policy for the classical model.

QUANTITY DISCOUNTS

As long as the charge c per unit of input is a constant, the total charge per unit time is fixed. Hence, there is no need to consider it in the cost model. We now turn to the case where c is a function

$$c = c(q) \tag{2.15}$$

of the input quantity q. Quantity discounts in purchasing furnish an illustration [11]. Maintaining all other assumptions of the classical model, the relevant cost per unit time becomes

$$C(q) = h\frac{q}{2} + s\frac{r}{q} + c(q)r \tag{2.16}$$

It is common to assume that

$$h = kc \qquad (2.17)$$

where k is a factor of proportionality. With this assumption we have

$$C(q) = \frac{1}{2} kcq + s\frac{r}{q} + c(q)r \qquad (2.18)$$

If $c(q)$ is a step function (as is the case with quantity discounts), then $c(q)$ can be treated as a constant c_i within each price range i. Let price range i be determined by the quantity range $l_i \leq q < u_i$. Then, the *local* minimum q_i of the cost function in range i is given by

$$q_i = \begin{cases} l_i & \text{if} & q_i{}^* \leq l_i \\ q_i{}^* & \text{if} & l_i \leq q_i{}^* \leq u_i \\ u_i & \text{if} & u_i \leq q_i{}^* \end{cases} \qquad (2.19)$$

where

$$q_i{}^* = \sqrt{\frac{2rs}{kc_i}} \qquad (2.20)$$

The corresponding minimum cost is

$$C_i = \begin{cases} C(l_i) & \text{if } q_i = l_i \\ C(q_i{}^*) = \sqrt{2rsh} + c_i r & \text{if } q_i = q_i{}^* \\ C(u_i) & \text{if } q_i = u_i \end{cases} \qquad (2.21)$$

The over-all minimum is found by selection of the smallest C_i. In practice, many simplifications are possible. A good approach is to find out for which price range $q_i = q_i{}^*$. Then all price ranges to the left can be excluded.

STORAGE COSTS AS A FUNCTION OF PRODUCTION COSTS

So far, we have treated the inventory carrying cost h as a constant. But since inventory carrying cost is usually computed as a fraction k of the unit cost of the product, and since the latter depends on the produced quantity q, the same is true of h. Let the variable production cost per unit be v. Then, the total production cost of a lot of size q is

$$s + vq \qquad (2.22)$$

and the unit production cost becomes

$$\frac{s}{q} + v \qquad (2.23)$$

Since the holding cost h is assumed to be a fraction k of unit production cost, we have

$$h = k \left(\frac{s}{q} + v \right) \tag{2.24}$$

Thus, total setup cost and inventory cost per unit time becomes

$$C = \frac{sr}{q} + k \left(\frac{s}{q} + v \right) \frac{q}{2}$$

$$= \frac{sr}{q} + kv \frac{q}{2} + \frac{ks}{2} \tag{2.25}$$

which leads to

$$\hat{q} = \sqrt{\frac{2rs}{kv}} \tag{2.26}$$

Obviously, only the variable cost v is relevant for the adjustment of the holding cost in the lot-size formula.

STEP FUNCTIONS FOR STORAGE COST

When storage space must be rented, it is likely that only fixed increments—corresponding to a lot-size q_0—can be rented. If the cost per

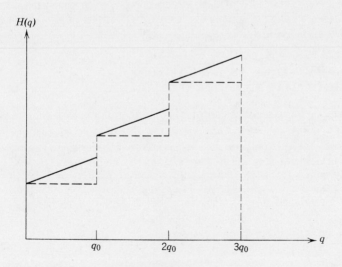

Fig. 2-3.

unit time of renting one increment is c_0, then the total storage cost per unit time will be (Fig. 2-3)

$$H(q) = \left[\frac{q}{q_0}\right] c_0 + \frac{h}{2} q \qquad (2.27)$$

where $[q/q_0]$ is the smallest integer $\geq q/q_0$, and q is the lot-size. Total cost per unit time of storage and setups becomes

$$C(q) = \left[\frac{q}{q_0}\right] c_0 + h \frac{q}{2} + s \frac{r}{q} \qquad (2.28)$$

This function can be minimized by analogy with the cost function for price breaks.

PRICE-DEPENDENT DEMAND

If the demand rate r depends on the sale price p per unit,

$$r = r(p) \qquad (2.29)$$

a second degree of freedom is introduced into the classical model: both the price p and the reorder quantity q become decision variables [60]. In this case the criterion for optimization is profit per unit time:

$$P = pr(p) - \left[s \frac{r}{q} + h \frac{q}{2} + cr(p) \right] \qquad (2.30)$$

where c is the unit production cost. The optimal lot-size for each given price level p is

$$\hat{q} = \sqrt{\frac{2sr(p)}{h}} \qquad (2.31)$$

and the profit associated with it is given by

$$P(\hat{q}, p) = pr(p) - \sqrt{2shr(p)} - cr(p) \qquad (2.32)$$

The optimal price may be obtained by maximizing this expression with respect to p. For illustrative purposes, assume

$$r(p) = ap + b \qquad (2.33)$$

where a and b are given constants. Then,

$$P = ap^2 + bp - \sqrt{2sh(ap + b)} - c(ap + b) \qquad (2.34)$$

By using the usual calculus approach, the following cubic equation for the optimal price $\hat{p}$ is easily derived:

$$8a^3\hat{p}^3 + (16a^2b - 8ca^3)\hat{p}^2 + (10ab^2 - 12ca^2b + 2c^2a^3)\hat{p} \\ + 2b^3 - 4cab^2 + 2c^2a^2b - sha^2 = 0 \qquad (2.35)$$

It may be solved by radicals or by numerical methods.

THE CLASSICAL MODEL FOR DISCRETE DEMAND (SLOW-MOVING ITEMS)

The idealization of continuous arrival of demand in time is quite reasonable as long as the quantities withdrawn from inventory at a time are small against the quantity produced or purchased at a time. But this assumption ceases to hold for "slow-moving items." Here, the classical economic-lot-size formula fails. On the other hand, economic-lot-size considerations may be particularly important for slow-moving items, including the question of whether the item should be stocked at all. We are thus led to adjust the classical model for discrete arrivals of demands.

Since we are dealing with static models, we assume that constant quantities a are demanded at constant time intervals with a frequency of n per unit time. Obviously, one will restrict the reorder quantity to multiples of the order size:

$$q = ka \qquad (k = 1, 2, \cdots) \qquad (2.36)$$

Furthermore, it can be assumed that input always takes place at one of the "demand points" in time. Consequently, the average inventory level is $a(k - 1)/2$, and the cost per unit time becomes

$$C(k) = \frac{ah}{2}(k - 1) + \frac{ns}{k} \qquad (2.37)$$

The optimization problem now becomes one of finding the particular integer $\hat{k} \geq 1$ which minimizes Eq. 2.37. Obviously, this is one of the two integers neighboring the real number

$$k^* = \sqrt{\frac{2ns}{ah}} \qquad (2.38)$$

The minimizing integer may be found by substituting both candidates in Eq. 2.37. Usually, the difference between the two alternatives is negligible, so that k^* may be rounded off to the nearest integer. The solution

$$\hat{k} = 1 \tag{2.39}$$

means that the item should be produced to order rather than stocked. Before determining $\hat{k}$ for a larger number of items by Eq. 2.38, it may be desirable to screen out those items which should not be stocked at all. Obviously, a necessary and sufficient condition for not stocking is that

$$C(1) \leq C(2) \tag{2.40}$$

or

$$ns - ah \leq 0 \tag{2.41}$$

This quantity can easily be tabulated for wide ranges of the parameters. Such tables may serve as useful screening devices.

CUTOFF POINT FOR SLOW-MOVING ITEMS

In large inventory systems with many active items it is often preferable to have a simpler rule for separating stock items from nonstock items.* Let n be the annual frequency of demand (number of orders) for an item. In the relevant range of slow-moving items, it may further be assumed that demand is for one unit at a time. In practice, it is common to use a rule of the following type:

If

$$\begin{array}{ll} n < j & \text{do not stock} \\ n \geq j & \text{do stock} \end{array} \tag{2.42}$$

The cutoff point j is the same for all items. How can it be optimally chosen? Assume that the system contains $f(n)$ items of annual frequency n. Furthermore, let the setup cost s be the same for all items. Then, the annual cost attributable to nonstock items is

$$\sum_{n=1}^{j-1} f(n)ns \tag{2.43}$$

As regards the stock items, we have to decide on an inventory policy. As in Eq. 2.37, we assume instantaneous replenishment at demand points. Then, the economic reorder quantity will generally be equal to two units in a certain range $n \leq N$ of slow-moving items. Adopting a reorder quantity of two units for all items in that range, Eq. 2.37

* A related problem is that of disposal of excess stock [52, 54]. See also Bibliography C, [43].

shows that the average inventory level will be 0.5 unit for all items. *If* $c(n)$ is the average value of an item taken over all items with frequency n, then $f(n) c(n)/2$ is the inventory investment in class n. The annual carrying cost will be assumed equal to a fraction k of the investment.

Since we order two units at a time, the annual setup cost in class n is $f(n) ns/2$. Finally, we assume that there is a fixed annual cost a associated with stocking an item. This cost may, for example, be interpreted as the cost of regular stock taking. Since we expect that $j < N$, it is sufficient to consider the cost attributable to all items with $n \leq N$. This cost is given by

$$C(j) = \sum_{n=1}^{j-1} f(n)ns + \sum_{n=j}^{N} f(n) \left[a + \frac{k}{2} c(n) + \frac{ns}{2} \right] \qquad (2.44)$$

The first difference of $C(j)$ with respect to j is easily seen to be

$$\Delta C(j) = C(j + 1) - C(j)$$

$$= f(j)js - f(j) \left[a + \frac{k}{2} c(j) + \frac{js}{2} \right] \qquad (2.45)$$

$$= f(j) \left[\frac{js}{2} - a - \frac{k}{2} c(j) \right]$$

Setting the first difference equal to zero, we obtain the following equation for the optimal cutoff point $\hat{j}$:

$$\frac{s}{2} \hat{j} - a - kc(\hat{j}) = 0 \qquad (2.46)$$

Since the solution will not normally be integral, the neighboring integers must be checked. Furthermore, care must be taken because the function $C(j)$ may not have a unique minimum. It is advisable to compute a number of differences $\Delta C(j)$ in the neighborhood of $\hat{j}$.

OPTIMAL ORDER OF WITHDRAWAL FOR SLOW-MOVING ITEMS

In the case of sporadic demand, complications may also be introduced by the obsolescence behavior of the *individual* item in stock so that the order of withdrawal becomes a decision problem. Derman and Klein [13] have investigated this problem, assuming that the utility of an item of age S is a known, decreasing function $U(S)$.

Consider n items on the ground which are numbered $i = 1, \cdots, n$ in the order of their arrival in stock. In other words, the first item is the oldest. The respective points in time corresponding to the next n demands are given. Let these demands be numbered consecutively in time by $j = 1, \cdots, n$. Since the function $U(S)$ is known, it then becomes possible to compute the utility a_{ij} associated with satisfying the jth demand by the ith item. The withdrawal policy with maximum total utility can obviously be found by solving the "assignment problem"* defined by the utility matrix a_{ij}.

Consider the special case where $U(S)$ is concave. This means that the rate of deterioration is increasing $[U'(S)$ decreasing, $U''(S) < 0]$. We assert that the optimal solution must contain the element a_{11}. Suppose that this was not the case. Then the solution would have to contain two elements a_{1j} and a_{i1} with $j \neq 1, i \neq 1$. But this solution could obviously be improved by picking the two elements a_{11} and a_{ij} instead.

For the relation

$$a_{11} + a_{ij} > a_{1j} + a_{i1} \tag{2.47}$$

or, equivalently,

$$a_{11} - a_{1j} > a_{i1} - a_{ij} \tag{2.48}$$

is a direct consequence of the concavity assumption: the oldest item $i = 1$ has the highest rate of deterioration in a given time span (here the span between the first and the jth demand). Consequently, the solution must contain a_{11} and, in the same way, all a_{ii}: for concave utility functions $U(S)$ the optimal withdrawal policy is "first in, first out" (FIFO). In completely analogous fashion it may be shown that for convex utility functions the optimal policy is "last in, first out" (LIFO). For further material on the problem, see [26, 38].

* See Mathematical Appendix

chapter 3
Static Probabilistic Models

The essential feature of a probabilistic model is that its measure of effectiveness—say, cost—depends not only on a set of decision variables x_1, x_2, $\cdots$ subject to the control of the decision maker but also on a set of uncontrollable parameters p_1, p_2, $\cdots$ which are only known subject to probability distributions. We may, therefore, write the following cost function:

$$C = C(x_1, x_2, \cdots; p_1, p_2, \cdots) \tag{3.1}$$

Furthermore let $f(p_1, p_2, \cdots)$ be the joint probability density of the parameters p_1, p_2, $\cdots$, so that

$$\int_{-\infty}^{+\infty} \cdots \int_{-\infty}^{+\infty} f(p_1, p_2, \cdots)\, dp_1\, dp_2 \cdots = 1 \tag{3.2}$$

It is necessary to redefine the notion of an optimal policy for probabilistic models. The most commonly used criterion for optimization is the expected value of the measure of effectiveness, i.e.,

$$E(C) = \int_{-\infty}^{+\infty} \cdots \int_{-\infty}^{+\infty} C(x_1, x_2, \cdots;$$
$$p_1, p_2, \cdots) f(p_1, p_2, \cdots)\, dp_1\, dp_2 \cdots \tag{3.3}$$

The particular policy $\hat{x}_1$, $\hat{x}_2$, $\cdots$ which minimizes $E(C)$ is called optimal. Note that $E(C)$ no longer depends on the uncertain parameters. Although the expected value is almost exclusively used as the optimization criterion for probabilistic models, it does not represent the only possibility of defining a meaningful criterion. Restrictions which had to be fulfilled in a strict sense in deterministic models may have to be replaced by restrictions which must hold with a specified probability (confidence).

In principle, it is possible to generalize all previously discussed deterministic models for the case of probabilistic parameters. However, the demand rate usually is the parameter of greatest interest. Furthermore, the great mathematical complexity added by the use of

25

expected values limits the usefulness of more sophisticated probabilistic models.   In the following, we shall, therefore, mainly dwell upon relatively simple models with probabilistic demand.   The static nature of the model is usually introduced by the assumption that demand per unit time comes from independent, identical probability distributions. By this assumption the probability distributions of demand during *any* time interval (lead time, checking interval) may also be considered as given.   Demand materializes continuously in time in such a way that a linear approximation of the inventory curve is meaningful.   Apart from these modifications concerning demand, the models fall within the same framework as outlined for the deterministic case, and the same notation is maintained.

THE SETTING OF REORDER POINTS

In the deterministic case it was possible to determine reorder points in such a way that no shortages occurred ($I_0 = 0$).   In the probabilistic case, shortages can be prevented only with a specified probability α_0 (confidence level).   By analogy with Eq. 2.1, let

$$G(R_L + R_t) \tag{3.4}$$

be the cumulative probability distribution of $R_L + R_t$.   The probability that no shortage will occur between times L and $L + t$ is

$$G(A + Q_L) = \alpha \tag{3.5}$$

It is customary to specify a critical value α_0 below which α must not fall.   If

$$G(H) = \alpha_0 \tag{3.6}$$

then we shall not order if

$$A + Q_L > H \tag{3.7}$$

or

$$A > H - Q_L \tag{3.8}$$

Hence, H is the reorder point for the generalized stock level if shortages are to be avoided with a confidence of α_0.   (See also [53, 61] and Bibliography C, [48].)

GENERALIZATION OF THE CLASSICAL MODEL

We maintain all assumptions of the deterministic classical model with the exception of these modifications.   Demand per unit time comes from a set of known, identical, independent probability distributions with mean r. The production rate is $p = \infty$. Shortages which can no longer be excluded give rise to a cost d per unit short but do not cause any cancellations of demand. The decision variables of the problem are reorder quantity q and reorder point P (Fig. 3-1). The lead time L is given. At any time, at most one order is "in the pipeline."

Our optimization criterion will be expected cost per unit time of setups, inventory, and shortages. First, consider inventory costs. Let x_1 and x_2 be the demand during two consecutive lead time intervals. This implies that the inventory gradually drops from the peak level $P - x_1 + q$ to the minimum level $P - x_2$. The latter may be negative. The cycle time T which elapses during this inventory reduction is a random variable whose distribution is well defined by our assumptions about demand. For a given set of values of the three random variables x_1, x_2, T we shall approximate the actual inventory level by a straight line connecting the peak with the next valley. The inventory level given by this line is designated by $I(t)$ where $0 \leq t \leq T$. We also define

$$I^+(t) = \begin{cases} I(t) & \text{if } I(t) \geq 0 \\ 0 & \text{if } I(t) < 0 \end{cases} \tag{3.9}$$

and

$$J = \frac{1}{T} \int_0^T I^+(t|x_1, x_2, T) \, dt \tag{3.10}$$

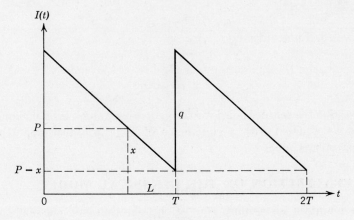

Fig. 3-1.

The inventory cost per unit time during the cycle under consideration is given by hJ, and its expected value by

$$h \int_{x_1} \int_{x_2} \int_T J f(x_1, x_2, T) \, dx_1 \, dx_2 \, dT \tag{3.11}$$

where $f(x_1, x_2, T)$ designates the joint probability density of x_1, x_2, T. The evaluation of the integral J requires a distinction of the cases $x_2 \leq P$ and $x_2 > P$. In the latter case, let T' be the time when the inventory reaches the zero level. It then follows from Fig. 3-1 that

$$J = \begin{cases} \dfrac{1}{2} (P - x_1 + q + P - x_2) & \text{for } x_2 \leq P \\[2ex] \dfrac{1}{2} \dfrac{T'}{T} (P - x_1 + q) & \text{for } x_2 > P \end{cases} \tag{3.12}$$

Thus, the expected inventory cost per unit time becomes

$$E(C_I) = \iiint_{x_2 \leq P} \frac{h}{2} (P - x_1 + q + P - x_2) \, f(x_1, x_2, T) \, dx_1 \, dx_2 \, dT$$

$$+ \iiint_{x_2 > P} \frac{h}{2} \frac{T'}{T} (P - x_1 + q) \, f(x_1, x_2, T) \, dx_1 \, dx_2 \, dT \tag{3.13}$$

We shall approximate this complex expression by a simpler one which somewhat underestimates the inventory cost. Considering the second integral, it follows from the geometry that

$$\frac{T'}{T} = \frac{P - x_1 + q}{P - x_1 + q + x_2 - P} \tag{3.14}$$

Consequently, the function under the integral becomes

$$\frac{T'}{T} (P - x_1 + q) = \frac{P - x_1 + q}{1 + \dfrac{x_2 - P}{P - x_1 + q}} \tag{3.15}$$

As long as we exclude from consideration policies with excessive shortages, we can assume

$$\frac{x_2 - P}{P - x_1 + q} \ll 1 \tag{3.16}$$

Using the first two terms of the Taylor expansion of Eq. 3.15, we obtain the following approximation:

$$\frac{T'}{T}(P - x_1 + q) \approx P - x_1 + q + P - x_2 \tag{3.17}$$

Clearly, we are somewhat underestimating the inventory term. But using this approximation, the complex expression for inventory cost in Eq. 3.13 simplifies to

$$h\left(\frac{q}{2} + P - \bar{x}\right) \tag{3.18}$$

where $\bar{x} = rL$ is the expected value of x_1 (and also of x_2).

The expected shortage cost per unit time is given by the expected value of

$$\frac{d}{T}(x - P)^+ \tag{3.19}$$

Strictly speaking, its evaluation requires knowledge of the joint density of T and x. But as long as T has a small coefficient of variation—a reasonable assumption—we can treat it as a constant and replace it by its expected value $E(T)$. The latter may be approximated as follows. The average consumption per unit time during the cycle under consideration is

$$\frac{q + x_2 - x_1}{T} \tag{3.20}$$

The expected value of this expression must equal r. Treating T as a constant $E(T)$, this leads to

$$E(T) \approx \frac{q}{r} \tag{3.21}$$

Substituting this expression in Eq. 3.19, we obtain the term

$$d\frac{r}{q}\int_P^\infty (x - P) f(x)\, dx = d\frac{r}{q} g(P) \tag{3.22}$$

for the expected shortage cost per unit time, where

$$g(P) = \int_P^\infty (x - P) f(x)\, dx \tag{3.23}$$

and $f(x)$ is the probability density of x (demand during lead time).

In the same manner it may be shown that the expected setup cost per unit time is approximately equal to sr/q. In summary, we arrive at the following total expected cost per unit time:

$$E(C) = s\frac{r}{q} + h\left(\frac{q}{2} + P - rL\right) + d\frac{r}{q}g(P) \tag{3.24}$$

Before we proceed with the determination of optimal values $\hat{q}$ and $\hat{P}$, we note that the derivative

$$g'(P) = F(P) - 1 \tag{3.25}$$

where $F(x)$ is the cumulative function of $f(x)$. This shows that $g(P)$ may be obtained as

$$g(P) = \int_P^\infty [1 - F(u)]\,du \tag{3.26}$$

This relation may be helpful for tabulating $g(P)$. By differentiating $E(C)$ partially with respect to both q and P, we are led to the following equations for the optimal quantities:

$$-\frac{r}{\hat{q}^2}[s + d\,g(\hat{P})] + \frac{h}{2} = 0 \tag{3.27}$$

$$d\frac{r}{\hat{q}}g(P) + h = 0 \tag{3.28}$$

From Eq. 3.27 we obtain

$$\hat{q} = \sqrt{\frac{2r[s + d\,g(\hat{P})]}{h}} \tag{3.29}$$

and from Eqs. 3.28 and 3.25,

$$\hat{q} = -\frac{dr\,g'(\hat{P})}{h} = \frac{dr[1 - F(\hat{P})]}{h} \tag{3.30}$$

These equations may be solved for $\hat{P}$ and $\hat{q}$ by elementary iterative methods.

It should be noted that the random variable x [demand during lead time with probability density $f(x)$] may also be defined in the case of probabilistic lead time L. Consequently, all results hold up with a slight reinterpretation of $f(x)$. The only change in the cost equation 3.24 is the replacement of the term rL by the mean $\bar{x}$ of $f(x)$. But as long as the demand rate and the lead time are independent random variables,

$$\bar{x} = r\,E(L) \tag{3.31}$$

where $E(L)$ is the expected value of lead time. For other treatments of probabilistic lead time, see [6, 19] and the section "Discrete Demand Models for Slow-Moving Items" in this chapter.

PROCESSES WITH NEGLIGIBLE SETUP COST

In continuous production and similar processes where setup cost plays no essential part, we are only concerned with balancing inventory and shortage costs. We assume that replenishment orders can be placed at given, equidistant checking points and are filled after the lead time L which is a multiple of the checking interval. The checking interval serves as the time unit so that L is an integer. The demand per checking interval comes from identical probability distributions, and the cost per checking interval is proportional to the *closing* level of inventory (or shortage). Both inventories (overages) and shortages are carried over to the next period.

Simple Feedback Rule

Let us introduce the following notations:

$$\left.\begin{array}{l} I_i = \text{inventory level at the end of period } i \\ q_i = \text{input received at the beginning of} \\ \qquad \text{period } i \\ r_i = \text{demand during period } i \\ S_i = \text{generalized stock level at the beginning} \\ \qquad \text{of period } i \text{ (sum of amount on hand and} \\ \qquad \text{amount on order)} \end{array}\right\}(i = 1, 2, \cdots)$$

h = cost per unit of closing inventory at the end of a period

d = cost per unit of shortage at the end of a period

$f(R)$ = probability density of total demand in $L + 1$ consecutive periods

$F(R)$ = cumulative function of $f(R)$

Further define

$$Q_i = S_i + q_{i+L} = Q \tag{3.32}$$

$$R_i = r_i + \cdots + r_{i+L} = R \tag{3.33}$$

and (for any real number I):

$$I^+ = \begin{cases} I & \text{for } I \geq 0 \\ 0 & \text{for } I < 0 \end{cases}$$

$$I^- = \begin{cases} 0 & \text{for } I \geq 0 \\ I & \text{for } I < 0 \end{cases} \tag{3.34}$$

At the beginning of each period i we must decide on the ordering quantity q_{i+L}. Since this quantity is not delivered until the beginning of period $i + L$, it seems reasonable to use the cost in period $i + L$ as the measure of effectiveness of the decision. At first glance, this might not lead to a cost-minimizing procedure in the strict sense, because the cost incurred later than period $i + L$ might also be influenced by the present ordering decision. We shall see later on that this is not the case (see Eq. 3.121). Obviously, the inventory level at the end of period $i + L$ is

$$I_{i+L} = Q_i - R_i = Q - R \tag{3.35}$$

and the cost associated with it is

$$C = h(Q - R)^+ - d(Q - R)^- \tag{3.36}$$

Thus, the expected cost for period $i + L$ is given by

$$E(C) = h \int_0^Q (Q - R) f(R) \, dR + d \int_Q^\infty (R - Q) f(R) \, dR \tag{3.37}$$

By a simple calculation it can be shown that Eq. 3.37 is minimized when $Q = \hat{Q}$, where $\hat{Q}$ is given by

$$F(\hat{Q}) = \frac{d}{h + d} \tag{3.38}$$

We, therefore, have the following ordering rule for determination of q_{i+L}:

$$Q_i = S_i + q_{i+L} = \hat{Q} \tag{3.39}$$

Since negative ordering quantities are impossible, the rule is interpreted to mean $q_{i+L} = 0$ for $S_i > \hat{Q}$. The ordering rule, Eq. 3.39, may be given a simpler and more practical form. By Eqs. 3.35 and 3.39, the optimal expected inventory level $E(I_{i+L})$ is given by

$$E(I_{i+L}) = \hat{Q} - E(R) = I_0 \tag{3.40}$$

where the "inventory target" I_0 is defined by Eq. 3.40. The optimal ordering rule Eq. 3.39 may now be written as

$$S_i + q_{i+L} - E(R) = I_0 \tag{3.41}$$

or

$$q_{i+L} = I_0 + E(R) - S_i \tag{3.42}$$

Now consider the long-run performance of this rule. We first note that

$$I_i = I_{i-1} + q_i - r_i \tag{3.43}$$

If we wish to start using the rule at the beginning of period $i = 1$, S_1 must be given as an initial condition. If Eq. 3.42 yields a negative value* for q_{L+1}, we order nothing until S_i has been sufficiently reduced. This only means that the actual use of the rule begins at a later time. We can, therefore, assume that

$$q_{L+1} = I_0 + E(R) - S_1 > 0 \qquad (3.44)$$

Now consider the later decisions. By definition,

$$S_i = I_{i-1} + q_i + q_{i+1} + \cdots + q_{i+L-1} \qquad (3.45)$$

$$S_{i+1} = I_i + q_{i+1} + \cdots + q_{i+L-1} + q_{i+L} \qquad (3.46)$$

so that

$$S_{i+1} - S_i = I_i - I_{i-1} + q_{i+L} - q_i \qquad (3.47)$$

By Eqs. 3.43 and then 3.42, this becomes

$$S_{i+1} - S_i = q_{i+L} - r_i \qquad (3.48)$$

$$= I_0 + E(R) - S_i - r_i$$

so that

$$S_{i+1} = I_0 + E(R) - r_i \qquad (3.49)$$

Replacing i by $i + 1$ in Eq. 3.42, we obtain

$$q_{i+L+1} = I_0 + E(R) - S_{i+1} \qquad (3.50)$$

But by Eq. 3.49, this becomes

$$q_{i+L+1} = r_i \qquad (i = 1, 2, \cdots) \qquad (3.51)$$

or, equivalently,

$$q_{i+L} = r_{i-1} \qquad (i = 2, 3, \cdots) \qquad (3.52)$$

We thus have the surprisingly simple result: from the second period on, we always order an amount equal to the actual demand in the immediately preceding period. Inputs lag L periods behind demand. The decision process is completely described by

$$q_i = \begin{cases} a_i & \text{for } i = 1, \cdots, L \\ I_0 + E(R) - S_1 & \text{for } i = L + 1 \\ r_{i-L-1} & \text{for } i = L + 2, L + 3, \cdots \end{cases} \qquad (3.53)$$

where the a_i are the amounts ordered prior to period 1 which are given as initial conditions. The behavior of the inventory level itself may

* Sometimes a negative value is permissible; this means that previously ordered amounts may be canceled or adjusted. This is particularly important when drastic demand changes occur.

be deduced from Eq. 3.35 under the assumption that the demands r_i are independent random variables with identical standard deviations σ. Since R comprises $L + 1$ such random variables and $Q = \hat{Q} = \text{const.}$, the inventory level will fluctuate about its target value I_0 with a standard deviation of $\sqrt{L + 1}\sigma$.

The solution of Eq. 3.38 suggests a general principle for balancing shortages and overages, which we shall have occasion to apply repeatedly. Let us generally introduce a control variable Q and a random variable R with known density, and two functions $A(Q, R) \geq 0$ and $B(Q, R) \leq 0$ which may be interpreted as overage and shortage levels, respectively. Let us further assume the fundamental property of "linear control":

$$\frac{d}{dQ} [E(A + B)] = \alpha \tag{3.54}$$

where E denotes the expected value and α is a constant. To minimize a cost function of the form

$$E(C) = h\, E(A) - d\, E(B) \tag{3.55}$$

we differentiate with respect to Q and then use Eq. 3.54, thus obtaining

$$\frac{d\, E(C)}{dQ} = h \frac{d\, E(A)}{dQ} - d \left[-\frac{d\, E(A)}{dQ} + \alpha \right] \tag{3.56}$$

This leads to the following condition for the optimal value $\hat{Q}$:

$$\frac{d\, E(A)}{dQ} = \frac{\alpha d}{h + d} \tag{3.57}$$

In other words, the derivative of the expected overage must equal the characteristic cost ratio in Eq. 3.57. In our previous example we had

$$A = (Q - R)^+ \tag{3.58}$$

$$\alpha = 1$$

By Eq. 3.57, this leads directly to the result of Eq. 3.38.

Damped Response Rule

Since by Eq. 3.53 the ordered quantity follows the demand rate, it is a random variable with standard deviation σ, whereas the standard deviation of the inventory level is $\sqrt{L + 1}\sigma$. Especially in production processes, input fluctuations of the order of σ may be unacceptable. They would mean that the random fluctuations of the market are directly reflected by the production pattern. As we shall see, the production fluctuations may be reduced at the expense of greater inventory fluctuations. Vassian [55] has shown by an application of servo theory that the ordering rule, Eq. 3.42, minimizes inventory fluctuations where minimization is over a certain class of linear feedback rules. The linear rule, Eq. 3.42, may be written in the form

$$q_{i+L} = E(r_{i+L}) - \left\{ \sum_{j=0}^{L-1} [q_{i+j} - E(r_{i+j})] + I_{i-1} - I_0 \right\} \quad (3.59)$$

The quantity in braces may be viewed as a correction quantity allowing for the present inventory discrepancy and already committed future production discrepancies. Discrepancy is defined as deviation from expected value. A slower production response can be achieved by multiplying the correction quantity with a damping factor k, where $0 < k < 1$:

$$q_{i+L} = E(r_{i+L}) - k \left\{ \sum_{j=0}^{L-1} [q_{i+j} - E(r_{i+j})] + I_{i-1} - I_0 \right\} \quad (3.60)$$

$$= E(r_{i+L}) - k \, \Delta_i$$

with an obvious definition of Δ_i. We shall first study the behavior of Δ_i under the ordering rule, Eq. 3.60. By definition,

$$\Delta_i - \Delta_{i-1} = q_{i+L-1} - q_i - E(r_{i+L-1}) + E(r_{i-1}) + I_{i-1} - I_{i-2}$$

$$= q_{i+L-1} - E(r_{i+L-1}) - [r_{i-1} - E(r_{i-1})]$$

By Eq. 3.60, this may be rewritten as

$$\Delta_i - \Delta_{i-1} = -k \, \Delta_{i-1} - [r_{i-1} - E(r_{i-1})]$$

or

$$\Delta_i = (1 - k) \, \Delta_{i-1} - [r_{i-1} - E(r)_{i-1})]$$

By continued iteration we obtain

$$\Delta_i = - \sum_{j=1}^{\infty} (1 - k)^{j-1} [r_{i-j} - E(r_{i-j})] \quad (3.61)$$

Turning to the inventory level, we observe that

$$I_{i+L} - I_0 = I_i + \sum_{j=1}^{L} (q_{i+j} - r_{i+j}) - I_0$$

$$= I_i - I_0 + \sum_{j=1}^{L} [q_{i+j} - E(r_{i+j})] - \sum_{j=1}^{L} [r_{i+j} - E(r_{i+j})]$$

$$= \Delta_{i+1} - \sum_{j=1}^{L} [r_{i+j} - E(r_{i+j})]$$

By Eq. 3.61 this becomes

$$I_{i+L} - I_0 = - \sum_{j=1}^{\infty} (1 - k)^{j-1}[r_{i-j+1} - E(r_{i-j+1})]$$

$$- \sum_{j=1}^{L} [r_{i+j} - E(r_{i+j})]$$

Since each difference $[r - E(r)]$ represents a random variable with mean zero and standard deviation σ, the inventory level will fluctuate about the target value I_0 with a variance of

$$\sigma^2 \left[L + \sum_{j=0}^{\infty} (1 - k)^{2j} \right] = \sigma^2 \left(L + \frac{1}{2k - k^2} \right)$$

Consequently, the standard deviation of the inventory level is

$$\sigma(I) = \sigma \sqrt{L + \frac{1}{2k - k^2}} \qquad (3.62)$$

The production fluctuations may be analyzed by observing from Eqs. 3.60 and 3.61 that

$$q_{i+L} = E(r_{i+L}) + k \sum_{j=1}^{\infty} (1 - k)^{j-1}[r_{i-j} - E(r_{i-j})] \qquad (3.63)$$

From this, the standard deviation of produced quantities is easily seen to be

$$\sigma(q) = \sigma \sqrt{\frac{k}{2 - k}} \qquad (3.64)$$

For $k = 1$, we get back our former results.

More generally, the quantities $r - E(r)$ may be viewed as forecasting errors and the quantities $E(r)$ as representing a production plan based on the forecast. In this interpretation, our results give insight into the deviations of inventories and production quantities from planned levels [39].

The results derived in the last two sections in an elementary fashion may also be obtained more directly by the z-transform techniques of servo theory. An exposition of the principles of this approach is found in [51, 55] as well as in the section on feedback behavior in Chapter 5.

Lost-Sales Case

Equation 3.35 and the theory following it rest on the assumption that shortages can be carried over to the next period; no demand is lost because of shortages. We now consider the lost-sales case where any excess of demand in a given period over the supply on hand at the beginning of the period is lost. As is shown in [3], the lost-sales inventory problem is intrinsically complicated and normally does not lead to a simple or explicit optimal ordering rule. The optimal ordering quantity generally depends in a complicated fashion on *all* "pipeline quantities" $q_i, \cdots, q_{i+L-1}$, not just on their sum. Since the complexity of the rule and the difficulty of obtaining it render it practically useless, we shall restrict ourselves to a plausible approximate solution. Consider the ordering quantity q_{i+L} which must be decided on at the beginning of period i. The first period under control is period $i + L$. We shall try to minimize the expected cost for that period. Let

r = demand per period with probability density $f(r)$;
  cumulative distribution $F(r)$
J = starting inventory level (after receipt of input
  for the period)
s = actual sales per period
h = cost of overage per unit of closing inventory
d = profit per unit if sold

Obviously, the parameter d assumes the role of a unit cost of shortage when the demand r exceeds the supply J. Thus, the relevant cost incurred in a period is

$$C = h(J - r)^+ - d(J - r)^- \qquad (3.65)$$

If we could control the starting level J for period $i + L$ in a deterministic sense, we would obviously choose $J = \hat{J}$, where $\hat{J}$ is given by

$$F(\hat{J}) = \frac{d}{h + d} \qquad (3.66)$$

The expected number of units sold, $E(s)$, would then be given by

$$E(s) \approx \int_0^{\hat{J}} r f(r) \, dr + \hat{J} \int_{\hat{J}}^{\infty} f(r) \, dr = v \qquad (3.67)$$

where v is merely a definition. In reality, J is a random variable, and we shall attempt to control it so that its expected value is $\hat{J}$. This can be accomplished by the following ordering rule where we have maintained the approximation, Eq. 3.67, for the expected sales per period:

$$I_i + q_i + \cdots + q_{i+L-1} + q_{i+L} - (L + 1)v = \hat{J} \qquad (3.68)$$

I_i is the closing inventory of period i, and q_{i+L} can be determined from Eq. 3.68. By analogy with the earlier theory, this rule may be implemented (in the long run) by letting the ordering quantity equal actual sales during the immediately preceding period (see Eq. 3.53). Since v is only an approximation of expected sales per period, the rule may lead to an average starting inventory which deviates somewhat from $\hat{J}$. If experience with the rule shows that this is the case, the target value $\hat{J}$ in Eq. 3.68 may have to be replaced by a slightly modified value. An estimate of expected cost may be obtained on the basis of Eq. 3.65, substituting $\hat{J}$ for J. Alternatively, the cost behavior can be explored by a simulated use of the rule. A similar approach may be taken when the probability distributions of demand change from period to period.

Demand Dependent on Delivery Time

In the previous section we assumed that all shortages were equivalent to lost sales. We shall now consider a model in which the probability distribution of actual sales per period depends in a more general way on the occurrence of shortages [29]. We shall, however, restrict ourselves to normal distributions of the withdrawal quantities (sales) per period. As before, production orders for the replenishment of inventory are placed at the beginning of given checking periods, say, weeks. Production lead time is L weeks. At the beginning of week 1 there are $L + 1$ production lots $q_1, \cdots, q_{L+1}$ in the production pipeline, including the quantity q_1 which has just left the production process, and the quantity q_{L+1} which has just been ordered (Fig. 3-2).

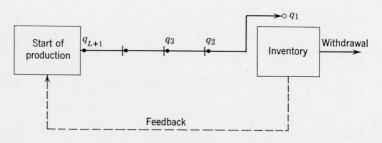

Fig. 3-2.

Generally speaking, the quantity q_i becomes available for withdrawal at the beginning of the ith week ($i = 1, \cdot \cdot \cdot, L + 1$). The ordering mechanism will be of the undamped type (Eq. 3.59); the withdrawal quantities r_{i+j} in Eq. 3.59 will be approximated by identical, independent normal random variables. Consequently, the inventory level is normally distributed about the target level I_0, and its standard deviation $\bar{\sigma}$ is $\sqrt{L + 1}$ times the standard deviation of the withdrawal quantity (see Eq. 3.62 for $k = 1$).

We interpret the withdrawal quantity as being equal to shipments if inventory on hand exceeds demand, otherwise as being equal to the total of shipments and uncancelled demand. Thus, a negative inventory level I (shortage) indicates total unfilled, uncanceled orders (backlog). We are particularly interested in the expectations of shortages and overages. If we define

$$\text{Overage} = \begin{cases} I & \text{if } I \geq 0 \\ 0 & \text{otherwise} \end{cases}$$

and

$$\text{Shortage} = \begin{cases} 0 & \text{if } I \geq 0 \\ I & \text{otherwise} \end{cases}$$

it follows that the expected value of the overage is

$$A = \frac{1}{\sqrt{2\pi}\,\bar{\sigma}} \int_0^\infty I \exp\left[- \frac{(I - I_0)^2}{2\bar{\sigma}^2} \right] dI \qquad (3.69)$$

and the expected value of the shortage is

$$B = \frac{1}{\sqrt{2\pi}\,\bar{\sigma}} \int_{-\infty}^0 I \exp\left[- \frac{(I - I_0)^2}{2\bar{\sigma}^2} \right] dI \qquad (3.70)$$

Note that always $B < 0$. Obviously, $A + B = I_0$.

If we define the "normalized" quantities

$$A_n = \frac{A}{\bar{\sigma}} \qquad B_n = \frac{B}{\bar{\sigma}} \qquad I_{0n} = \frac{I_0}{\bar{\sigma}} \qquad (3.71)$$

Eqs. 3.67–3.69 can be rewritten as follows:

$$A_n = \frac{1}{\sqrt{2\pi}} \int_0^\infty I \exp\left[- \frac{(I - I_{0n})^2}{2} \right] dI \qquad (3.72)$$

$$B_n = \frac{1}{\sqrt{2\pi}} \int_{-\infty}^0 I \exp\left[- \frac{(I - I_{0n})^2}{2} \right] dI \qquad (3.73)$$

where $A_n + B_n = I_{0n}$.   The functions

$$A_n = A_n(I_{0n}) \qquad B_n = B_n(I_{0n}) \tag{3.74}$$

have been tabulated in Table 3-1.

Both A_n and B_n are monotonic functions of I_{0n} so that the inverse functions $A_n{}^{-1}$ and $B_n{}^{-1}$ are defined.   In particular, it follows from Eq. 3.74 that the function

$$y = A_n B_n{}^{-1}(x) \tag{3.75}$$

measures the "normalized overage" y as a function of the "normalized shortage" x.   This relation will be used repeatedly.   An important feature of Table 3-1 is that it furnishes this direct relation between shortages and overages.

Now suppose that the weekly *demand* for a product is normally distributed with means s and standard deviation σ, but the expected weekly *sales* are equal to a fraction of expected demand which depends on the average delivery time t resulting from the inventory policy. Let this fraction be denoted by $\alpha(t)$.   Since in this case the sales revenue is sensitive to the inventory policy, the question arises: What inventory policy strikes the best balance between inventory costs and sales revenue?

According to our assumptions, the weekly withdrawal quantity (sales) is normally distributed with mean

$$s(t) = \alpha(t)s \tag{3.76}$$

and standard deviation

$$\sigma(t) = \alpha(t)\sigma \qquad (0 \leq \alpha(t) \leq 1) \tag{3.77}$$

The function $\alpha(t)$ is decreasing and approaches zero for $t \to \infty$.   If the inventory policy is conducted such that an average delivery time t results from it, then the inventory level is normally distributed with the parameters

$$\{I_0; \sqrt{L + 1}\, \sigma(t)\} \tag{3.78}$$

where I_0 is the target level.   Let $|B|$ equal the expected shortage of the inventory fluctuation described by Eq. 3.78.   Since $|B|$ is the average backlog and $s(t)$ is the output rate of the system, an incoming order,

Table 3-1
Normalized Overages and Shortages

I_{on}	A_n	B_n	I_{on}	A_n	B_n	I_{on}	A_n	B_n	I_{on}	A_n	B_n
−0.0	0.40	−0.40	−1.00	0.08	−1.08	0.0	0.40	−0.40	1.00	1.08	−0.08
−0.10	0.35	−0.45	−1.10	0.07	−1.17	0.10	0.45	−0.35	1.10	1.17	−0.07
−0.20	0.31	−0.51	−1.20	0.06	−1.26	0.20	0.51	−0.31	1.20	1.26	−0.06
−0.30	0.27	−0.57	−1.30	0.05	−1.35	0.30	0.57	−0.27	1.30	1.35	−0.05
−0.40	0.23	−0.63	−1.40	0.04	−1.44	0.40	0.63	−0.23	1.40	1.44	−0.04
			−1.50	0.03	−1.53				1.50	1.53	−0.03
−0.50	0.20	−0.70	−1.60	0.02	−1.62	0.50	0.70	−0.20	1.60	1.62	−0.02
−0.60	0.18	−0.78	−1.70	0.02	−1.72	0.60	0.78	−0.18	1.70	1.72	−0.02
−0.70	0.14	−0.84	−1.80	0.01	−1.81	0.70	0.84	−0.14	1.80	1.81	−0.01
−0.80	0.12	−0.92	−1.90	0.01	−1.91	0.80	0.92	−0.12	1.90	1.91	−0.01
−9.90	0.10	−1.00	−2.00	0.01	−2.01	0.90	1.00	−0.10	2.00	2.01	−0.01

on the average, has a waiting time of approximately $|B|/s(t)$. This can be used as an approximation for the average delivery time so that

$$t = -\frac{B}{s(t)} \tag{3.79}$$

and

$$B = -t\,s(t) \tag{3.80}$$

In words: "The expected shortage equals the product of output rate and average delay."   Let p be the profit per unit sold, not taking into account the costs of overages due to the inventory policy, and let h be the overage cost per unit of the weekly closing inventory.

Table 3-2
Decay Function of Demand

t, weeks	$\alpha(t)$
0	1.00
0.2	0.92
0.4	0.84
0.6	0.77
0.8	0.71
1.0	0.66
1.2	0.62
1.4	0.58
1.6	0.56
1.8	0.54
2.0	0.52

Since the function $A_n B_n^{-1}$ measures the normalized overage as a function of the normalized shortage, the expected profit associated with the inventory policy is

$$E(P) = p\,s(t) - h\,\sqrt{L+1}\,\sigma(t)\,A_n B_n^{-1}\left(-\frac{ts}{\sqrt{L+1}\,\sigma}\right) \tag{3.81}$$

We can now state the problem of balancing holding costs and delivery time in mathematical terms.   Given the function $\alpha(t)$ which measures the fraction of demand that will materialize as sales when the average delivery time is t, and given the unit profit p and the unit overage cost h, find the particular value $\hat{t}$ of t which maximizes the expected profit, Eq. 3.81, subject to the restriction

$$0 \leq t \leq L \tag{3.82}$$

The extreme case $t = L$ is equivalent to production to order.

The order rule for maintaining the optimal policy is given by

$$E(I_{L+1}) = V + \sum_{i=1}^{L+1} q_i - (L + 1) s(\hat{t}) = \hat{I}_0 \qquad (3.83)$$

where V is the actual inventory level at the beginning of week 1 and I_0 is the optimal target level corresponding to the optimal delivery time $\hat{t}$ by the relation

$$B_n \left[\frac{\hat{I}_0}{\sqrt{L + 1}\, \sigma(\hat{t})} \right] = - \frac{\hat{t}s}{\sqrt{L + 1}\, \sigma} \qquad (3.84)$$

Particularly because of the complexity of the functions A_n and B_n, the maximization must be carried out numerically by tabulating or graphing $E(P)$ as a function of t.

As an example, consider the decay function $\alpha(t)$ defined by Table 3-2. Further assume that $L = 3$, $s = 1000$ units, $\sigma = 500$ units, $p = \$10.00$, and $h = \$10.00$ per unit per week. Table 3-3 exhibits how the values for $E(P)$ can be calculated. Figure 3-3 pictures $E(P)$ as a function of t and shows that the optimal delivery time is approximately one week.

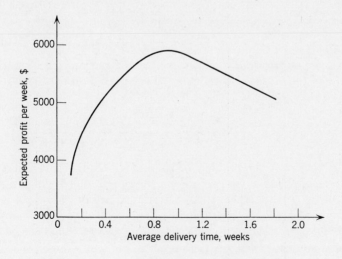

Fig. 3-3.

Table 3-3
Calculation of $E(P)$

$$\bar{\sigma} = \sqrt{L+1}\,\alpha(t)\sigma \qquad B_n = \frac{-ts}{\sqrt{L+1}\,\sigma}$$
$$= 1{,}000\alpha(t) \qquad\qquad = -t$$

t	$\alpha(t)$ $=1{,}000\alpha(t)$	B_n $=-t$	A_n	$\bar{\sigma}A_n$	$h\bar{\sigma}A_n$	$ps(t)$	$E(P)$
0	1.00 1,000	0	∞	∞	∞	10,000	∞
0.2	0.92 920	−0.20	0.70	644	6440	9,200	2,760
0.4	0.84 840	−0.40	0.40	336	3360	8,400	5,040
0.6	0.77 770	−0.60	0.25	193	1930	7,700	5,770
0.8	0.71 710	−0.80	0.17	121	1210	7,100	5,890
1.0	0.66 660	−1.00	0.10	66	660	6,600	5,940
1.2	0.62 620	−1.20	0.07	43	430	6,200	5,770
1.4	0.58 580	−1.40	0.05	29	290	5,800	5,510
1.6	0.55 550	−1.60	0.02	11	110	5,500	5,390
1.8	0.54 540	−1.80	0.01	5	50	5,400	5,350
2.0	0.52 520	−2.00	0.01	5	50	5,200	5,150

THE OPTIMAL RESERVE INVENTORY
LEVEL BETWEEN MACHINES

We define a reserve inventory as an inventory set up between machines 1 and 2 (see Fig. 3-4), where the output from machine 1 is the input to machine 2. The purpose of the reserve inventory is to prevent idle time of machine 2 in case machine 1 breaks down. Let

S = level of reserve inventory
μ = mean time interval between breakdowns of machine 1
τ = duration of breakdown
$g(\tau)$ = probability density of τ
d = cost per unit time of idle time of machine 2
h = cost per unit time of carrying one unit of reserve inventory
r = consumption rate (per unit time) of machine 2

We shall be interested in finding the optimum value of S. It is assumed that the reserve inventory level is at a constant level S as long as no breakdowns occur, and will be replenished to that level within a short time after each breakdown, perhaps by overtime production on machine 1. More specifically, we assume that the duration of the breakdown and the replenishment time taken together are small in comparison with the mean time μ between breakdowns (Fig. 3-5). As far as inventory costs are concerned, it is then possible to treat the inventory level $I(t)$ as remaining constant at level S. The inventory cost per unit time is hS.

Obviously, the idle time of machine 2 during a breakdown of machine 1 will be

$$t = \begin{cases} 0 & \text{if } S \geq r\tau \\ \tau - \dfrac{S}{r} & \text{if } S < r\tau \end{cases} \qquad (3.85)$$

Consequently, the expected cost of idle time per breakdown is

$$d \int_{S/r}^{\infty} \left(\tau - \frac{S}{r} \right) g(\tau)\, d\tau \qquad (3.86)$$

Fig. 3-4.

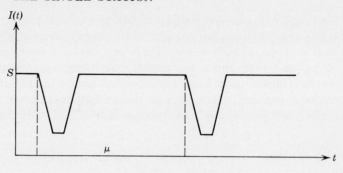

Fig. 3-5.

Since there are on the average $1/\mu$ breakdowns per unit time, the total cost per unit time becomes

$$C = hS + \frac{d}{\mu} \int_{S/r}^{\infty} \left(\tau - \frac{S}{r} \right) G(\tau) \, d\tau \qquad (3.87)$$

where $G(\tau)$ is the cumulative function of $g(\tau)$.

It follows that

$$\frac{dC}{dS} = h - \frac{d}{r\mu} \left[1 - G\left(\frac{S}{r}\right) \right] \qquad (3.88)$$

The optimum reserve level $\hat{S}$ is thus given by

$$G\left(\frac{\hat{S}}{r}\right) = 1 - \frac{r\mu h}{d} \qquad (3.89)$$

If

$$r\mu h > d \qquad (3.90)$$

no reserve inventory should be held since one unit of idle time of machine 2 is less expensive than carrying r units of product between breakdowns.

THE NEWSBOY PROBLEM AND OTHER FINITE PROCESSES

The models considered thus far assumed infinite processes. A somewhat different type of problem arises when the inventory process is terminated after a finite duration. The "newsboy problem" is typical: an optimal *one-time* supply S for meeting a probabilistic demand R is sought [4, 11, 39, 59, 35].   One may think of a seasonal good which is produced only once.   There is a charge h for each unit produced but not sold, and a charge d for each unsatisfied demand; h may be interpreted as salvage loss per unit and d as the loss of potential profit per unit.   Let $f(R)$ be the probability density of R. Under these assumptions, the cost function is of the already familiar form

$$h \int_0^S (S - R) f(R) \, dR + d \int_S^\infty (R - S) f(R) \, dR \qquad (3.91)$$

which leads to an optimal supply level $\hat{S}$ given by

$$F(\hat{S}) = \frac{d}{h + d} \qquad (3.92)$$

where $F(R)$ is the cumulative probability distribution of R.

A somewhat different problem arises when the salvage loss for left-over units is negligible but a significant holding cost h per unit time is incurred.   It is assumed that the demand R materializes in a linear fashion during a given planning interval T (Fig. 3-6).   The shortage charge is assumed proportional to the area under the negative part of

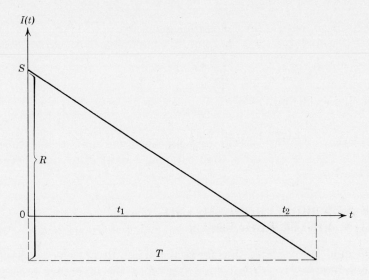

Fig. 3-6.

the inventory curve.   If the total cost per unit time is designated C, the cost incurred during the interval T will be

$$CT = \begin{cases} h\left(S - \dfrac{R}{2}\right)T & \text{for } R \le S \\[2ex] \dfrac{h}{2}St_1 + \dfrac{d}{2}(R - S)t_2 & \text{for } R > S \end{cases} \tag{3.93}$$

where t_1 and t_2 are defined as in Fig. 3-6.   Consequently, we have the following expression for expected cost per unit time:

$$E(C) = h\int_0^S \left(S - \frac{R}{2}\right)f(R)\,dR + h\int_S^\infty \frac{S}{2}\frac{t_1}{T}f(R)\,dR$$
$$+ d\int_S^\infty \frac{(R - S)}{R}\frac{t_2}{T}f(R)\,dR \tag{3.94}$$

From the geometry it follows that

$$\frac{t_1}{T} = \frac{S}{R}$$
$$\frac{t_2}{T} = \frac{R - S}{R} \tag{3.95}$$

Thus,

$$E(C) = h\left[\int_0^S \left(S - \frac{R}{2}\right)f(R)\,dR + \int_S^\infty \frac{S^2}{2R}f(R)\,dR\right]$$
$$+ d\int_S^\infty \frac{(R - S)^2}{2R}f(R)\,dR \tag{3.96}$$
$$= h\,E(A) - d\,E(B)$$

with obvious definitions of $E(A)$ and $E(B)$.   It is easily seen that

$$E(A) + E(B) = \int_0^\infty \left(S - \frac{R}{2}\right)f(R)\,dR \tag{3.97}$$
$$= S - \frac{E(R)}{2}$$

This shows that we have "linear control" with $\alpha = 1$ (see Eq. 3.54). Following our general principle of balancing shortages and overages, (see Eq. 3.57) we compute

$$\frac{d\,E(A)}{dS} = \int_0^S f(R)\,dR + S\int_S^\infty \frac{f(R)}{R}\,dR = L(S) \tag{3.98}$$

The optimal solution is given by

$$L(\hat{S}) = \frac{d}{h + d} \tag{3.99}$$

A similar but more general problem is discussed in [27].

We now return to the newsboy problem with the modification that the initial supply is a random variable q whose distribution depends on the ordered quantity q_0; in other words, both supply q and demand r are probabilistic. We restrict ourselves to the case of two independent normal distributions with parameters (r_0, σ_r) for the demand and (q_0, σ_q) for the supply; q_0 is the decision variable, all other parameters are given constants. If we let

$$\sigma^2 = \sigma_r{}^2 + \sigma_q{}^2 \tag{3.100}$$

the inventory level

$$u = q - r \tag{3.101}$$

will be normally distributed with the density

$$f(u \mid q_0) = \frac{1}{\sqrt{2\pi}\sigma} \exp\left[- \frac{(u - q_0 - r_0)^2}{2\sigma^2} \right] \tag{3.102}$$

The expected cost is given by

$$E(C) = h \int_0^\infty u f(u \mid q_0)\, du - d \int_{-\infty}^0 u f(u \mid q_0)\, du \tag{3.103}$$

Introducing

$$v = u - q_0 \tag{3.104}$$

it follows that

$$f(u \mid q_0) = \frac{1}{\sqrt{2\pi}\sigma} \exp\left[- \frac{(v - r_0)^2}{2\sigma^2} \right] \tag{3.105}$$

$$= g(v)$$

and

$$E(C) = h \int_{-q_0}^\infty (v + q_0)\, g(v)\, dv - d \int_{-\infty}^{-q_0} (v + q_0)\, g(v)\, dv \tag{3.106}$$

$$= h\, E(A) - d\, E(B)$$

with obvious definitions of $E(A)$ and $E(B)$.

The relation

$$E(A) + E(B) = r_0 + q_0 \tag{3.107}$$

shows that we have linear control with $\alpha = 1$. Since $g(v)$ does no longer contain q_0 as a parameter, the optimal solution is given by

$$1 - G(-\hat{q}_0) = \frac{d}{h + d} \tag{3.108}$$

where $G(v)$ is the cumulative function of $g(v)$.

THE BASE STOCK SYSTEM FOR PATIENT CUSTOMERS

The so-called base-stock system introduces a new type of ordering mechanism. The inventory process begins with an initial inventory of B units. Whenever a customer order for r units is received, an inventory replenishment order for r units is placed immediately. Replenishment orders are filled after the (deterministic) lead time L. The customer order is filled, as far as possible, from the supply on hand. Should the total unfilled customer demand exceed the supply on hand (negative inventory level), then we assume that customers will not cancel any orders but await the arrival of sufficient stock. It follows from our assumptions that the sum of inventory on the ground and on order is constant in time and equal to B, the so-called base stock. At a given time, let x be the amount which was demanded during the immediately preceding time span of length L. Then x units are on order at the particular time. Consequently, the amount of inventory on the ground is $B - x$. If we let $f(x)$ be the probability density of demand during a time span L, the expected cost per unit time of overages and shortages attributable to the inventory on the ground is

$$E(C) = h \int_0^B (B - x) f(x) \, dx + d \int_B^\infty (x - B) f(x) \, dx \tag{3.109}$$

where h and d are the unit costs per unit time of overage and shortage, respectively. It follows that the optimal base stock is given by

$$F(B) = \frac{d}{h + d} \tag{3.110}$$

where $F(x)$ is the cumulative function of $f(x)$. For the case of impatient customers, see the section on "Discrete Demand Models for Slow-Moving Items" in this chapter. A rather thorough analysis of base-stock control is given in [22]. In Chapter 9 we shall give a generalization for series of stations.

THE ARROW-HARRIS-MARSCHAK MODEL

The Arrow-Harris-Marschak (AHM) model is a highly generalized inventory model which comprises most of the previously discussed inventory situations as special cases [2, 3]. Contrary to our frequent use of plausible approximate criteria in previous models, it addresses itself to a rigorous minimization of long-run expected cost. The price paid for such generality and rigor is that—except in the most simple cases—the solutions cannot be obtained in explicit form, and numerical solutions can only be obtained with a computational burden rarely warranted in practice. However, in exceptional situations involving very costly inventories, the use of the model may be justifiable.

The model assumes equidistant checking points and identical, independent probability distributions $g(r)$ of the demand r during checking intervals. Orders are filled instantaneously and shortages are carried over to the next period. An ordering policy at a given checking point is defined as a decision function

$$y = y(x) \tag{3.111}$$

where x is the stock on hand (before ordering) and $y - x$ is the amount to be ordered ($y \geq x$). The cost incurred during one period is assumed to be of the form $C(x, y, r)$.

Consider first a finite process which lasts for n periods. Since there are n ordering decisions, the desired solution will consist of n optimal ordering functions $y_k(x)$ corresponding to the n checking points ($k = 1, \cdots, n$). These functions will be derived recursively. Given x and y, the expected cost in any period is a function

$$L(x, y) = E(C(x, y, r)) \tag{3.112}$$

Clearly, $y_n(x)$ can be found by minimizing $L(x, y)$ with respect to y for each value of x. Thus, if the minimum value of the expected cost in the nth period is designated by $f_n(x)$, we have

$$f_n(x) = \min_{y \geq x} L(x, y) \tag{3.113}$$

Computationally, this derivation of $y_n(x)$ and $f_n(x)$ requires a series of one-dimensional minimizations with respect to y, one for *each* value of x. We then proceed to the derivation of $y_{n-1}(x)$ and $f_{n-1}(x)$; the latter function is defined as the minimum expected cost for the last two periods ($n - 1$ *and* n), given the stock level x at the beginning of period

$n - 1$. If we tentatively order up to the level y at the beginning of period $n - 1$, the stock level before ordering at the beginning of period n will be

$$y - r_{n-1} \tag{3.114}$$

where r_{n-1} is the demand during the $(n - 1)$th period. We then follow the just derived optimal decision rule for the last period, i.e., we order up to $y_n(y - r_{n-1})$. This combined policy, which makes a tentative decision for period $n - 1$ and thereafter the optimal decision for period n, gives rise to the total cost

$$C(x, y, r_{n-1}) + C(y - r_{n-1}, y_{n-1}(y - r_{n-1}), r_n) \tag{3.115}$$

where r_n is the demand in the last period. The expected value of this expression relative to the joint density $g(r_{n-1}) g(r_n)$ is easily seen to be equal to

$$L(x, y) + \int_0^\infty f_n(y - r_{n-1}) g(r_{n-1}) dr_{n-1} \tag{3.116}$$

Clearly, the optimal ordering decision for period $n - 1$ is one which minimizes the expected cost of the combined policy. Therefore, $y_{n-1}(x)$ and $f_{n-1}(x)$ are given by

$$f_{n-1}(x) = \min_{y \geq x} \left[L(x, y) + \int_0^\infty f_n(y - r) g(r) dr \right] \tag{3.117}$$

In completely analogous fashion, the full set of recurrence relationships

$$f_{k-1}(x) = \min_{y \geq x} \left[L(x, y) + \int_0^\infty f_k(y - r) g(r) dr \right]$$
$$(k = 2, \cdots, n) \tag{3.118}$$

can be derived, where $f_k(x)$ is the minimum expected cost for periods k through n, and $y_k(x)$ is the corresponding optimal ordering rule for checking point k. At each step, a series of one-dimensional minimizations is required.

The whole procedure is also known as "dynamic programming" [7, 8, 49]; it is dynamic in the sense that it yields a whole set of solutions which permit—even after deviations from the optimal policy—making the optimal decision for the *remaining* time without further calculation. It is not difficult to see that the assumption of identical density functions for the different periods is not essential.

Turning to the infinite process, it becomes necessary to discount the cost of all future periods k by a factor α^k, where $0 < \alpha < 1$. This keeps total future costs finite.   It is plausible that the optimal decision function $y(x)$ should be the same for all checking points, and Eq. 3.117 suggests (letting $n \to \infty$) that $y(x)$ and the associated minimum cost $f(x)$ for all future can be obtained by solving the integral equation

$$f(x) = \min_{y \geq x} \left[L(x, y) + \alpha \int_0^\infty f(y - r) \, g(r) \, dr \right] \qquad (3.119)$$

As already mentioned, the existence of explicit solutions $f(x)$ and $y(x)$ is the exception rather than the rule.

It has been shown by various authors [3, 14, 15] that very general conditions (such as certain convexity properties) imposed on the cost functions and probability densities suffice to render the optimal policy $y(x)$ of the (S, s) type; this means that the optimal policy employs the well-known concepts of reorder point and reorder quantity, where the reorder point is s and the reorder quantity is $(S - s)^+$.   As an example, consider the case of negligible setup cost.   Then, the expected cost per period is of the form

$$L(x, y) = G(y) \qquad (3.120)$$

Let the absolute minimum of $G(y)$ be designated by $\{S; G(S)\}$.   It is clear that no realistic long-run inventory policy has to concern itself with the case $x > S$ because this condition will not be permitted to arise.   We, therefore, assume $x \leq S$ for all periods.   Consequently, we can realize the minimum possible cost in each period by following the rule

$$y(x) = S \qquad (3.121)$$

Clearly, this is also the long-run optimal policy.   This is a special case of an (s, S) policy where $s = S$.   In the case of a fixed ordering cost (setup cost) the interaction of periods cannot be avoided.   Hence, the solution is more complicated.

If delivery is not instantaneous (lead time $L > 0$), then the optimal ordering policy can be shown to be of the form

$$y = y(x + Q_0) \qquad (3.122)$$

where Q_0 is the quantity due in at the time of ordering.   Most results obtained in the case of instantaneous delivery hold up in terms of the generalized stock level $x + Q_0$.   However, this is not the case, when shortages are lost rather than carried over [3].

DISCRETE-DEMAND MODELS
FOR SLOW-MOVING ITEMS

All models considered thus far assumed continuous arrivals of demand and continuous decision variables. This model approximation may have to be dropped for slow-moving items which are demanded rather sporadically in time, so that only a few—if any—items are kept in inventory. In that case "discrete models" are required which take into account the discrete arrivals of demands in time and restrict the decisions to a few discrete alternatives. The previously discussed continuous models may be adjusted for slow-moving items by discretizing their decision variables and probability distributions [30]. We already encountered an example of this kind when we generalized the classical deterministic lot-size model for discrete arrivals of demand. The same principles hold for probabilistic models. As regards the mathematical techniques for optimization, it may become necessary to employ finite difference methods rather than differential calculus. In principle, nothing new is added by such discretizations, and we do not give further examples here. However, a few original concepts have also been developed.

A Queuing Model of the Base-Stock System

If reordering decisions can be made after each transaction, queuing theory lends itself to the treatment of certain discrete problems [18, 32, 45, 46, 57]. The base stock system (see Eq. 3.109) seems particularly appropriate for items with sporadic demand and hence will be used to illustrate the use of queuing concepts. We shall have to borrow certain elementary concepts and results from queuing theory. The number of items in the base stock, B, may be viewed as the number of channels of a queuing facility. An item on the ground is an idle channel, an item on order a busy channel. It is assumed that demands arrive one at a time in Poisson fashion. The (probabilistic) lead time for a reordered item corresponds to the service time. Its probability distribution is assumed to be of the Erlang type. Customer demand which cannot be satisfied immediately is *lost*. The inventory problem of finding the optimal base stock has thus been brought into the form of the well-known queuing problem of optimizing the number of channels. To formulate the problem mathematically, let

λ = arrival rate of demand
   (mean number of demands per unit time)
T = mean lead time

We now borrow from queuing theory that the probability of there being exactly m idle channels is

$$P_m = \frac{(\lambda T)^{B-m} e^{-\lambda T}}{(B-m)! E_B(\lambda T)} \qquad (0 \le m \le B) \qquad (3.123)$$

where

$$E_B(x) = e^{-x} \sum_{n=0}^{B} \frac{x^n}{n!} \qquad (B = 0, 1, 2, \cdots) \qquad (3.124)$$

It can then be shown that the expected number of idle channels is given by

$$\bar{m} = B \frac{D_{B-1}(\lambda T)}{E_B(\lambda T)} \qquad (3.125)$$

where

$$D_B(x) = E_{B+1}(x) - \frac{x}{B+1} E_B(x) \qquad (B = 0, 1, 2, \cdots) \quad (3.126)$$

Tabulations of the functions $E_B(x)$ and $D_B(x)$ are given in [45].

Finally, the expected number of services performed per unit time is

$$\bar{S} = \lambda(1 - P_0) \qquad (3.127)$$

In the inventory interpretation, the quantities $\bar{m}$ and $\bar{S}$ represent the expected level of inventory on the ground and the expected number of sales per unit time respectively. These quantities may be viewed as functions of the only control variable B. Let p be the profit per unit sold, not considering ordering and inventory charges. Further assume that the cost of ordering is s, and the cost of holding one unit in inventory (on the ground) is h per unit time. Then, the expected profit per unit time will be

$$E(P) = (p - s) \bar{S}(B) - h \bar{m}(B) \qquad (3.128)$$

This function may be evaluated for different values of B, and the profit maximizing value $\hat{B}$ may be selected directly. Alternatively, the first difference of $E(P)$ with respect to B may be set equal to zero to find $\hat{B}$. If we permit replenishment orders for more than one unit we must also consider the setup cost per order. The queuing model employed for the base-stock system may be generalized to include this case. It then leads to certain modifications of the classical economic-lot-size formula [45]. For some critical remarks about inventory models of the queuing type, see [28].

Markov Processes

In the queuing formulation just given, the treatment of the inventory problem rests essentially on the derivation of the probabilities P_m of there being m units in stock. The same principle may be employed for the treatment of inventory systems with predetermined, equidistant checking points. If the statistical situation with regard to demands remains the same from period to period, then there is no reason to change the reorder rule; it can be prescribed so that steady-state behavior satisfies some optimal criteria. The steady-state probabilities P_m are, therefore, of prime interest. For the sake of generality, m will be allowed to assume negative values also (shortages), but finite upper and lower bounds for m are assumed. The probabilities p_{mk} of transition of the system from state m at the beginning of a period to state k at the beginning of the next period are determined by the reorder rule and the statistical situation with regard to demands and replenishment. Once these are established, the steady-state probabilities P_m may be obtained by solving the linear system

$$P_m = \sum_k P_k p_{km} \qquad (3.129)$$

In other words, the steady-state probabilities are the components of the characteristic vector associated with the Markovian matrix p_{km}. A solution of these equations exists, and is unique if the matrix p_{km} is ergodic. Specific examples for the application of this principle, including cases with probabilistic lead time and impatient customers (lost-sales case), are found in [22, 46]. A similar treatment of continuous-review systems is given in [20]. Gaver [21] has applied the related notions of renewal theory to the analysis of inventory processes. See also [3].

BIBLIOGRAPHY B

Static Single-Station Models

1. Abrams, I. J., *Contributions to the Stochastic Theory of Inventory*, Dissertation, University of California, 1957.
2. Arrow, K. J., Harris, Th., Marschak, J., "Optimal Inventory Policy," *Econometrica*, **19**, No. 3 (July 1951), 250–272.
3. Arrow, K. J., Karlin, S., Scarf, H., *Studies in the Mathematical Theory of Inventory and Production*, Stanford, California: Stanford University Press, 1958.
4. Barnett, H. H., "Initial Provisioning with Confidence," *Operations Research*, Vol. 9, No. 1, (Jan.–Feb. 1961), 127–128.
5. Beale, E. M. L., Morton, G., Land, A. H., "Solution of a Purchase-Storage Programme," *Operational Research Quarterly*, **9**, No. 3 (Sept. 1958).
6. Beckman, M., Muth, R., "An Inventory Policy for a Case of Lagged Delivery," *Management Science*, **2**, No. 2 (Jan. 1956), 145–155.

7. Bellman, R., *Dynamic Programming*, Princeton, New Jersey: Princeton University Press, 1957.

8. Bellman, R., Glicksberg, I., Gross, O., "On the Optimal Inventory Equation," *Management Science*, **2**, No. 1 (Oct. 1955), 83–104.

9. Bowman, E. H., Fetter, R. B., *Analysis for Production Management*, Homewood, Illinois: Richard D. Irwin, 1957.

10. Case Institute of Technology, *Proceedings of the Conference on Operations Research in Production and Inventory Control* (Jan. 1954).

11. Churchman, C. W., Ackoff, R. L., Arnoff, E. L., *Introduction to Operations Research*, New York: John Wiley & Sons, 1957.

12. Clark, Charles E., and Rowe, Alan J., "Inventory Policies and Related Numerical Approximations," *Journal of Industrial Engineering*, **12**, No. 1 (Jan.–Feb. 1960).

13. Derman, C., Klein, M., "Inventory Depletion Management," *Management Science*, **4**, No. 4 (July 1958), 450–456. "A Note on the Optimal Depletion of Inventory," *ibid.*, **5**, No. 2 (Jan. 1959), 210–213.

14. Dvoretzky, A., Kiefer, J., Wolfowitz, J., "The Inventory Problem," *Econometrica*, **20**, No. 2 (Apr. 1952), 187–122. *Ibid.*, No. 3 (July 1952), 450–466.

15. Dvoretzky, A., Kiefer, J., Wolfowitz, J., "On the Optimal Character of the (S,s)-Policy in Inventory Theory," *Econometrica*, **21**, No. 4 (Oct. 1953), 586–596.

16. Eilon, S., "A Note on the Optimal Range," *Management Science*, **7**, No. 1 (Oct. 1960), 56–61.

17. Finch, P. D., "Note on a Stock Model," *Operational Research Quarterly*, **9**, No. 1 (March 1958).

18. Flagle, C. D., "Queuing Theory and Cost Concepts Applied to a Problem in Inventory Control," in: *Operations Research for Management, Vol. II*, J. F. McCloskey and J. M. Coppinger (eds.), Baltimore: The Johns Hopkins Press, 1956.

19. Freeman, R. J., "Ss Inventory Policy with Variable Delivery Time," *Management Science*, **3**, No. 4 (July 1957), 431–434.

20. Galliher, H. P., Morse, Ph. M., Simond, M., "Dynamics of Two Classes of Continuous-Review Inventory Systems," *Operations Research*, **7**, No. 3 (May–June 1959), 362–384.

21. Gaver, D. P., Jr., "Renewal-Theoretic Analysis of a Two-Bin Inventory Control Policy," *Naval Research Logistics Quarterly*, **6**, No. 2 (June 1959), 141–164.

22. Gaver, D. P., Jr., "On Base-Stock Level Inventory Control," *Operations Research*, **7**, No. 6 (Nov.–Dec. 1959), 689–703.

23. Gluss, B., "Cost of Incorrect Data in Optimal Inventory Computations," *Management Science*, **6**, No. 4 (July 1960), 491–497.

24. Gordon, J. J., Taylor, W. J., "The Condition for Lot Size Production," *Journal of the American Statistical Association*, **51**, (Dec. 1956), 627–636.

25. Grassi, R. C., Gradwohl, A. J., "Obsolescence and Economic Lot Size," *Journal of Industrial Engineering*, **11**, No. 5 (Sept.–Oct. 1959).

26. Greenwood, J. A., "Issue Priority: Last In First Out (LIFO) vs. First In First Out (FIFO) as a Method of Issuing Items from Supply Storage," *Naval Research Logistics Quarterly*, **2**, No. 4 (Dec. 1955), 251–268.

27. Hadley, G., Whitin, T. M., "An Optimal Final Inventory Model," *Management Science*, **7**, No. 2 (Jan. 1961), 179–183.

28. Hadley, G., Whitin, T. M., "Replenishment Times, Service Times, and the Independence Assumption," *Operations Research*, **9**, No. 1 (Jan.–Feb. 1961), 132.

29. Hanssmann, F., "Optimal Inventory Location and Control in Production and Distribution Networks," *Operations Research*, **7**, No. 4 (July–Aug. 1959), 483–498.

30. Heyvaert, A. C., Hurt, A., "Inventory Management of Slow Moving Parts," *Operations Research*, **4**, No. 5 (Oct. 1956), 572–580.

31. Jackson, R. R. P., "A Stock Model," *Operational Research Quarterly*, **7**, No. 4 (Dec. 1956).

32. Karush, W., "A Queuing Model for an Inventory Problem," *Operations Research*, **5**, No. 5 (Oct. 1957), 693–703.

33. Kellerer, H., "Lagerumschlag und Lagerdauer in Handelsbetrieben," *Archiv fuer mathematische Wirtschafts- und Sozialforschung*, **VI**, (1940), 120–130.

34. Klein, M., Rosenberg, L., "Deterioration of Inventory and Equipment," *Naval Research Logistics Quarterly*, **7**, No. 1 (Mar. 1960), 49–62.

35. Levitan, R. E., "The Optimum Reject Allowance Program," *Management Science*, **6**, No. 2 (Jan. 1960), 172–186.

36. Levy, J., "Loss Resulting from the Use of Incorrect Data in Computing an Optimal Inventory Policy," *Naval Research Logistics Quarterly*, **5**, No. 1 (Mar. 1958), 75–82.

37. Levy, J., "Further Notes on the Loss Resulting from the Use of Incorrect Data in Computing an Optimal Inventory Policy," *Naval Research Logistics Quarterly*, **6**, No. 1 (Mar. 1959), 25–32.

38. Lieberman, G. J., "Lifo Versus Fifo in Inventory Depletion Management," *Management Science*, **5**, No. 1 (Oct. 1958), 102–105.

39. Magee, J. F., *Production Planning and Inventory Control*, New York: McGraw-Hill Book Company, 1958.

40. Mellon, W. G., "A Selected, Descriptive Bibliography of References on Priority Systems on Related, Nonprice Allocators," *Naval Research Logistics Quarterly*, **5**, No. 1 (Mar. 1958), 17–27.

41. Mickey, M. R., "A Method for Determining Supply Quantity for the Case of Poisson Distribution of Demand," *Naval Research Logistics Quarterly* **6**, No. 4 (Dec. 1959), 265–272.

42. Mills, E. S., "Expectations and Undesired Inventory," *Management Science*, **4**, No. 1 (Oct. 1957), 105–109.

43. Modigliani, F., Muth, J. F., "Optimum Lot Size Under Uncertainty and Joint Costs," *ONR Research Memorandum* No. 6; No. 21.

44. Morris, W. T., "Inventorying for Unknown Demand," *Journal of Industrial Engineering*, **11**, No. 4 (July–Aug. 1959).

45. Morse, P. M., *Queues, Inventories and Maintenance*, New York: John Wiley & Sons, 1958.

46. Morse, Ph.M., "Solutions of a Class of Discrete-Time Inventory Problems," *Operations Research*, **7**, No. 1 (Jan.–Feb. 1959), 67–78.

47. Naddor, E., "Elements of Inventory Systems," in: *Operations Research and Systems Engineering*, C. D. Flagle—W. H. Huggins—R. H. Roy (eds.), Baltimore: The Johns Hopkins Press, 1960, 175–220.

48. Naddor, E., "Some Models of Inventory and an Application," *Management Science*, **2**, No. 4 (July 1956), 299–312.

49. Sasieni, M., "Dynamic Programming and Inventory Problems," *Operational Research Quarterly*, **11**, Nos. 1–2 (Mar.–June 1960).

50. Savage, I. R., "Cycling," *Naval Research Logistics Quarterly*, **3**, No. 3 (Sept. 1956), 163–175.

51. Simon, H. A., "On the Application of Servomechanism Theory in the Study of Production Control," *Econometrica*, **20**, No. 2 (Apr. 1952), 247–268.

52. Simpson, J. R., "A Formula for Decisions on Retention or Disposal of Excess Stock," *Naval Research Logistics Quarterly*, **2**, No. 3 (Sept. 1955), 145–156.

53. Solomon, M. J., "A Scientific Method for Establishing Reorder Points," *Naval Research Logistics Quarterly*, **1**, No. 4 (Sept. 1954), 289–294.

54. Sussams, J. E., "The Surplus Stock Formula," *Operational Research Quarterly*, **8**, No. 3 (Sept. 1957).

55. Vassian, H. J., "Application of Discrete Variable Servo Theory to Inventory Control," *Operations Research*, **3**, No. 3 (Aug. 1955), 272–282.

56. Vazsonyi, Andrew, "Comments on a Paper by Karush," *Operations Research*, **8**, No. 3 (May–June 1960), 418–420.

57. Ventura, E., "Sur l'utilization des intégrales de contour dans les problèmes de stocks et de délais d' attente," *Management Science*, **6**, No. 4 (July 1960), 423–443.

58. Watkins, H. R. W., "The Cost of Rejecting Optimum Production Runs," *Operational Research Quarterly*, **8**, No. 4 (Dec. 1957).

59. Whitin, T. M., *The Theory of Inventory Management*, Princeton, New Jersey: Princeton University Press, 1953.

60. Whitin, T. M., "Inventory Control and Price Theory," *Management Science*, **2**, No. 1 (Oct. 1955), 61–68.

61. Whitin, T. M., Youngs, J. W. T., "A Method for Calculating Optimal Inventory Levels and Delivery Time," *Naval Research Logistics Quarterly*, **2**, No. 3 (Sept. 1955), 157–174.

chapter 4
Applications of Static Single-Station Models

In the literature of recent years, a considerable number of case studies dealing with the installation of scientific inventory control systems testifies to the fact that the simple static models discussed in the preceding chapters have found widespread application in business and industry as well as in military supply operations [2, 11, 12, 13, 17, 23, 24, 25, 34, 35, 47, 53, 56, 60]. Of course, no real situation is static in the strict sense, but, fortunately, changes often occur so gradually that simple static models may be used to good advantage if their parameters are adjusted periodically. Furthermore, few real inventory systems consist of a single station. Systems with several thousand parallel stations are the rule rather than the exception. However, as long as there are no significant interactions between the parallel stations, these may be treated independently as single stations. This assumption is valid for many inventory systems, especially when inputs are ordered from outside sources rather than produced inside the operation of which the inventory system is a part. Before we turn to specifics, we shall discuss the principles that govern the application of scientific models in general.

GENERAL PRINCIPLES FOR APPLICATIONS

Application of scientific production and inventory models is here taken to mean the full cycle of conceptualization, solution, and implementation which was discussed in the "Introduction". The purpose of an application is to yield an improvement in some sense over an existing way of making decisions. Before a full-fledged application is undertaken, a crude feasibility study should determine whether or not a significant improvement can reasonably be expected. Only then the study should enter the conceptualization phase in which a formalized model of the real situation is constructed. This requires a more detailed collection of data and other facts by the research team.

The conceptualization phase is fundamental in that its success or failure determines the success or failure of all later phases. How can the success of model construction be judged? Obviously, the desired property of a model is its ability to make correct predictions of the outcomes of various possible courses of action. This property ensures that the optimal decision rule extracted from the model will indeed yield the best possible decision relative to the chosen criterion, and implementation will produce the results claimed by the operations research study. Thus, the predictions made by an operations research model are not predictions of the future in general but predictions of the future as a function of alternative courses of action. To make such predictions, some form of causal determinism is exploited. A few basic considerations will further explain this point and be of help in practical model construction. The essence of an operations research model is a set of causal functional relationships between controllable (independent) variables subject to decision and dependent variables by which the performance of the system is measured. Ideally, all dependent variables can be condensed into a single measure of effectiveness. The model must be explanatory rather than merely descriptive; otherwise its causality may be questionable, and the model may become worthless for decision making. The previously presented mathematical models are of the explanatory type. The *validity* of a causal model is established as follows. The values of the independent and dependent variables as well as all model parameters are measured without any reference to the model. The measured data refer, of course, to a well-defined historical period. The values of the parameters and independent variables are then fed into the model, and theoretical values of the dependent variables are calculated from its functional relationships. If the theoretical values and the measured values of the dependent variables are consistent, the model will be considered valid, at least for a certain range of the independent variables. Thus, validity is established by a retrospective test.

With a validated model at hand, we can proceed to optimization. If system performance is judged by a single criterion such as total cost, then the optimal values of the independent variables can be mathematically derived from the validated model. But obviously the optimal values depend on the model parameters some of which are only retrospectively known. Therefore, these optimal solutions are not to be confused with optimal decision rules. Only as the optimal solution is supplemented by forecasting devices for those parameters that are not known at decision time, it becomes a decision rule. Clearly, a decision rule must be based only on known information.

These considerations show that the causal model alone is not sufficient for evaluation of *system performance* under optimal decision rules. What is required is a *prediction model* embracing the forecasting rule, the decision rule, and the validated causal model. The prediction model is the heart of an operations research study. This remains true even in those cases where mathematical complexity forbids the derivation of optimal solutions from the causal model. We shall discuss examples later on where the decision rule is based on a simplified decision model which is different from the validated causal model. But whatever the *origin* of the decision rule, its *performance* must always be evaluated by the prediction model. Obviously, one expects the prediction model to be much more complex than the causal model. For this reason, performance evaluation may require a "simulation," i.e., a simulated step-by-step use of the decision rule. This may be done by hand methods or computer methods. Unfortunately, it is not needless to say that the only reason for resorting to a simulation is the complexity of the model which prevents one from writing down the desired measure of performance in closed, "analytical" form. There are strong similarities between simulation and certain complex algorithms in mathematics which produce a final result via a large number of intermediate steps. Particularly, a simulation approach does not relieve the researcher of any of his responsibilities for model construction and validation. Simulation is a method of calculating values of the dependent system variables where the rules of calculation are given by a previously constructed model. The fact that the rules of calculation are in part of the logical rather than of the analytical type is not relevant. After the system performance under optimal decision rules has been determined and found to be substantially better than under present rules, the optimal decisions should be scrutinized for feasibility. A restriction, hitherto unknown to the researcher, may have been violated. If this is the case, the restriction must be incorporated in the model, and new optimal decision rules must be derived and evaluated. When satisfactory decision rules have been found and system performance is still attractive, one can turn to the problems of implementation.

In summary, we may distinguish the following phases in the process of application:

1. Crude feasibility study: estimation of payoff potential.
2. Collection of data and other relevant facts, especially inventory history of item.
3. Selection of basic structure of the causal model.

4. Determination of model parameters, especially demand parameters.
5. Retrospective validation of the causal model.
6. Construction of forecasting devices, especially for demand.
7. Determination of cost parameters for decision model.
8. Derivation of decision rules.
9. Evaluation of system performance under proposed rules, using prediction model.
10. Feasibility check on proposed decision rules.
11. Implementation.

These phases will now be discussed in more detail, some of them in later sections.

PHASES OF APPLICATION

To conduct a reliable feasibility study is a difficult art, and it is not easy to give some reasonably general principles. What should always be done is to find out where the sales are and where the inventory is; by this we mean which products contribute how much to the total inventory and sales. Many companies have tabulations or other records which supply the necessary information; otherwise, it may be obtained from samples and the aggregate figures. It is helpful to rank products in descending order of their contributions to sales and draw the corresponding cumulative curves of sales and dollar value of inventory. Such graphs are helpful in estimating what range of products might reasonably be expected to come under a scientific control scheme.* Obviously, it does not pay to apply the usually more costly scientific procedures to the "tail" of the product line which comprises a large number of low-volume products. Study can then be confined to the inventory attributable to the relatively small number of high-volume items. From experience, a scientific control scheme may be expected to result in an inventory reduction of about 20%. Reductions of more than 30% appear to be rare exceptions. Using some of these figures and crude estimates of the cost parameters of interest (such as inventory carrying cost), one is in a position to give an order-of-magnitude estimate of achievable savings. These must be weighed against the increased costs that are anticipated. As already mentioned, the scientific control procedures are in themselves more costly than informal ones. From the range of items considered, a crude estimate can be made. Some crude time studies of procedures may

---

* A stratification of control schemes by volume classes has long been a common practice in business, industry, and military [16, 32].

be helpful.   If an electronic data-processing system is contemplated
as a tool for keeping stock records and for decision-making calculations
and forecasting, a crude estimate of computer time and cost may also
be obtained with relative ease.   If no significant net savings appear
the value of a detailed study is doubtful.   If the results look promising,
a second look should be taken at the possible inventory reduction.
A sample of items and their contributions to inventory should be
analyzed.   Are the inventories reasonable in light of the lead times?
Are the protective stocks justified in light of the actual sales fluctuations?   If not, what reduction could be expected from a very crude
forecast and inventory model?   What would this reduction be in
terms of the whole system?   (The latter kind of inference from the
sample is often facilitated by the fact that the probability distribution
of sales per product is logarithmic-normal; for more detail see the section "Inferences for the Total System".)   Bounding techniques are
generally helpful.   For example, if the potential gain derived from a
deterministic model, assuming perfect forecasts, is negligible, a more
realistic treatment could only worsen the results.   Setup costs, shortage costs, and total costs must be treated similarly.   With these
remarks we shall have to dismiss the subject of the feasibility study.

If a detailed study is decided upon, the next step is a more detailed
collection of data and facts relevant to model construction.   For a
random sample of individual items, possibly comprising from 2% to
10% of all items, demand history, inventory history,* ordering and
delivery history should be obtained.   This information must be complete enough to permit the estimation of all performance data and
model parameters with the exception of cost parameters, especially
those pertaining to probability distributions of lead times and demand
patterns.   Ideally, there should also be information on the occurrence
of shortages, but usually it is not obtainable from the records.   The
more history, the better.   Usually, the availability of data is the limiting factor.   Furthermore, the intrinsic characteristics of each item
should be obtained: unit cost, quantity discounts, selling price, etc.
In addition to numerical data, other facts must be gathered.   Flow
charts of existing procedures, paper work, and materials flow are
essential and very helpful in model construction.   What are the
restrictions on ordering procedures?   How frequently can orders be
placed?   What are the required and existing information lead times?
Does the nature of the product exclude certain control schemes?   Are
there any restrictions in neighboring areas, for example, transportation

* The problems of recording errors and of measuring physical inventories have
received little attention in the literature [57, 8].

and materials handling?   What measure of effectiveness is approved by management?   What are the decisions which must be made? Is there significant interaction between products?   Are the time patterns reasonably static?   With this information available, the basic structure of a causal model will soon begin to crystallize in the mind of the researcher.   The term "structure" refers especially to the identification of the variables to be included in the model.   The researcher will usually be able to use one of the mathematical models in this book as a point of departure, but certain modifications and extensions are almost always required; sometimes models have to be built from scratch.   With the basic structure of the model chosen, only the numerical values of the parameters remain to be determined from the data.   However, the final approval or disapproval of the model is not decided by the researcher's intuition but by an objective test of the goodness of fit between reality and model.

We shall discuss two examples of validation of causal models, one employing an analytical model and one employing a simulation model. Suppose we are to establish economic-lot-sizes for a simple, reasonably stable inventory process with negligible lead time.   No safety stock is carried.   The model which comes to mind is the simple classical model described by

$$I = \frac{q}{2} \quad N = \frac{r}{q} \tag{4.1}$$

where I = average inventory level in physical units
N = number of orders placed per year
r = demand per year in physical units
q = lot size in physical units

In our terminology, r is a parameter, q an independent variable, and I and N are dependent variables.   The model is highly idealized in that it assumes lot sizes which are constant in time.   But this does not necessarily invalidate it.   It may still be a valid model in terms of averages. From the data we can obtain numerical values for r and for the average lot size $\bar{q}$ during an historical test period of one year.   We can also measure the dependent variables N and I.   Care must be taken in calculating I from the stock records.   Perhaps inventory is always recorded when it is close to its high point or low point.   Then the average of the recorded inventory levels would give a seriously biased result.   The precise mathematical definition of the average inventory level must be kept in mind.   After all variables have been measured for the year in question, we can check whether the relations

$$I = \frac{\bar{q}}{2} \qquad N = \frac{r}{q} \tag{4.2}$$

are fulfilled.   There are many reasons why they might not.   In that case, the process must be studied more closely, and the model must be refined.   We here assume that satisfactory agreement between theoretical and measured values of the dependent variables has been found. It should be noted that this test can be performed although the present ordering rule is not known and probably not formalized.   The validation of probabilistic models would have to follow the same principles. But, as we shall see in the section on forecasting, probability distributions of demand do not exist apart from a formalized forecasting procedure.   Therefore, although the knowledge of existing decision rules is not required for testing, a formalized forecasting procedure furnished by the researcher *is* required.   It is, so-to-speak, a part of the probabilistic model.

Returning to the deterministic model, we assume that the cost parameters s and h have been determined.   We can then write the optimal solution

$$\hat{\bar{q}} = \sqrt{\frac{2rs}{h}} \tag{4.3}$$

which minimizes the cost

$$C = hI + sN \tag{4.4}$$

incurred during the test year.
We also assume that a forecasting function

$$r^* = g(r_0) \tag{4.5}$$

is available where r^* = forecast of demand for test year

r_0 = demand for the year preceding the test year

The optimal solution, Eq. 4.3 then leads to the optimal decision rule

$$\hat{\bar{q}} = \sqrt{\frac{2s \, g(r_0)}{h}} \tag{4.6}$$

This rule could be implemented by always ordering an equal amount (that given by the formula) when the inventory level has dropped to zero.   Then, the average ordering quantity would obviously be equal to $\hat{\bar{q}}$ and, by Eq. 4.2, the cost incurred under this "optimal" rule would be

$$C = \frac{h}{2} \sqrt{\frac{2s\ g(r_0)}{h}} + sr \sqrt{\frac{h}{2s\ g(r_0)}} \qquad (4.7)$$

This is the prediction model which must be used for evaluating the performance of the optimal decision rule. The example is oversimplified, especially because a forecast would hardly remain unrevised for a whole year. But it illustrates the essential points. If—more realistically—a new forecast is prepared whenever an order must be placed, then it is no longer possible to calculate the average order size $\bar{q}$ by a simple closed expression. The prediction model becomes relatively complicated despite the simplicity of the causal model.

As a second example consider a complex military supply establishment for which more efficient inventory control rules are to be devised. The present rules for a typical class of items might be as follows:

For items currently stocked

1. Check balance on hand and on order biweekly
2. Calculate average monthly usage, based on last six months or on total available history if the latter is less than six months.
3. If average monthly usage is nonzero, and balance on hand and on order exceeds a three-month supply (based on rule 2) do not order.
4. If average monthly usage is nonzero, and balance on hand and on order is less than a three months' supply (based on rule 2), order a two-month supply.
5. If average monthly usage is zero, and the total available history is less than 12 months, do not order.
6. If average monthly usage is zero, but the item was requested within the last 12 months, do not order.
7. If average monthly usage is zero, and the item was not requested within the last 12 months, remove item from the stocking list and scrap balance on hand.

For items not currently stocked

8. If there is no request, do not order.
9. If there is a request, and the available history is less than six months, order the requested amount.
10. If there is a request, and the item has been demanded at least three times during the past six months, add the item to the stocking list, and order a five-month supply based on the last six months.
11. Upon request, add any item to the stocking list and order the requested initial amount.

In a system of this complexity, a considerable number of dependent variables is of interest: average inventory investment, average number of items on the stocking list (this relates to the cost of stock taking), number of orders placed per year, fraction of all requests filled from stock, total value scrapped, etc. The decision variables are also numerous, and their effect on the dependent variables is not easily visualized. One does not expect to come up with an analytical model in this case. Rather, the model must be molded after the details of the actual process. It is not possible to summarize the effect of the details on the dependent variables as compactly as an analytical model can do. Here, simulation has its place.* The inventory control rules of the system already show great resemblance with the structure of a computer flow chart so that a computer suggests itself as the appropriate tool for calculation. Prior to any calculations, a causal model relating the decision variables with the dependent variables must be constructed. As an example, consider average inventory level as the dependent variable. We subdivide the test period by a mesh of equidistant points in time which we number $i = 1, \cdots, n$. Let

I_i = inventory level at time i
q_i = quantity received at time i
d_i = quantity ordered at time i (decision)
r_i = demand between times $i - 1$ and i
$$\rho_i = \begin{Bmatrix} 1 \text{ if item is not} \\ 0 \text{ if item is} \end{Bmatrix} \text{deleted from stocking list at time } i \qquad (4.8)$$

We further assume that we have established a probability distribution of lead times from which we can draw samples λ (Monte-Carlo technique); let the time unit for λ be the time interval between mesh points. The average inventory level I is then given by

$$I = \frac{1}{n} \sum_{i=1}^{n} I_i^+ \qquad (4.9)$$

where

$$I_i = \begin{cases} I_{i-1} + q_i - r_i & \text{for } \rho_{i-1} = 1 \\ 0 & \text{for } \rho_{i-1} = 0 \end{cases} \qquad (4.10)$$

and

$$q_i = \sum_{j + \lambda(j) = i} d_j \qquad (4.11)$$

* Examples of inventory studies based on simulation models are found in [23, 28, 53, 56]. See also the "Report of System Simulation Symposium" (1957), sponsored jointly by the *AIIE*, *TIMS*, and *ORSA*.

where $\lambda(j)$ is the lead time sample associated with the ordering decision d_j; the summation is taken over all values of j for which $j + \lambda(j) = i$. Equations 4.8–4.11 constitute the causal model which relates the decision variables d_i and ρ_i with the dependent variable I. The next step is the testing of this simulation model. It may be fallacious to assume that the model is so similar to the real process in all details that testing is superfluous. A simulation model needs to be tested just as much as an analytical model. The test could be made by measuring the quantities r_i, d_i, ρ_i, and I_i for $i = 1, \cdot \cdot \cdot, n$; feeding the measured values r_i, d_i, and ρ_i into the model; calculating a theoretical value of I; and comparing it with the measured value of I for the test period. On the other hand, it may be simpler not to measure the decision variables d_i, ρ_i and, instead, to take advantage of the fact that the present decision rules are formalized. This means that the decision variables d_i, ρ_i can be set up as functions of the demand history up to time i. Thus, only the demand parameters r_i need be measured, and the computer can calculate the values of the decision variables from the complex decision rules discussed earlier. It is here that the computer has its greatest potential. The testing of other dependent variables is done in analogous fashion.

After successful testing, we can turn to the design of new decision rules for d_i and ρ_i; the decision rules, combined with the causal model, yield a reliable prediction model. In the present case, the causal model is too complicated to permit convenient derivation of optimal solutions. (Optimality is defined relative to total relevant cost.) To avoid the simulation of a great number of alternative decision rules, researchers often resort to a highly simplified "decision model" for the derivation of decision rules. In the present case it could be argued that a major weakness of the ordering rule 4 is its disregard of costs of ordering and stocking. Therefore, one possibility would be to change this ordering rule to

$$d = \sqrt{\frac{2sr}{h}} \qquad (4.12)$$

where d = quantity ordered
r = forecast demand per unit time
s = fixed cost per order
h = unit carrying cost per unit time

The demand r would be forecast by present rules, and all other decision rules would remain unchanged. Thus, the classical economic-lot-size model has served as the decision model, but, obviously, it cannot be used as the prediction model. To predict system performance under the new decision rules, we must resort to the elaborate simulation model whose validity was established earlier.

One might argue that the use of a decision model which does not have the ability to predict is questionable. But experience shows that substantial improvements over existing rules can often be achieved with the aid of highly simplified models. A plausible reason is that the model falsifies the system response to alternative decisions in a consistent fashion. Thus, the "best" decision rule derived from the model may come quite close to the true optimal rule. Depending on the circumstances, the mathematical models presented in this book may serve as both prediction models and decision models, or only as decision models. Thus far, the problems of model validation and performance prediction have been discussed in terms of the individual stock item. The problems that arise in making the step from the individual item to the total system will be discussed in a separate section. Other sections are also devoted to the fundamental topics of forecasting and determination of cost parameters.

Assuming that all steps up to and including the evaluation of system performance under the proposed rules have been successfully completed, it now becomes necessary to scrutinize the proposed rules for feasibility. It is almost never true that the researcher has a complete list of the pertinent restrictions when he first formulates the problem; he normally discovers restrictions in stages. Especially when he thinks he is through with the problem he is likely to be told: "Yes, but we can't do this because . . . ." The iteration process arising from this inevitable fact of life is a legitimate part of the research. Even if the client does not question the results, it is dangerous to be satisfied with a successful performance evaluation. Certain characteristics of the solution must also be determined and be discussed with the decision maker. Magee [46] has an illustrative case where the introduction of economic-lot-sizes in manufacturing led to unacceptable fluctuations of production loads. Only after a damped production response rule (see Eq. 3.60) had been devised, feasibility was achieved at slightly higher cost. In these cases it is comforting that the minimum of the cost function is usually quite flat. One may also discover that the proposed scheme overloads or underloads transportation facilities which were previously considered outside the scope of the study. It is not so easy after all to practice the often advocated whole-system approach. In summary, the responsible decision-maker must be satisfied with all aspects of the solution prior to implementation. Some remarks about the problems of implementation are found in a later section of this chapter.

FORECASTING

Decision making is concerned with the future. Hence, the demand parameters of decision-making models must be descriptive of the future. This can only be accomplished by a forecast of the parameter values. Thus, forecasting appears as a special case of parameter estimation. It differs, however, from the usual kind of statistical estimation when the variable to be characterized by the forecast is statistically unstable in time. This is the rule rather than the exception.

Most of the material in this chapter is applicable to forecasting in general. Demand or sales forecasting are the special cases of primary interest in production and inventory control. After a brief general account of principles and methods, we shall discuss in more detail those forecasting techniques which have been most frequently used in production and inventory control.

There are various possible objects of a forecast. Most frequently, the object is a future *value* of the variable under consideration. Occasionally other objects may be more suitable or may be capable of being forecast more accurately. An example is the *direction of change*. In Chapter 6 we shall discuss a case study which is concerned with a raw-material purchasing strategy. In this particular case, a knowledge of the rank ordering of future prices was sufficient for making the optimal decision. Obviously, the direction of price changes can be forecast much more reliably than the prices themselves. In many speculative decisions the direction of change is all that matters. Another possible object is the *largest (or smallest) likely value*. More precisely, such values are defined in terms of probabilities. Thus, the largest likely value may be defined as the value which will not be exceeded with a probability of 0.95. Some authors speak of the "maximum reasonable demand" [7, 46]. It is clear that such notions are particularly useful in production and inventory control. The relationship with the protective stock in mathematical inventory models is obvious.

A forecast is always prepared with the aid of the forecasting function which relates certain *input variables* with the object of the forecast. Much of the forecasting problem consists of finding the right input variable (or variables). We may distinguish the following groups of possible input variables. *External* variables describe, as the name implies, the environment of the business under consideration. Examples are: population, national income, savings, employment, the Federal Reserve Board's durable goods index, and other general economic and social variables; these variables are generally more useful for long-range forecasts covering one or more years than for forecasts of the immediate future which are of great interest in production and inventory control.   *Internal* variables describe the operations of the business itself.   Examples are the amount of orders on the books as an input variable for industry activity and raw material prices; or previous sales of machines as an input variable for spare parts sales. We except from the internal variables the forecasting object itself; the history of the variable to be forecast is a frequently used input variable.   Finally, *subjective forecasts* in the form of judgmental estimates or opinions may provide a point of departure for more objective and more accurate forecasting, or may even be the best possible forecasts in a given situation.

The forecasting function may be viewed as the equivalent of a *forecasting model*.   There are *descriptive models* with only statistically established forecasting functions, *explanatory* models based on a causal understanding of the system, and mixtures of both.*   As a rule, descriptive models require more frequent revision while explanatory models are more powerful predictors and may even give a certain amount of control over the variable in question.   An almost trivial but sometimes forgotten requirement for a forecasting model is that it must incorporate a *time lag* between input variables and the variable to be forecast.   Even the most perfect causal relationship between, say, national income and sales of a given product during identical time periods is not usable as a forecaster.   In this particular case, a forecasting function could be established by supplementing the causal relationship by a descriptive forecasting model for national income, based on history of national income.   The compound relationship established in this way is usable for forecasting purposes.   Forecasting based on the history of the object itself is an important example of the use of descriptive models.   Most descriptive models relate the variable to be forecast to its various historical values by a linear function. Moving average techniques are examples.   But some other functions have also proved useful, for example, the maximum or minimum value of the variable during a certain historical time span, multiplied with a certain factor.   This method exploits the autocorrelation of the time series.   Descriptive models may also be used in connection with subjective forecasts.   In one case, a weighted average of three subjective forecasts, prepared independently by three persons, proved to be a good predictor.   Such weights can correct for the bias that is often present in subjective forecasts.

* An interesting causal forecasting model for spare parts requirements is used in [60]; see also [5, 55, 67].

Once the forecasting function has been chosen, the probability distribution of the forecasting error can be determined retrospectively. However, this should not be done with the same data that were used to develop the forecasting function. It cannot be overemphasized that some information concerning the magnitude of the forecasting error is as essential as the forecast itself. When the forecasting function is put to use, the error distribution can be made the basis of a statistical control device which signals the need for revision of the forecasting function. These points will be discussed in some more detail later on.

After these general remarks we turn to some points of special importance in production and inventory control. It sometimes comes as a shock to "practical men" that no scientific inventory control can be established without a demand forecast for each *individual stock item* to be controlled. But this should not be so surprising since ordering and production decisions must also be made for each individual item. Thus, the traditional business forecasts for aggregate groups of items are of little help. On the other hand, a scientific control scheme will normally be confined to the usually small fraction of all products that accounts for the larger portion of sales and inventory. Nevertheless, the required number of forcasts may be considerable and may require automatic computing machinery to be done economically.

The *frequency* with which forecasts are prepared is suggested by the frequency with which decisions must be made, but it also depends on economic considerations. Obviously it is useless to forecast more frequently than decisions must be made.* But it may be quite reasonable to forecast less frequently, using the same forecast for several subsequent decisions. This may be looked at as sampling in time. Similarly, detailed forecasts may be prepared for a sample of products, and the balance of products be forecast by statistical inference, using a forecast for the aggregate of all products. Normally, less frequent forecasting and other simplifications of the forecasting problem will worsen the quality of decisions. This means added costs. On the other hand, the cost of preparing forecasts is also reduced. Few studies become so refined that this cost-balancing problem is solved scientifically; usually, it is solved on an intuitive basis.

Similar considerations hold for the time span to be covered by the forecast. Obviously, it is useless to forecast farther into the future than is necessary for making the immediate decisions. The appropriate length of the decision horizon can only be deduced from the mathematical decision rule itself. A decision rule like the smoothing formula of Eq. 6.1 shows the rapidly declining influence of forecasts

---

* In some cases, the decision frequency is under control and may then be fitted to the availability and quality of forecasts.

of the distant future.   Similarly, other decision rules give indications of the relevant forecasting horizon.

Almost all of the previously mentioned input variables and forecasting models have found their applications in production and inventory control, though to varying degrees.   Subjective forecasts may sometimes be obtained in the form of salesmen's estimates.   The fact that such forecasts are often very crude need not preclude their usefulness. Especially when the stock items to be controlled are not the finished products themselves but, say, parts which must be assembled into finished products, then a crude forecast for finished assemblies may be translatable into a fairly reliable parts forecast.   This is due to the fact that parts requirements for different assemblies usually overlap; therefore, total parts requirements are not too sensitive to forecasting errors for individual finished products, provided that these errors are independent.   The parts forecasts may be obtained by an "explosion" of the assembly forecasts [62, 2].   If an operation has a large enough backlog of assembly orders already on hand, one can go to an objective forecasting method: the forecasting problem reduces itself to an explosion of orders on hand.   This is an example of a causal model based on internal variables.   Whenever forecasts are based on internal or external variables it is essential that all categories of demand for a given item are covered.   For example, if parts are also used for repairs it is obviously not sufficient to have forecasts for new assemblies. It should be clear from these few remarks that the organization of routine forecasting may require considerable changes in the flow of information in the company.   An example of this kind of reorganization is found in [2], Chapter 2.

Although it is true that subjective, internal, and external variables have been used in practice, it nevertheless appears that the vast majority of all case studies resorts to forecasting schemes that are based on the demand history of the individual stock item.   Suppose that forecasts are to be prepared at the end of period n, and that recorded demand history $r_1, \cdots, r_n$ is available.   Then each forecast r^*_k for a future period $k > n$ is obtained as a function

$$r_k^* = f_{nk}(r_1, \cdots, r_n) \qquad (4.13)$$

The forecasting problem is identical with that of finding a suitable set of functions f_{nk}.   Without loss of generality, we confine ourselves to the problem of forecasting the next period, $n + 1$.   We can then write

$$r^*_{n+1} = f_{n+1}(r_1, \cdots, r_n) \qquad (4.14)$$

The search for a suitable set of functions f_j (where $j = n + 1, n + 2,$

$\cdots, \infty$) inevitably involves some trial and error with actual data. It is essential that only a portion of the available data, say, periods $n = 1, \cdots, m$, be used in this trial-and-error phase, and the rest, say, periods $n = m + 1, \cdots, N$, be reserved for an impartial test of the selected alternative.   Let f_j be the set of forecasting functions selected in the trial-and-error phase.   We then prepare forecasts $r_{m+1}^*, \cdots, r_N^*$ and study the sequence of forecasting errors

$$r_{m+1} - r_{m+1}^*, \cdots, r_N - r_N^* \tag{4.15}$$

If we treat this sequence of numbers as a random sample from a single error distribution associated with our forecasting method, then we can calculate estimates μ and σ of the mean and standard deviation, respectively, of the error distribution.   We shall then say that the demand r_{N+1} comes from a probability distribution with mean $r_{N+1}^* + \mu$ and standard deviation σ.   If $\mu = 0$, the forecasting method will be called unbiased.   Parameters other than μ and σ can be estimated in the same fashion.   In summary, the probability distribution of the demand r_{N+1} is identical with the error distribution, superimposed on the forecast.   This is how the probability distributions required for mathematical inventory models are established.

From time to time, the forecasting functions will need to be adjusted. The most natural indicator for the necessity to do so is the forecasting error itself.   Statistical control chart techniques (see Mathematical Appendix) may be employed for early discovery of the fact that the forecasting error is "out of control."   The control limits are, of course, based on the previously established error distribution.   There are also some self-adjusting methods.   The use of these control techniques for item-by-item forecasting can be made economical although this may require automatic computing machinery.

We shall discuss more specifically the most popular and successfully applied forecasting techniques of the form of Eq. 4-14.   It appears that all of these use linear forecasting functions:

$$r_{n+1}^* = f_{n+1}(r_1, \cdots, r_n) \tag{4.16}$$

$$= \sum_1^n a_i r_i$$

where the coefficients a_i do not depend on $r_1, \cdots, r_n$.

The "moving average" technique is defined by

$$r_{n+1}^* = \frac{1}{k}(r_{n-k+1} + \cdots + r_n) \tag{4.17}$$

where k is an integer.   In other words, the forecast is obtained as the average demand of the k periods immediately preceding the time of forecasting.   The best choice of k must be relegated to the trial-and-error approach suggested earlier.   It greatly depends on the properties of the time series under consideration.   If the demands in different periods have low correlation, a large value of k is likely to give smaller forecasting errors.   This becomes obvious by considering the theoretical limiting case of identical probability distributions of demand for all periods.   In that case, the best estimate of distribution parameters is obtained by using the largest sample size.   On the other hand, when short-term trends or significant autocorrelation are present, smaller values of k yield better results.   These are rather general principles which hold for all cases where there is a choice of using different amounts of historical information.

The moving average technique picks up trends slowly.   A faster response is obtained by fitting a regression line to the time series of demand for the k periods preceding prediction, and using this trend line for extrapolation of demand.   Since the coefficients of the regression line are themselves linear functions of the demand data, we again have a linear forecaster.   The continuous updating of the coefficients may be done economically by quite simple linear formulas; for details see [7].   This method may be regarded as self-adjusting.

Exponential smoothing [65] is defined by

$$r_{n+1}^* = \alpha r_n + (1 - \alpha)r_n^* \tag{4.18}$$

where α is a weighting factor with $0 < \alpha < 1$.   By recursive application of the definitional equation it is easily seen that r_{n+1}^* is in fact a linear function of all previous demands

$$r_{n+1}^* = \sum_{i=0}^{\infty} \alpha(1 - \alpha)^i r_{n-i} \tag{4.19}$$

The coefficients decay exponentially with the distance i from the present period n.   Hence the name of the technique.   The most obvious advantage of this technique is that it requires minimum storage of historical information.   Another advantage is the possibility of varying the sensitivity to most recent history on a continuous scale by selecting different values of α.   On the other hand, it can be proved by an application of servo theory that this kind of forecast never catches up with a consistent trend [7].   An exponential smoothing technique with a trend correction which eliminates this deficiency is defined as follows:

$$r_{n+1}^* = \alpha r_n + 2(1 - \alpha)r_n^* - (1 - \alpha)r_{n-1}^* \tag{4.20}$$

Obviously, r_n^* in Eq. 4.18 has been replaced by a value which is larger by the amount $r_n^* - r_{n-1}^*$; this amount is a simple measure of trend. The choice of a numerical value for α is critical.   Brown [7] suggests $\alpha = 0.1$ as a good starting point.   For certain values of α, the forecast will become oversensitive and overshoot and undershoot actual demand.   Once again, servo theory can shed light on this phenomenon of oscillation, and can help to avoid it.   When a marked change in trend occurs, a temporary increase of α may be desirable.   Exponential smoothing is a special case of weighted-average techniques.

Repeatedly, reference has been made to servo theory as a tool for exploration of forecast behavior with respect to stability and systematic error.   The most useful concept in this connection is the so-called z-transform which is discussed in Chapter 5 in connection with dynamic decision rules (see the section on feedback behavior).   As soon as the z-transform of a mechanism—be it a dynamic decision rule or a forecasting rule—has been established, some important statements can be made concerning the stability of the time series generated by the mechanism.

The forecasting problem furnishes a good example of how mathematical decision-making models can point up the need for information. This is one of the greatest merits of scientific models.   All too often, information systems in general and electronic data processing systems in particular are designed without sufficient analysis of the decision-making process.   The obvious results are lack of essential information and excess of irrelevant information.   Unfortunately, this often is the difficulty encountered in the implementation of a new inventory control system.   Then, a redesign of the information system is inevitable.   For some case studies with special emphasis on practical forecasting problems, see [2, 5, 21, 26, 31, 35, 55, 60, 67].

COSTS

The mathematical inventory models tacitly assume the existence of certain cost parameters such as setup cost s, carrying cost h, and shortage cost d.   However, the meaning of these costs in specific situations —let alone their quantitative determination—is far from obvious. Some of the conceptual problems that arise are discussed in [46]. Difficulties occur at three levels: (a) the definition of total system cost; (b) the allocation of total system cost to individual functions in the system; (c) the general framework of assumptions and restrictions governing the system as a whole as well as the cost allocation process.

At all three levels, significant differences between the cost concepts of accounting and the cost concepts required by operations research will become apparent.

When a business enterprise is viewed as a whole system, it is clear that certain operating costs are associated with it in a meaningful way. During each accounting period or unit of time, a well-defined cost of labor, materials, depreciation of equipment and fixtures, and the like is incurred. A fairly typical and exhaustive list of cost categories $1, \cdots, m$ is found in Table 4.1. These *natural costs* as

Table 4-1
Total System Costs as Influenced by Changes in Individual Activity Levels*

Functions (Activities) / Natural Costs for Total System		Carrying of Inventory		Carrying of Shortages	Setting up	Hiring	Laying off
		Steady State	Transient Period				
	1. Conventional costs						
V_1	Materials	u or c	c		c		
V_2	Payroll and supplementary benefits	u	c	c	u or c	c	c
	Equipment and fixtures	u	u				
	Space and real estate	u or c	u				
	Supplies	u	u				
	Utilities	u	c				
.	Transportation	u	c	c			
.	Travelling and communication	u	u	c	c		
	Insurance	c	u				
.	Other services purchased	u	u				c
	Taxes (except on income)	c	u				
	Interest	u	u				
V_m	Miscellaneous	u	u				
S	**2. Sales**			c	c	c	c
R	**3. Potential income from other investments**	c←					
T	**4. Income taxes**						

* c = changed; u = unchanged.

opposed to expense center or functional costs, together with sales revenue S and income taxes T, constitute the income statement (profit and loss statement) of the business enterprise. They may, therefore, be referred to as conventional accounting costs. These costs are strictly internal to the enterprise. For the purposes of operations research, at least two external "quasi cost" categories must be added to the list of natural costs. Both are of the nature of opportunity costs. The first one is the potential income (return R) which the capital invested in the business could earn if invested elsewhere. It is clear that this idea is a significant departure from accounting concepts. For example, if the potential rate of return were greater than the actual rate achieved by the business, then the inclusion of the quasi cost in the income calculation would lead to the conclusion that the business is operating at a loss. But whereas a consistent loss in the accounting sense leads to certain ruin of the enterprise, a consistent loss in the novel sense just introduced may be associated with a highly profitable enterprise (in the accounting sense). The loss occurs only relative to other opportunities. Accounting is concerned with absolute standards, operations research with relative standards which help to evaluate alternative courses of action relative to each other, and thus to arrive at a decision. This is not to say that some accounting data cannot be used for decision-making purposes. But they can rarely be used as they stand because they were collected and calculated for another purpose, primarily that of finding out retrospectively what the profit of the business has been. Usually, additional measurements or estimates, dismantling and recomposition of accounting data are necessary to arrive at decision-making data that are useful to operations research. The other quasi cost has to do with sales revenue. If the system can be operated in two modes A and B, where mode A results in a lower sales volume, then there is an opportunity cost of mode A relative to mode B equal to the marginal profit differential between the two modes. But it is quite important to note that the profit differential must be calculated exclusive of the cost differential attributable to a change from mode A to mode B. For example, A and B could be two levels of advertising. The opportunity cost of A relative to B would be the difference in profits, where profits are calculated exclusive of the cost of advertising. The final comparison between the two modes would be made by a cost equation which would include both the opportunity cost and the advertising cost. Of course, this is nothing more than a calculation of over-all profits associated with the two modes, but it is mathematically convenient to use cost notions throughout. This principle is true in general: operations research compares alternative courses of action on the basis of "profits" associated with them, where "profit" is the sum of conventional profit (in the accounting sense) and additional earnings from other investments financed by a reduction of the investment in the business. For the purpose of such comparisons it is sufficient to work with profit differentials rather than total profits, and it is only a matter of mathematical convenience in production and inventory control that the relevant elements of the profit differential are cast into the form of costs.

It should now be clear that a basic feature of costs in operations research is their relativity. There are no costs "as such," but only costs relative to specific courses of action and specific assumptions. It is of the greatest importance, especially in presentations to management, that this *framework of assumptions* be made explicit. Otherwise the nature of the potential savings claimed by an operations research study may be completely misunderstood. Of special importance are assumptions concerning the reinvestment of any funds freed from the business. Where will the funds be invested, and what will be the expected rate of return? A bank rate, a rate of return on investment in securities, or in other businesses, and in which ones? Other important assumptions will be discussed later. To be sure, all these assumptions must be spelled out *before* an operations research solution is carried out. But they must be repeated when the results are presented. For example, when an operations research study claims a potential profit increase of x dollars, it should be stated that y dollars of this sum represent an increase of conventional profit in the accounting sense—i.e., y dollars will show on the income statement of the enterprise—whereas $x - y$ dollars represent the earnings from assumed reinvestment of liquidated funds in government bonds. Only in this way the communications gap between business men and researchers can be bridged, and disastrous misunderstandings can be avoided.

After this discussion of the costs associated with the system as a whole we turn to the problem of allocating these costs to individual functions such as the carrying of inventory or shortages, setting up for production or other activities, hiring of labor, etc. The costs which we shall associate with these activities are properly regarded as *functional costs*. Even when only the conventional costs of the whole system are to be allocated, the definition of functional cost is not straightforward. A number of rather arbitrary practices is in common use in cost accounting. If the function to be costed is "production of product 1," it is quite usual that the readily identifiable "direct costs" are established for all products, and a portion of the so-called indirect costs and overhead (for example administrative cost) is allocated to the various products in proportion to their direct costs.   As we shall see, such functional costs are not what is needed in operations research.   Furthermore, the functional breakdown of the system required by operations research will often be different from that used in accounting.   For example, few accounting systems will have setup costs or hiring costs readily available.   Thus, the allocation process must be redone, but it may be possible to use the raw data collected by accounting.   To arrive at a definition of functional costs which is useful in operations research, we must postulate a *fundamental principle:* functional costs which are to be used as parameters in mathematical decision-making models must be so defined that there is agreement between the potential savings predicted by the model and the savings which will be verifiable on the income statement and in the form of returns from new investments after implementation of the mathematical solution.   It will become apparent that this is not a triviality. Let us turn once again to the total (conventional) cost per accounting period which appears on the income statement.   This cost can be decomposed into a number of contributions each of which is the product of a unit cost c_i and a volume factor V_i.   For example, the labor cost per month is the product of the monthly pay per worker and the number of workers in the system.   With some imagination, similar volume factors and unit costs may be defined for all natural cost categories.   We may, therefore, write the total (conventional) cost in the form

$$C = \sum_{i=1}^{m} c_i V_i \qquad (4.21)$$

It is immediately obvious that the income statement will show no change in costs unless a change of the system variables V_i is made. This observation is of the greatest importance.   For example, it may well be that the direct labor cost associated with setting up for production is substantial, and that the economic-lot-size formula calls for higher inventories and less frequent setups.   But if management is unwilling to reduce the numbers of workers (the relevant system variable in this case) despite the reduction of setups, and prefers to have them sweep the floor more frequently, then the income statement will not show a cost reduction but an increased cost because of higher inventories.   We conclude that our functional costs must be defined relative to a specific set of assumptions concerning the changes of system variables.   These assumptions are part of the general framework of assumptions mentioned earlier, and should also be presented to management when the nature of possible savings is discussed. More specifically, one has to perform the following conceptual experiment. A change is made in the "activity level" of a given function. A statement is made as to which system variables are to be held constant during the experiment, and which ones may be adjusted to their respective minimum levels required for operating the system in its steady state after the transition. The new set of system variables for the steady state is computed. Then, Eq. 4.21 yields the new system cost. The difference between the old and the new system cost is, by definition, the functional cost attributable to the particular change in activity level. The details of the change are fixed by the framework of assumptions. Similarly, we define the investment which enters the calculation of opportunity cost. We locate the particular subset of system variables V_i which change only temporarily, that is during the transient period. Obviously, the (conventional) cost determined by this subset also changes temporarily. It is the amount of this change which defines the investment that can be liquidated or must be pumped into the system as a consequence of the change in activity level. The details of the change are fixed by the framework of assumptions.

We shall discuss some illustrative examples. Consider first the problem of determining the *inventory carrying cost* for a finished goods inventory in a manufacturing operation. The good is consumed (and produced) at a given average rate. A suitable measure of the activity level of the inventory carrying function is the (average) number of physical units in stock. To determine the carrying cost per physical unit per unit time, we perform the conceptual experiment of reducing the inventory level by a number of units. We assume that this will be accomplished by cutting production temporarily while consumption continues at its previous rate. We first examine the system variables in the steady state, that is after production has returned to its previous level (see Table 4.1). V_1, the volume of raw materials consumed by the production process per unit time, will probably be unchanged. Conceivably, it could be somewhat lower because less spoilage might result from the lower inventory*. Accounting records on spoilage are sometimes available. Assuming the first case, the cost of raw materials will not change. The same is true for labor cost and depreciation of equipment. The storage space requirements for the new inventory will undoubtedly be lower. Whether the cost will be low-

---

* A similar problem is that of obsolescence. Sometimes the danger of obsolescence can be reduced by proper communication between engineering and production. For an example see [12], Chapter 2. The influence of design changes is discussed in [55].

ered depends on whether or not the actual amount of space owned or rented by the company is reduced. If not, no allowance for storage space should be included in the inventory carrying cost. The cost of insurance will be changed only if the terms of the insurance policy are changed. Similarly with other items which may have to be considered: taxes, heat and light, alarm service, stock maintenance labor, supervision, supplies, and so on. This procedure establishes the "conventional cost" component of the inventory carrying cost per unit per unit time. Clearly, reference to accounting data is made continuously, but they are regrouped and reinterpreted. To mention a likely exception, the storage requirement for an inventory of a given size will normally have to be measured directly.

In order to establish the opportunity cost component of carrying cost, we first examine the system variables for the transient period. Undoubtedly, the cost of materials will be temporarily reduced. If— and only if—temporary layoffs are made, the cost of labor will be temporarily reduced. Similarly, the cost of utilities used by the plant and the transportation cost for raw materials may be reduced. It all depends on the assumptions and restrictions imposed on the transient process. A change in storage cost is not a temporary but a permanent change and should not be considered here. All other variables are treated similarly. In our particular example, temporary savings—say, out of an unchanged cash budget—can be realized in the areas of materials, labor, utilities, and transportation. The investment liquidated in this way—and only this amount—will be considered as capital capable of earning a return from other investments. Further assumptions would have to be made about the specifics of reinvestment so that a rate of return would be determined. The annual return on the investment liquidated per physical unit is then added to the "conventional cost" part of the annual carrying cost per unit. Most empirical studies arrive at a total annual carrying cost of between 10% and 25% of investment. Some accounting systems charge a so-called imputed interest of, say, 4% of the book value of inventories. This practice has nothing in common with the operations research approach just presented. The book value is based on production cost which includes, for example, depreciation and overhead. This fact alone shows that the book value has nothing to do with the capital that can actually be liquidated and produce additional earnings.

The *cost of carrying shortages* is even more distant from accounting notions of cost, and is undoubtedly most difficult to determine in practice. Once again, great emphasis must be placed on the general framework of assumptions. What will happen when an excess of demand over supply occurs? In highly competitive situations, as in food retailing, or in the case of highly fashionable or seasonal products, the customer will not be willing to wait, and a shortage is almost certainly equivalent to a lost sale. (Parenthetically, it appears that nothing sensible can be said about possible long-run losses due to customer aggravation. These are not considered here.) If the average level of shortage were reduced, steady-state sales revenue would increase by the same amount. Other system variables in the area of conventional costs would have to be adjusted in order to support the higher sales activity. The profit differential between the two states, the so-called marginal profit, assumes the role of opportunity cost in this case. A good approximation to marginal profit can be found by separating the system variables into those which are likely to remain constant when sales are increased, and those which will vary in proportion with sales (fixed and variable costs). As in the inventory case, it would be fallacious to use accounting data about the profitability of given products. The marginal profit is usually greater than these data would indicate. In other cases, the customer may be willing to wait for a limited amount of time, and the company may take special action such as expediting, provisioning from other sources, use of overtime in production. Specific assumptions must be made as to just what will be done. Payroll, transportation, traveling and communication may be affected but, to repeat, only if the system variables are changed as a consequence of special action, and not if the system is flexible enough to absorb such shocks. In some instances it may be possible to divide the chances between the lost-sales case and the expediting case. On occasion, it may also be desirable to give consideration to the cost of shortage to the customer, especially when the supplier and the customer are part of a larger over-all system. In a study of spare parts provisioning for aircraft maintenance, it was argued that a lower stock reliability would, in fact, force the customer to increase his fleet of airplanes. In such cases the cost of shortage can be based on the increased cost of stand-by equipment. Some military applications make use of "essentiality factors" for spare parts [41]. Because of the difficulties in obtaining numerical estimates of shortage costs, many studies avoid this concept altogether: the mathematical problem is modified by introducing a restriction on the *frequency* of shortages, or by prescribing a "maximum reasonable demand" which the system should be prepared to handle routinely [7]. But even when no numerical estimate can be obtained, the cost of shortage remains a useful mathematical device. This point will further be discussed in the section "The Method of Efficient Surfaces" where the role of the cost parameters as Lagrangian multipliers is uncovered. Another somewhat indirect approach is sometimes useful. By considering the presently pursued inventory policy as optimal relative to an unknown shortage cost, it is possible to calculate the "implied" shortage cost with the aid of a mathematical model. The result of such calculations may be surprising and cause management to come up with a more reasonable cost of shortage which may then become the basis for arriving at a more truly optimal inventory policy.

During our discussion thus far, the important principles and the methodology for determination of functional cost parameters have been exposed. We shall, therefore, restrict ourselves to some brief remarks about the remaining functions listed in Table 4.1. As regards *setup cost*, "lost production" should be a consideration only if the plant is working at capacity and if fewer setups would actually increase sales so that a marginal profit could be earned. Other items which may or may not be included, depending on the framework of assumptions, are (quoted from [12], Chapter 2):

1. *Office setup.* Before anything is done in the shop, the Production Planning Department must plan the production and the Standards Department must prepare necessary drawings and control forms.
2. *Shop setup cost.* This consists of the cost of actually adjusting the production equipment to perform the required operations, the cost of scrap which is involved in making adjustments at the beginning of the run, and the cost of setting up the quality inspection procedure.
3. *Shop takedown costs.* This involves the cost of entering the finished product into stock and performing the necessary paperwork attached thereto.
4. *Office takedown.* This is the cost of the analysis performed by the Cost Analysis Section.

If stock items are ordered from outside sources, the fixed charge s per order may have to include the cost of communication (telephone call, etc.) and the cost of paper work of the purchasing department. It must also be kept in mind that the setup cost under a new control system may be higher than the present value because of more costly procedures such as formal preparation of forecasts, use of mathematical decision rules, keeping of additional records, etc. The determination of such new cost elements may even require some experimentation with and time studies of the new procedures.

Possible factors in the *cost of hiring* are interviewing, advertising, lost production because of learning and training problems, paper work. Similarly, for a *cost of layoff*, one may have to consider paper work, contributions to an unemployment fund, rearrangement of job assignments according to union seniority rules, and the learning and training problems associated with such changes.

All in all, the determination of functional costs for decision-making models is not an easy task. It is perhaps a good rule that it should not be carried out without frequent reference to the income statement of the enterprise, with the principles of this section in mind. The effect of errors in cost parameters will be studied in a later section. The fact remains that in some cases the cost parameters cannot be determined satisfactorily. As mentioned earlier, this should not be an argument against the concept of these parameters which remain practically useful as Lagrangian multipliers (see the section "The Method of Efficient Surfaces").

INFERENCES FOR THE TOTAL SYSTEM

It is essential to keep in mind that the final goal of every inventory study must be to make statements about the total system rather than the individual item. In the following, the term "total system" refers to *all items included in the scientific control scheme*. Management is not and cannot be interested in detail information but will base the ultimate acceptance or rejection of a proposed control system on a few aggregate characteristics. It is of great importance that the aggregate evaluation be given in terms which are meaningful to management. Typically, management wishes answers to the following questions.

1. Considering the total system, what will be the:
   a. average inventory investment J (in dollars)?
   b. stock reliability λ (percentage of the total number of demands per year which is filled directly from stock)?
   c. number N of replenishment orders per year under the proposed control system?
2. How does this compare with present performance?

The breakdown (a), (b), (c) will normally be desired regardless of whether or not a common cost denominator for these three conflicting factors has been found. Since a detailed inventory study must normally be restricted to a sample of all items in the system, we are faced with the problem of drawing inferences for the total system from the sample investigated in the study. To be specific, we shall assume that our decision model is the generalized (probabilistic) classical economic-lot-size model (see Eq. 3.24). Deviating somewhat from the exact mathematical model with its interrelationship of reorder point P

and reorder quantity q, we can approximately determine these quantities (see [2]) by the formulas

$$F(\hat{P}) = \frac{d}{hL + d} \tag{4.22}$$

and

$$\hat{q} = \sqrt{\frac{2s\bar{r}}{h}} \tag{4.23}$$

where hL = carrying cost of one unit of product during lead time L
   d = cost per shortage delay
   $F(x)$ = cumulative probability distribution of demand during lead time L
   $\bar{r}$ = mean demand per unit of time

When no meaningful cost of shortage can be obtained, Eq. 4.22 is replaced by

$$F(\hat{P}) = \alpha \tag{4.24}$$

where α is a prechosen (usually high) confidence level. To enhance routine use of Eqs. 4.22–4.23, it is useful to construct nomographs which allow to read off $\hat{P}$ and $\hat{q}$ as functions of the relevant parameters [2]. This is almost a necessity in any large system not utilizing computers.

Equation 4.24 may frequently be written in the form

$$\hat{P} = \bar{r}L + \beta\sigma \tag{4.25}$$

where σ is the standard deviation of demand during lead time L, and β is a constant which depends on the confidence level α in Eq. 4.24. Indicating the parameters of the ith item by a subscript i, we may then write the average inventory investment in item i with unit value c_i:

$$J_i = c_i \left(\beta\sigma_i + \sqrt{\frac{s_i\bar{r}_i}{2h_i}} \right) \tag{4.26}$$

If there are m items in the system, the total average investment is given by

$$J = \sum_{1}^{m} c_i \left(\beta\sigma_i + \sqrt{\frac{s_i\bar{r}_i}{2h_i}} \right) = \sum_{1}^{m} J_i \tag{4.27}$$

A direct evaluation of this expression by computing the contributions of all items would be very tedious and costly. Rewriting J in the following form

$$J = m \left(\frac{1}{m} \sum_{i=1}^{m} J_i \right) = m \bar{J} \qquad (4.28)$$

shows that the problem may be viewed as one of estimating the mean J of the quantity J_i taken over the population of all items i. We may, therefore, expect sampling theory to be helpful in our evaluation. Of course, there is no basis for drawing a sample unless something is known about the (joint) distribution of the basic quantities on which J_i depends. Such knowledge may have to be gained by processing certain basic data for *all* items, but this will normally be easier than processing the J_i for all items. To simplify the situation somewhat, assume that the setup cost has the same value s for all items, and that $h_i = kc_i$. Then,

$$J_i = \beta \sigma_i c_i + \sqrt{\frac{s}{2k}} \sqrt{c_i \bar{r}_i} \qquad (4.29)$$

To estimate the mean of $\sqrt{c_i \bar{r}_i}$, one may tabulate the quantities $u_i = c_i \bar{r}_i$ for all items and establish the respective fractions of the total population which fall into certain ranges of u_i. In many companies such tabulations are prepared on a routine basis.

Then the values $\sqrt{u_i}$ (which *cannot* be computed on tabulating equipment) may be sampled by drawing items from the different ranges of u_i in proportion to the fractions just established, and the mean of $\sqrt{u_i}$ may be estimated from the sample. This method has its greatest potential for simulation models where the function to be sampled is *not* theoretically known but the parameters which it depends upon can be identified. In the present example, it may be easier to fit a continuous theoretical distribution $g(u)$ to the historgram of u_i and to obtain the mean of $\sqrt{u_i}$ by the integration

$$E(\sqrt{u}) = \int_0^\infty \sqrt{u} \, g(u) \, du \qquad (4.30)$$

Even when numerical integration is necessary—as will normally be the case—this requires considerably less effort than computing thousands of square roots. Of course, the numerical integration is equivalent to computing $\sqrt{u}$ for the mid-point of each class interval of u_i, and weighting the results by the respective fractions of the population which fall into the class intervals.   The evaluation of such integrals is especially convenient when $g(u)$ is a logarithmic-normal distribution. This seems to be frequently the case.   The logarithmic-normal distribution is defined by

$$g(u) = \frac{1}{\sqrt{2\pi}\sigma}\frac{1}{u}\exp\left[-\frac{(\ln u - \mu)^2}{2\sigma^2}\right] \tag{4.31}$$

where $\ln u$ is the natural logarithm of u.   The parameters μ and σ are not to be confused with the mean and standard deviation, respectively, of the random variable u.   The mean of u is given by

$$\bar{u} = e^{\mu + \sigma^2/2} \tag{4.32}$$

and the standard deviation of u by

$$\sigma(u) = \bar{u}\sqrt{e^{\sigma^2} - 1} \tag{4.33}$$

The logarithmic-normal distribution has the remarkable property that any power $z = u^k$ of u is also logarithmic-normally distributed with the same parameter σ.   The expected value of u^k is given by

$$E(u^k) = \bar{u}^k \exp\left[k(k-1)\frac{\sigma^2}{2}\right] \tag{4.34}$$

Thus, we have an explicit formula for evaluating integrals of the form of Eq. 4-30.   For more detailed information concerning the logarithmic-normal distribution, see [7].

All quantities of interest (J, λ, N) may be determined in analogous fashion.   (The reliability factor λ is determined indirectly by finding the expected number of shortage delays.)   If necessary, sampling theory may also be used to derive confidence limits for the results. The quantities (J, λ, N) may then be compared with the set (J_1, λ_1, N_1) describing performance under present procedures.   If meaningful cost parameters k, d, s have been established, the annual system costs to be compared are

$$C = kJ + d(1 - \lambda)R + sN \tag{4.35}$$

and

$$C_1 = kJ_1 + d(1 - \lambda_1)R + sN_1 \tag{4.36}$$

where

$$R = \sum_{i=1}^{m} \bar{r}_i \tag{4.37}$$

These estimates of total cost are (at most) as reliable as the estimates of the cost parameters k, d, s. Since there is usually some doubt about the reliability of the latter, it is advisable to ask the question: how much error in the cost parameters could be tolerated before the proposed decision rules would become inferior to the present rules, i.e., before $C > C_1$ would hold? By Eqs. 4.35–4.36, the condition $C > C_1$ is equivalent to

$$k(J - J_1) + dR (\lambda_1 - \lambda) + s(N - N_1) > 0 \qquad (4.38)$$

This relation may be used to find the ranges of k, d, s for which the proposed rules will be superior. If these ranges are relatively wide and the cost estimates lie well inside the ranges, one will be less reluctant to implement the "optimal" policy.

Finally, a new control system may bring about changes in the parameters of the inventory system. Most important of all, increased stock reliability $\lambda > \lambda_1$ may lead to increased sales so that the parameters $\bar{r}_i$ would be distorted. Sometimes this is the major reason for introducing a new control system. Then the historical data are no longer valid for the testing of the control system. Since the new sales picture usually is quite intangible, some assumptions are inevitable. We shall use the asterisk to denote quantities corresponding to the increased sales level. Let the increased level be equal to γ times the old sales level. Regardless of what will be the particular value of γ, it seems reasonable to assume that

$$\frac{\bar{r}_i{}^*}{\bar{r}_i} = \gamma \qquad (4.39)$$

$$\frac{\sigma_i{}^*}{\sigma_i} = \frac{\bar{r}_i{}^*}{\bar{r}_i} = \gamma \qquad (4.40)$$

The second assumption is conservative since the sales picture normally becomes smoother with increasing volume. If we split the inventory investment J_i into its components (see Eq. 4.29),

$$J_{i1} = \beta \sigma_i c_i \qquad (4.41)$$

$$J_{i2} = \sqrt{\frac{s}{2k}} \sqrt{c_i \bar{r}_i} \qquad (4.42)$$

it becomes evident that

$$\frac{J_{i1}{}^*}{J_{i1}} = \gamma \qquad (4.43)$$

$$\frac{J_{i2}{}^*}{J_{i2}} = \sqrt{\gamma} \qquad (4.44)$$

In other words, the "buffer stock" is proportional to sales, and the "variable inventory" is proportional to the square root of sales as long as the product mix is not changing (Eq. 4.39).   By Eq. 4.35, we may therefore write the total cost of an optimal inventory policy at an increased sales volume:

$$C^* = k(J_1{}^* + J_2{}^*) + d(1 - \lambda)R^* + sN^*$$
$$= k(\gamma J_1 + \sqrt{\gamma}J_2) + d\gamma(1 - \lambda)R + s\sqrt{\gamma}N \qquad (4.45)$$

The third term follows from the fact that for each item the number of orders per year is given by

$$N_i = \frac{\bar{r}_i}{\sqrt{(2s\bar{r}_i)/kc_i}} = \sqrt{\frac{kc_i\bar{r}_i}{2s}} \qquad (4.46)$$

so that

$$\frac{N_i{}^*}{N_i} = \sqrt{\gamma} \qquad (4.47)$$

The advantage of Eq. 4.45 lies in the fact that the quantities J_1, J_2, R, and N can be evaluated against actual history, and the results may then be extrapolated to arbitrary sales levels with very little effort. This may be carried out for different levels λ of reliability (note that J_1 is a function of λ since β depends on λ).

THE METHOD OF EFFICIENT SURFACES (PARAMETRIZATION OF COSTS)

We now turn to the case where meaningful cost parameters s, h, d cannot be established.   As in Eqs. 4.22–4.23, we consider only (S, s)-policies of inventory control with the decision variables P_i and q_i for the single item $(i = 1, \cdots, m)$.   Since there is no longer a single measure of performance, inventory policies must be evaluated by the performance variables J, N, B, where

J = average inventory investment
N = number of orders placed per year
B = number of shortage delays per year (assuming backlogging of unfilled demand)

These variables measure the attainment of three conflicting objectives.   Each given inventory policy leads to a *compromise* between these conflicting objectives.   We now define an *efficient compromise* as follows.   For generality's sake assume that there are k conflicting performance variables $V_1, \cdots, V_k$ and n decision variables $x_1, \cdots, x_n$.

Assume further that higher values of V_1 are less desirable than lower ones (example: V_1 is a cost). A compromise

$$V_1 = a_1$$
$$\cdot$$
$$\cdot \tag{4.48}$$
$$\cdot$$
$$V_k = a_k$$

will be called efficient if

$$a_1 = \min_{x_1, \ldots, x_n} V_1(x_1, \cdots, x_n) \tag{4.49}$$

where minimization is subject to the restrictions

$$V_2(x_1, \cdots, x_n) = a_2$$
$$\cdot$$
$$\cdot \tag{4.50}$$
$$\cdot$$
$$V_k(x_1, \cdots, x_n) = a_n$$

In other words, a_1 is the lowest achievable value of V_1 for specified values a_j of all other performance variables ($j = 2, \cdots, k$). In that case, we shall refer to the point ($V_1, \cdots, V_k$) as an efficient point; the corresponding policy will be called an efficient policy. The totality of efficient points constitutes the "efficient surface" of the system in the k-dimensional space. For rather general convexity properties of the functions V_j ($j = 1, \cdots, k$), it can be shown that the efficient surface is independent of the particular objective j selected for minimization (or maximization). It is clear that the search for a "best" policy can be restricted to efficient policies since these are by definition superior to nonefficient policies. (Note that this notion of superiority does not presuppose a single measure of performance.) However, the selection of a "best" policy from among the *efficient* policies requires a value judgment. Since it has been assumed that the value judgment cannot be expressed in terms of relative weights of the conflicting objectives, the only alternative is to present the decision maker with a complete survey of the possible efficient compromises, and have him select what he judges to be the "best" compromise.

This method of efficient surfaces is in many ways superior to the method of preassigned weights (cost parameters s, h, d in the inventory example; see Eqs. 4.22–4.23). It does not assume a linear value scale; all it requires is a rank ordering of the different states of each variable V_j (topological scale). This can be of great importance in treating even such seemingly simple variables as cost of inventory investment.

It is true that this cost may often be treated as a linear function of investment in a certain range, but as investment approaches a level at which it may critically affect the company's credit rating or become inconsistent with top management policy, inventory cost becomes highly nonlinear. The efficient surface lets the executive be aware of what he chooses in terms of total system performance whereas an "optimal policy" based on estimated microparameters s, h, d may lead to surprises in total system performance. This is a strong argument in favor of introducing the value judgment *after* rather than before the mathematical solution (minimization). Thus, the efficient surface may be the best basis for making the required value judgment. This point may further be illustrated by the following example. Assume two conflicting variables, V_1 and V_2. Figure 4-1 shows two hypothetical efficient curves for two different systems. In the case of the lower curve, the value a_1 of V_1 can be achieved with a much lower value of V_2 than is the case for the upper curve. Consequently, the decision maker is likely to settle for a higher value of V_1 in the case of the upper curve. In other words, the nature of the relationship between achievable levels of conflicting objectives will influence the value judgment of the decision maker. This fundamental fact can be reflected by preassigned weights only in a rather imperfect manner.

When it is decided to use the method of efficient surfaces the task of operations research reduces to the construction of the efficient surface and its presentation in a form which is meaningful to management. Computationally, the construction of many efficient points means, of course, an increase in effort in comparison with the single measure of performance. The minimization Eq. 4.49, may be carried out by the

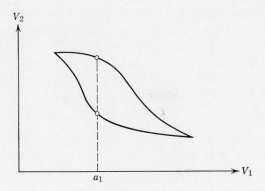

Fig. 4-1.

method of Lagrangian multipliers.   The Lagrangian function may be written as

$$V_1 + \mu_2(V_2 - a_2) + \cdots + \mu_k(V_k - a_k) \qquad (4.51)$$

where $a_2, \cdots, a_k$ are given and the minimum value a_1 of V_1 is sought. By standard methods, the system of equations for the unknowns

$$x_1, \cdots, x_n \qquad \mu_2, \cdots, \mu_k$$

is given by

$$\frac{\partial}{\partial x_u}(V_1 + \mu_2 V_2 + \cdots + \mu_k V_k) = 0 \qquad (u = 1, \cdots, n) \qquad (4.52)$$

$$V_j = a_j \qquad (j = 2, \cdots, k) \qquad (4.53)$$

In this formulation the a_j play the role of data inputs which are varied in order to obtain different efficient points.   Alternatively, one may consider the μ_j as the varying data inputs and the a_j as unknowns. Then the problem is greatly simplified.   Equations 4.52 now constitute a separate system for $x_1, \cdots, x_n$; its solutions may be substituted in Eq. 4.53 to obtain the a_j $(j = 2, \cdots, k)$; a_1 is obtained in the same way.   Since all equations are satisfied, we have the same solution which we would have derived had we postulated the obtained values a_j $(j = 2, \cdots, k)$ at the start.   This may also be seen more directly.   Equations (4.52) are conditions for the minimization of the function

$$V(x_1, \cdots, x_n) = V_1 + \mu_2 V_2 + \cdots + \mu_k V_k \qquad (4.54)$$

for given constants μ_j.   The solutions $x_1, \cdots, x_n$ of this minimization problem lead to the values a_j of V_j $(j = 1, \cdots, k)$.   Clearly, a_1 is the minimum value of V_1 achievable under the restrictions of Eq. 4.53 since, otherwise, $\Sigma_1^k a_j$ would not, in fact, be the minimum value of $V(x_1, \cdots, x_n)$.   Thus, for each set of Lagrangian multipliers μ_j, an efficient point is obtained by minimizing the function 4.54.   This offers an interesting interpretation of the Lagrangian multipliers.   In fact, we would have obtained the same criterion function 4.54 had we had preassigned weights for the variables $V_1, \cdots, V_k$.   Each μ_j $(j = 2, \cdots, k)$ may be interpreted as a ratio of weights so that our method is equivalent to a parametrization of weights.   The construction of the efficient surface may be viewed as a process of mapping the $(k - 1)$-dimensional space of weight ratios into the k-dimensional space of objectives.

Returning to the inventory problem, we have the three performance variables J, B, N; Eq. 4.54 written in terms of weight ratios takes the form

$$V = N + \frac{k}{s} J + \frac{d}{s} B = N + \mu_1 J + \mu_2 B \qquad (4.55)$$

where

$$\mu_1 = \frac{k}{s}; \qquad \mu_2 = \frac{d}{s} \qquad (4.56)$$

For each choice of values (μ_1, μ_2) the function 4.55 is to be minimized with respect to the decision variables q_i, P_i $(i = 1, \cdots, m)$. Since the function V can be split in the following manner,

$$V = \sum_{i=1}^{m} V_i(q_i, P_i) \qquad (4.57)$$

where each contribution V_i depends only on one item i, differentiation leads back to familiar decision rules for each individual item. Thus, a point N, J, B of the efficient surface is obtained in a straightforward manner. It is, of course, more reasonable to translate B into a reliability factor

$$\lambda = \frac{B}{R} \qquad (4.58)$$

where R is the total number of units demanded per year. The efficient surface will be of the type shown in Fig. 4-2.

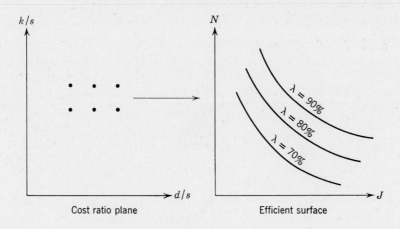

Cost ratio plane   Efficient surface

Fig. 4-2.

G. Feeney [23] has used the method of efficient surfaces in an inventory study for a major railroad which involved many thousands of items. In this particular case study, calculation of the quantities N, J, λ was carried out by a computer simulation based on actual demand history for a sample of about 400 items. Thus, the prediction model was a simulation model.* The decision model was the generalized classical model (see Eq. 3.24). The forecast was of the simple type, "the next six months will be like the last six months." It should be noted that the construction of each efficient point requires a new simulation of all 400 items over the test period. As one would expect, the point describing the actual performance of the system did not lie on the efficient surface. The graph of the efficient surface was presented to management and after some discussion lead to the selection of a point (N, J, λ) which represented the desired compromise between the conflicting objectives. The corresponding decision rules were implemented and, after a transition period with peak inventories, led to a steady state with 20% inventory reduction and no significant change in either stock reliability or number of orders processed. This result was in accordance with prediction. For similar studies in retailing, see [53, 56]. Feeney has also offered the interesting opinion that the cost parameters s, h, d—as well as any other internal cost of a business enterprise—are not to be regarded as "real" costs at all; they should only be considered as "dial settings" reflecting management philosophy of resource allocation. Thus, the Lagrangian multipliers are not further interpreted.

THE USE OF DATA-PROCESSING EQUIPMENT IN PRODUCTION AND INVENTORY CONTROL

We have briefly mentioned the use of computer simulations as a research tool. Data-processing equipment may also be useful in the actual day-to-day control operations. As many other activities within a complex system, the activities related to production and inventory control may be partially or fully mechanized. The extent to which this can be done depends—aside from economics—on the degree of formalization of rules. As long as ordering decisions involve judgment they cannot be made mechanically; but when mathematical decision rules are used, mechanization becomes possible. Thus, the

---

* Recently a special-purpose data-processing system for this type of analysis was developed at Stanford Research Institute. See D. A. D'Esopo and B. Lefkowitz, "An Inventory System Evaluator," abstract in *Operations Research* **9**, Supplement 1 (Bulletin), Spring 1961.

optimal ordering rules provided by operations research may lead to a double payoff through better inventory decisions and higher potential for mechanization, provided that mechanization can be done economically. Depending on the degree of formalization, the following typical activities may lend themselves to mechanization:

1. Record keeping of:
   a. stock on hand;
   b. stock on order;
   c. stock movements.
2. Forecasting of requirements (demand).
3. Making ordering decisions—order issuance.

Although a considerable number of computer applications in inventory control has been reported in various magazines (for a survey see the sections "Inventory Control," "Material Control and Production Control," and "Order Processing" in [10]), few seem to go beyond step 1. In this connection it may be worth while to note that the term "control" in business language usually refers to some kind of historical record keeping. Its meaning does not include any decision making or action—obviously a very unfortunate use of the word control which markedly differs from the usage preferred in this book (see Introduction). Of course, mechanization of record keeping must precede steps 2 and 3. Therefore, the present stage of mechanization is, in part, a natural evolutionary stage but also reflects the reluctance of management to "trust" either the formalized forecasting and decision rules, or the computer, or both.

The most important media used for record keeping in large inventory systems are magnetic tape, cards, and magnetic-disk storage [9]. The latter is used in IBM's RAMAC (random-access memory), a popular device for warehouse record keeping. In the case of tape, a segment of a "master tape" is assigned to each item for recording of certain characteristics of the item and a certain amount of inventory and movement history. One of the most important pieces of information is, of course, the balance on hand. As withdrawals from stock and receipts into stock occur, a machine-readable record of these transactions must be made. Either directly or indirectly, the transactions are recorded on a "transactions tape." Usually, the information on the transaction tape must first be sorted into the item sequence used on the master tape. Then, the computer updates the master tape by posting all transactions to their proper account. In many inventory systems, billing and other accounting transactions are inevitably linked with physical inventory transactions. These can often be handled by the computer at very small additional cost and are an important consideration in relation to computer economics. As can be seen from this sketch, sorting, merging, collating, addition, and subtraction are the ever recurring elements of business record keeping. A good business computer must be able to perform these quite elementary functions efficiently. One of the major cost items is the original recording of transactions in machine language. Sometimes this problem can be simplified by prepunching a larger number of cards corresponding to the various physical units in stock ("tub file" method). As transactions occur, cards are added or deleted. The tub file becomes in effect an analog of the physical stock. The following quotation from [10], p. 492 is an interesting contribution toward an evaluation of mechanized record keeping: "Maybe it is just coincidence, but we have searched the literature in vain for claims of actual cost savings, or other dollar benefits, in the approaches just discussed". But it should not be overlooked that mechanized record keeping may substantially reduce the reporting lag and give more up-to-date inventory information; this, in turn, is equivalent to a decrease in lead time and may enhance a substantial reduction of safety stocks.

The next logical step is to let the computer calculate forecasts and ordering decisions based on the historical data on the master tape. Computers also lend themselves to certain other routine forecasting methods, for example, explosion of orders on hand to determine parts requirements. Such applications often involve elementary matrix algebra, especially matrix multiplication in the case of parts listing by explosion and determination of materials requirements for a given production schedule [62, 50]. Similarly, work loads for machine centers and other information of interest in scheduling may be projected. These applications may also be considered as mechanized order processing. When decision-making functions are performed by a computer, substantial savings can result. In the case of an inventory system at Sperry Gyroscope Company, annual savings of $100,000 in operating cost were reported [59, 10]. But it is not clear how much of these savings were due to improved decision rules and how much to mechanization. It is wise to investigate carefully this question in each individual case. Finally, it should be kept in mind that a number of items may require handling by exception. For example, if certain items are included in a sales promotion program, then the computerized forecasting scheme based on historical movement becomes meaningless.

Generally speaking, all ground rules and principles for automation and mechanization are equally valid in the specific area of production and inventory control activities.   A number of more detailed discussions and case studies can be found in [18, 19, 20, 25, 30, 45, 50, 58].

PROBLEMS OF TRANSITION AND IMPLEMENTATION

It has been pointed out earlier that no "scientific" inventory control system can be implemented unless demand forecasts have been provided for.   It is, therefore, not surprising that inventory studies have often given rise to the first systematic forecasting activity in an operation, or have led to considerable improvement in information processing and paper work, occasionally to the point of a major reorganization.   Here lie major payoffs which, indirectly, are to the credit of inventory theory.   An example of this kind is a study done for Cummins Engine Company which involved installation of reorder points and reorder quantities for parts with price breaks but ultimately produced an integrated process control system with substantially reduced production lead time because of improved parts availability and acceleration of paper work, in addition to significant out-of-pocket savings [2].   In some extreme cases, companies have been able to reduce their inventories by as much as 50% and, simultaneously, give improved delivery to the customer.   It is clear that such results rest essentially on better information about customer demand.

Therefore, one of the first and most important steps in implementation is to organize a formal forecasting activity.   Similarly, procedures for the use of the decision rules must be spelled out.   In this area, new problems may arise for such simple reasons as the fact that inventory records are often out of phase with the actual inventory. This difficulty can be met by incorporating the reporting lag in the mathematical model (i.e., by setting higher reorder points).   Alternatively, one may try to reduce the reporting lag by organizational changes.   Sometimes, the use of electronic computers may be warranted to obtain up-to-date inventory information (see previous section).   As mentioned earlier, the cost of a formal forecasting activity as well as any other change in procedures must not be overlooked.   If after consideration of all factors the savings are small, one will usually prefer to avoid the disturbance which is inevitably caused by the introduction of a new system.

The period of transition from an existing to a new control system poses a considerable problem in most applications.   For example, when greater lot sizes are recommended, more storage facilities may be required; the higher inventories must be financed; in production, care must be taken that the occurrence of shortages is not drastically increased in the transition period; to realize savings, staff reductions are necessary. Companies often shrink back from layoffs so that the staff reduction may have to be accomplished through attrition. All in all, it will seldom be possible to make a quick transition. Especially in production, lot sizes must be changed gradually in the direction of economic-lot-sizes. In one case, the installation of economic-lot-sizes for the production of parts had to be planned over a period of two years [12].

Even when an inventory reduction is ultimately expected under a new system, the transition period may lead to peak inventories since all items with too low inventory levels under the new system are immediately ordered, but no compensating effect is present for those items with too high levels under the new system. Sometimes it is necessary to change the system only for a few items at a time.

OTHER APPLICATIONS OF INVENTORY CONCEPTS

The elementary concepts of inventory control have also been applied to a number of problems whose interpretation as inventory problems is not immediately apparent. This is true of the reorder point concept in particular. Normally, a reorder point for a decreasing inventory level is sought. Demand is assumed to be statistically stable. In some cases, however, the role of inventory level is assumed by the slack capacity of facilities used to satisfy a *changing* demand. The question arises when, that is, at what level of demand, new capacity should be ordered. We shall discuss several examples.

In evaluating the adequacy of airport parking lots [39] for a given future year, it is necessary to forecast the probability distribution of demand for parking spaces for that year. The optimal size of the lot is defined as that size which minimizes total expected cost of overage and shortage of spaces for the year under consideration. If this optimal size falls below the actual size, the lot is still adequate. The cost of shortage in this application was taken to consist of lost parking lot revenues, airport revenues, and administrative cost of responding to bad will created among displaced parking lot patrons. The cost of overage is the cost of building and operating an excess space. These costs could be determined. The forecast of demand for parking spaces was based on forecasts of air traffic and related traffic magnitudes and patterns.

A similar study was conducted for an electric utility company [1]. Here the question was: When should additional generating capacity be added to the existing system? In this case, no cost of shortage associated with inability to satisfy customer demand for power could be established. Rather, it was determined at what point of time the *probability* of shortage would rise above a certain specified level. This could be done by using historical data about generator outages and a forecast of demand for power. To give management all the pertinent information, the forecasting error of demand as well as several other variables of interest were parametrized. This approach has also been used for timing the acquisition of new electronic computing capacity (unpublished report, Case Institute of Technology); see also [40]. A very interesting application to engineering works is found in Bibliography D [45]. Here, a fixed cost was associated with each installation.

The newsboy model has almost universal applicability. Whenever there is a problem of balancing costs of overages and shortages in a situation involving uncertainties, it is likely to be of the newsboy type. Determination of the optimal raw materials input for a production process with uncertain (probabilistic) yield [51], setting of targets for specifications of a product which is manufactured with random errors [33], stocking of "style goods" for an essentially one-time demand [31], stocking of spare parts which are manufactured only once during the lifetime of certain equipment, are but a few examples. In the manufacture of steel rails, scrap losses could be reduced by 4% by setting the length target optimally. Similar examples have been reported in the food packaging industry [52].

BIBLIOGRAPHY C

Applications of Static Single-Station Models

1. Arnoff, E. L., Chambers, J. C., "On the Determination of Optimum Reserve Generating Capacity in an Electric Utility System," *Operations Research*, **4**, No. 4 (Aug. 1956), 468–479.
2. Arnoff, E. L., Kania, E. B., Small Day, E., "An Integrated Process Control System at the Cummins Engine Company," *Operations Research*, **6**, No. 4 (July–Aug. 1958), 467–497.
3. Beckmann, M. J., "An Inventory Policy for Repair Parts," *Naval Research Logistics Quarterly*, **6**, No. 3 (Sept. 1959), 209–220.
4. Beckmann, M. J., "An Inventory Model for Repair Parts—Approximations in the Case of Variable Delivery Time," *Operations Research*, **7**, No. 2 (Mar.–Apr. 1959), 256–258.
5. Beckmann, M. J., Bobkoski, F., "Airline Demand: An Analysis of Some Frequency Distributions," *Naval Research Logistics Quarterly*, **5**, No. 1 (Mar. 1958), 43–52.
6. Bowman, E. H., Fetter, R. B., *Analysis for Production Management*, Homewood, Illinois: Richard D. Irwin, 1957.

7. Brown, Robert G., *Statistical Forecasting for Inventory Control*, New York: McGraw-Hill Book Company, 1959.

8. Brown, W. M., "Measuring Physical Inventories," *Journal of the American Statistical Association*, **43** (Sept. 1948), 377–390.

9. Canning, R. C., *Electronic Data Processing for Business and Industry*, New York: John Wiley & Sons, 1956.

10. Canning, Sisson and Associates, *EDP Idea Finder, Data Processing Digest 1957 · 1958 · 1959*, Los Angeles, California: Canning, Sisson and Associates, Inc., 1960.

11. Chambers, J. C., Bond, A. F., Leake, J. H., "Optimum Lot Sizes for Parts Used in Aircraft Production," *Operations Research*, **6**, No. 3 (May–June 1958), 385–398.

12. Churchman, C. W., Ackoff, R. L., Arnoff, E. L., *Introduction to Operations Research*, New York, John Wiley & Sons, 1957.

13. Clark, C. E., "Mathematical Analysis of an Inventory Case," *Operations Research*, **5**, No. 5 (Oct. 1957), 627–643.

14. Clark, W. V. A., Jr., Ritchie, W. E., "Economic Lot Size and Inventory Control," *NACA Bulletin*, **34**, No. 6 (Feb. 1953), 772–782.

15. Collcutt, R. H., Banburry, J., Massey, R. G., Ward, R. A., "A Method of Fixing Desirable Stock Levels, and of Stock Control," *Operational Research Quarterly*, **10**, No. 2 (June 1959).

16. Culbertson, R. W., Holt, Ch. C., "Production Control and Inventory Control Practices and Problems as Evidenced by a Survey of Eleven American Companies," *Middle Atlantic Conference Transactions*, American Society for Quality Control, 1956.

17. Davis, R. H., "Optimal Inventory Control Decision Rules for a Large Supply System," *Operations Research*, **7**, No. 6 (Nov.–Dec. 1959), 764–782.

18. Day, L. W., "Production Control by Electronics," *Systems*, **19**, No. 4 (July–Aug. 1955), 22–23.

19. DeCarlo, C. R., "The Use of Automatic and Semi-Automatic Processing Equipment in Production and Inventory Control," *Proceedings of the Conference on Operations Research in Production and Inventory Control*, Cleveland, Ohio: Case Institute of Technology, 1954.

20. DeCarlo, C. R., "Application of Electronic Computing Machines to Operations Research Problems," *Operations Research*, **2**, No. 3 (Aug. 1954), 348.

21. English, J. A., Jerome, E. A., "Statistical Methods for Determining Requirements of Dental Materials," *Naval Research Logistics Quarterly*, **1**, No. 3 (Sept. 1954), 191–199.

22. Evans, G. W., "A Transportation and Production Model," *Naval Research Logistics Quarterly*, **5**, No. 2 (June 1958), 137–154.

23. Feeney, G. J., "A Basis for Strategic Decisions on Inventory Control Operations," *Management Science*, **2**, No. 1 (Oct. 1955), 69–82.

24. Flagle, C. D., "Queuing Theory and Cost Concepts Applied to a Problem in Inventory Control," in: *Operations Research for Management, Vol. II*, J. F. McCloskey and J. M. Coppinger (eds.), Baltimore: The Johns Hopkins Press, 1956.

25. Gainen, Leon, "Inventory Control—Exploiting the Electronic Data Processor in the Air Force," *Journal of Industrial Engineering*, **11**, No. 1 (Jan.–Feb. 1959).

26. Garrett, J. H., "Characteristics of Usage of Supply Items Aboard Naval Ships and the Significance to Supply Management," *Naval Research Logistics Quarterly*, **5**, No. 4 (Dec. 1958), 287–306.

27. Geisler, M. A., "Some Principles for a Data-Processing System in Logistics," *Naval Research Logistics Quarterly*, **5**, No. 2 (June 1958), 95–105.

28. Geisler, M. A., "The Simulation of a Large-Scale Military Activity," *Management Science*, **5**, No. 4 (July 1959), 359–368.

29. Harling, J., Bramson, M. J., "Level of Protection Afforded by Stocks (Inventories) in a Manufacturing Industry," *Proceedings of the 1st International Conference on Operational Research*, Bristol, England: John Wright and Sons, 1958, 372–389.

30. Harper, W. F., McGinnity, W. J., "A Completely Mechanized Material Control System," *NACA Bulletin*, **31**, No. 11 (July 1950), 1371–77.

31. Hertz, D. B., Schaffir, K. H., "A Forecasting Method for Management of Seasonal Style-Goods Inventories," *Operations Research*, **8**, No. 1 (Jan.–Feb. 1960), 45–52.

32. Hetter, F. L., "Navy Stratification and Fractionation for Improvement of Inventory Management," *Naval Research Logistics Quarterly*, **1**, No. 2 (June 1954), 75–78.

33. Heumann, H., Nobis, E., "Bestimmung des durchschnittlichen und des wirtschaftlichen Materialverbrauches von Kunststoff bei Kabel- und Leitungsisolierungen," *Metrika*, **2**, No. 3 (1959), 230–238.

34. Heyvaert, A. C., Hurt, A., "Inventory Management of Slow Moving Parts," *Operations Research*, **4**, No. 5 (Oct. 1956), 572–580.

35. Hollingshead, E. F., "An Application of Statistical Techniques to Management of Overseas Supply Operations," *Naval Research Logistics Quarterly*, **1**, No. 2 (June 1954), 82–89.

36. Horne, R. C., "Developing an Engineering Productivity Standard," *Naval Research Logistics Quarterly*, **1**, No. 3 (Sept. 1954), 203–206.

37. Hugli, W. C., Jr., "Production Planning Through Inventory Control," *Management Technology*, **1**, No. 2 (Dec. 1960), 59–65.

38. Hurni, M., "The Use of Operations Research in Inventory Control," *Proceedings of the Conference on Operations Research*, New York: Society for Advancement of Management, (Jan. 1954).

39. Hurst, F. V., Jr., "Evaluating the Adequacy of Airport Parking Lots," *Operations Research*, **3**, No. 4 (Nov. 1955), 522–535.

40. Isaac, E. J., "Note on Selection of Capital Equipment with Uncertain Delivery Date," *Operations Research*, **4**, No. 3 (June 1956), 354–356.

41. Karr, H. W., "A Method of Estimating Spare Parts Essentiality," *Naval Research Logistics Quarterly*, **5**, No. 1 (Mar. 1958), 29–42.

42. Levary, G., "A Pocket-Sized Case Study in Operations Research Concerning Inventory Markdown," *Operations Research*, **4**, No. 6 (Dec. 1956), 738–739.

43. Llewellyn, R. W., "Order Sizes for Job Lot Manufacturing," *Journal of Industrial Engineering*, **11**, No. 3 (May–June, 1959).

44. Lynch, C. F., "Notes on Applied Analytical Logistics in the Navy," *Naval Research Logistics Quarterly*, **1**, No. 2 (June, 1954), 90–102.

45. Macdonald, N., "A Big Inventory Problem and the IBM 702," *Computers and Automation*, **4**, No. 9 (Sept. 1955), 6–12, 38.

46. Magee, J. F., *Production Planning and Inventory Control*, New York: McGraw-Hill Book Company, 1958.

47. Marshall, B. O., Jr., Boggess, W. P. II, "The Practical Calculation of Reorder Points," *Operations Research*, **5**, No. 4 (Aug. 1957), 513–517.

48. McShane, R. E., "Science and Logistics," *Naval Research Logistics Quarterly*, **2**, Nos. 1 and 2 (Mar–June 1955), 1–7.

49. Meade, R., Jr., Fischer, C. A., "Mobile Logistics Support in the 'Passage to

Freedom' Operation," *Naval Research Logistics Quarterly*, **1**, No. 4 (Dec. 1954), 258–264.

50. Mitchell, H. F., "Electronic Computers in Inventory Control," *Proceedings of the Conference on Operations Research in Production and Inventory Control*, Cleveland, Ohio: Case Institute of Technology, 1954.

51. Page, E. S., Muris, S., "The Effect of Departures from Assumption When Manufacturing to a Specification," *Operations Research*, **5**, No. 1 (Feb. 1957), 68–74.

52. Paradiso, L. J., "Significance of Inventories in the Current Economic Situation," *Journal of the American Statistical Association*, **43** (Sept. 1948), 361–376.

53. Pessemier, E. A., "The Management of Grocery Inventories in Supermarkets," *Economic and Business Studies Bulletin No. 32*, Pullman: Washington State University, 1960.

54. Petersen, J. W., Geisler, M. A., "The Costs of Alternative Air Base Stocking and Requisitioning Policies," *Naval Research Logistics Quarterly*, **2**, Nos. 1 and 2 (Mar.–June 1955), 69–82.

55. Petersen, J. W., Steger, W. A., "Design Change Impacts on Airframe Parts Inventories," *Naval Research Logistics Quarterly*, **5**, No. 3 (Sept. 1958), 241–256.

56. Radell, N. J., "An Operations Research Application in Retailing," *Retail Control*, **28**, No. 10 (June 1960), 33–49.

57. Rinehart, R. F., "Effects and Causes of Discrepancies in Supply Operations," *Operations Research*, **8**, No. 4 (July–Aug. 1960), 543–564.

58. Russell, M. E., "A UNIVAC System of Material Control," *Computers and Automation*, **4**, No. 4 (Apr. 1955), 15.

59. Schaefer, Ch. G., "Electronic Brain Manages Sperry Inventory," *Aeronautical Purchasing* (Sept. 1958), 19–21.

60. Shaunty, J. A., Hare, V. C., Jr., "An Airline Provisioning Problem," *Management Technology*, **1**, No. 2 (Dec. 1960), 66–84.

61. Steers, N. I., Jr., "A Past System of Inventory Control," *NACA Bulletin*, **33**, No. 6 (Feb. 1952), 753–760.

62. Vazsonyi, A., "The Use of Mathematics in Production and Inventory Control: I. Theory of Parts Listing. II. Theory of Scheduling," *Management Science*, **1**, No. 1 (Oct. 1954), 70–85; **1**, Nos. 3 and 4 (Apr.–July 1955), 207–223.

63. Whitin, T. M., "On the Span of Central Direction," *Naval Research Logistics Quarterly*, **1**, No. 1 (Mar. 1954), 16–24.

64. Wilson, A. H., Finn, W. R., "Improvise or Plan?," *Naval Research Logistics Quarterly*, **4**, No. 4 (Dec. 1957), 263–267.

65. Winters, Peter R., "Forecasting Sales by Exponentially Weighted Moving Averages," *Management Science*, **6**, No. 3 (Apr. 1960), 324–342.

66. Young, W. M., "Priorities in the Naval Supply System," *Naval Research Logistics Quarterly*, **1**, No. 1 (Mar. 1954), 16–24.

67. Youngs, J. W. T., Geisler, M. A., Brown, B. B., *The Prediction of Demand for Aircraft Spare Parts Using the Method of Conditional Probabilities*, Santa Monica, California: Rand Corporation, Jan. 1955 (Research Memorandum RM-1413).

68. Youngs, J. W. T., Geisler, M. A., Mirkovich, A. R., *Confidence Intervals for Poisson Parameters in Logistics Research*, Santa Monica, California: Rand Corporation, Sept. 1954 (Research Memorandum RM-1357).

chapter 5
Dynamic Models

We have called a model "dynamic" when its parameters change in time. We assume that these parameters or at least their probability distributions are known as functions of time for a certain span of time extending into the future. Usually the parameter of greatest interest in dynamic models is the demand rate. The definition of a long-run optimal policy in a dynamic situation encounters great conceptual difficulty because of the fact that decisions must be based on a continuously changing knowledge of the future. All solutions offered for this problem employ the concept of a "planning horizon."

PLANNING HORIZONS

The method of the "shifting planning horizon" proposes to make decisions in the following way. A time interval of constant length T which immediately follows time t_1 is defined as the planning horizon at time t_1. For this planning horizon, define an expected measure of effectiveness—say, expected cost—relative to the probability distributions *as known at time* t_1. This measure is a function of the planned policy during the horizon and of history up to time t_1. At time t_1, determine the optimal plan by minimizing expected cost for the horizon. Begin implementation of the optimal plan. At a later time t_2, make a new optimal plan based on the horizon at time t_2 and on the knowledge of history up to time t_2. Adjust implementation according to the new plan. Table 5-1 illustrates this procedure for equidistant decision times t_1, t_2, $\cdots$. The ith time period is defined by its endpoints t_i and t_{i+1}. The planning horizon comprises n periods. It should be noted that only the first decision of each plan is final; all others are tentative. Which planning horizon yields the best long run results is a difficult theoretical question which is not discussed here. In practice, it can be answered by simulating the system using different planning horizons. Alternatively, one may include those periods in the horizon to which the immediate decision is most sensitive.

The method of the "fixed planning horizon" proceeds as follows. The time interval T following time t_0 is fixed as the planning horizon once for all. Let t be an arbitrary point of time within this horizon. It seems reasonable that the decision at time t should be a function of t and the history up to time t. (The history up to time t may include information which is equivalent to an improved forecast.) For simplicity's sake, assume that the history can be summarized by a single state variable, say the inventory level I. Then, the decision rule for, say, the quantity to be produced in the next time segment, should be of the form

$$q(t) = g(t, I) \tag{5.1}$$

where I depends on earlier decisions and on the values of random variables which have materialized up to time t. The optimal decision rule

Table 5-1
Decision Plans D_i for a Shifting Horizon of n Periods

Time ＼ Period	1	2	3	$\cdots$	n	$n+1$	$n+2$	$\cdots$	Final Decisions
t_1	D_1'	D_2'	D_3'		D_n'				D_1'
t_2		D_2''	D_3''		D_n''	D_{n+1}''			D_2''
t_3			D_3'''		D_n'''	D_{n+1}'''	D_{n+2}'''		D_3'''
$\cdot$									$\cdot$
$\cdot$									$\cdot$
$\cdot$									$\cdot$

is given by the particular function $g(t, I)$ which minimizes the expected cost for the horizon. It should be noted, however, that expected cost is now defined relative to a preconceived *type* of decision rule (Eq. 5.1) as well as a given relationship between forecast and history for each point of time. Once the optimal function $f(t, I)$ has been determined, decisions are made without further calculations by simply evaluating the decision function at each decision point t. The dynamic programming solution of the Arrow-Harris-Marschak model in Chapter 3 is an example of the fixed-horizon approach.

Combinations of both methods are conceivable. Mathematically, both methods have in common the minimization of expected cost for a given planning horizon. The following discussion will be centered on this minimization (or maximization) problem for specific models.

DYNAMIC VERSION OF THE CLASSICAL MODEL

The classical model is concerned with the minimization of total setup cost and inventory carrying cost. Consider a planning horizon of n decision periods, and assume that the demands r_i for the different periods $i = 1, \cdots, n$ are given. When a quantity $q_i > 0$ is produced in period i, a setup cost s_i is incurred; on the other hand, a positive inventory level I_i at the end of period i gives rise to a holding cost of amount $h_i I_i$. Variable production costs per unit are assumed to be the same for all periods. Since both shortages and overages are fully carried over to the next period, the closing inventory in period i is

$$I_i = I_0 + \sum_{j=1}^{i} (q_j - r_j) \qquad (i = 1, \cdots, n) \qquad (5.2)$$

where I_0 is the starting inventory at the beginning of the horizon. We shall only consider production policies which avoid shortages:

$$I_i \geq 0 \qquad (i = 1, \cdots, n) \qquad (5.3)$$

The problem of balancing total setup cost and inventory carrying cost may be stated as follows. Minimize

$$C = \sum_{1}^{n} (s_i x_i + h_i I_i) \qquad (5.4)$$

with respect to $q_1, \cdots, q_n$ subject to the restrictions

$$q_i, I_i \geq 0 \qquad (i = 1, \cdots, n) \qquad (5.5)$$

where x_i is defined as

$$x_i = \begin{cases} 0 & \text{if } q_i = 0 \\ 1 & \text{if } q_i > 0 \end{cases} \qquad (5.6)$$

Since this model is a special case of the finite Arrow-Harris-Marschak model (with changing demand distributions of variance zero), it can be solved by dynamic programming. However, we shall present a simplified method of solution developed by H. M. Wagner and T. M. Whitin [66].

It may be assumed that $I_0 < r_1$. Consequently, production must take place in the first period. If we now redefine r_1 as the actual demand during the first period minus the actual starting inventory, we can treat the problem under the assumption of zero starting inventory.   The following properties of an optimal solution are plausible but may easily be substantiated by rigorous proof [66]:

1. No production will take place unless the inventory level has dropped to zero.

2. If production takes place, the production quantity q_k is exactly equal to the total demand for a number of future periods:

$$q_k = \sum_{j=k}^{i} r_j \tag{5.7}$$

for some i with $k \leq i \leq n$.   In other words, no fractions of periods are served.

Now let M_i be the minimum achievable cost for the *first* i periods. Out aim is to determine M_n and the corresponding production decisions.   Consider the problem of finding M_i when all M_k with $k < i$ are already known.   It is clear that minimum cost for the first i periods can be achieved only if $I_i = 0$.   Therefore, if q_k ($q_k > 0$, $k \leq i$) is the last production run made in the optimal plan for the first i periods, it follows from properties 1 and 2 that

$$q_k = \sum_{j=k}^{i} r_j \tag{5.8}$$

and

$$I_{k-1} = 0 \tag{5.9}$$

Consequently, the optimal policy for the first i periods is composed of the optimal policy for the first $k - 1$ periods and one additional production decision q_k for a particular value of k.   To find this particular value, it suffices to examine the just described composite policies for all values of k ($1 \leq k \leq i$) and to select the policy with lowest cost. The cost of an optimal policy for the first $k - 1$ periods is M_{k-1}.   The cost from period k on is s_k plus the inventory charge for periods k through i.   The inventory level in period u, where $k \leq u \leq i$ is given by

$$
\begin{aligned}
I_u &= q_k - \sum_{v=k}^{u} r_v \\
&= \sum_{j=k}^{i} r_j - \sum_{v=k}^{u} r_v
\end{aligned}
\tag{5.10}
$$

The total cost of the composite policy is now seen to be

$$C_{ki} = M_{k-1} + s_k + \sum_{u=k}^{i} h_u \left(\sum_{j=k}^{i} r_j - \sum_{v=k}^{u} r_v \right)$$

$$(1 \le k \le i) \quad (5.11)$$

where

$$M_0 = 0 \qquad M_1 = s_1 \qquad (5.12)$$

We may equivalently write,

$$C_{ki} = \begin{cases} M_{k-1} + s_k + \sum\limits_{u=k}^{i-1} \sum\limits_{j=u+1}^{i} h_u r_j & \text{for } 1 \le k \le i - 1 \\[2em] M_{i-1} + s_i & \text{for } k = i \end{cases} \qquad (5.13)$$

Clearly, M_i is now found by the following minimization process:

$$M_i = \min_{1 \le k \le i} C_{ki}$$

$$= \min \left[M_{i-1} + s_i, \min_{1 \le k \le i-1} \left(M_{k-1} + s_k + \sum_{u=k}^{i-1} \sum_{j=u+1}^{i} h_u r_j \right) \right]$$

$$(5.14)$$

This recurrence relationship holds for all $i = 1, \cdots, n$. Thus it becomes possible to derive M_n and the corresponding production decisions. For rapid computation Table 5-2 is useful. When the column minima M_i are selected the corresponding optimal values of k may be marked at the same time by circling the appropriate cell of the table. It can be shown that the sequence of optimal values of k is nondecreasing (for increasing i). This may be exploited to further simplify computations. The maximum number of calculations of C_{ki}-values is $[n(n + 1)]/2$ which compares favorably with the total number 2^{n-1} of possible production programs.

We now turn to the case where the inventory cost is proportional to the time integral of the positive inventory level rather than to the closing inventory level. The cost parameters s and h are assumed to be constant for the entire horizon of length T. Inputs to the inventory are permitted at arbitrary points of time during the horizon. Shortages are not allowed. The demand rate is a given function $r(t)$ defined in the interval $0 \le t \le T$. Let the cumulative demand at time t be $R(t)$. We first consider the problem of finding the policy with minimum inventory holding cost for a given number m of setups. As before, we may assume that the process starts with zero inventory

Table 5-2
Costs C_{ki} of Composite Policies

Data	s_1	s_2	s_3	$\cdots$	s_n
	r_1	r_2	r_3	$\cdots$	r_n
Optimization Horizon i	1	2	3	$\cdots$	n
Time of Last Order, k					
1	C_{11}	C_{12}	C_{13}	$\cdots$	C_{1n}
2	—	C_{22}	C_{23}	$\cdots$	C_{2n}
.	—	—	C_{33}	$\cdots$	C_{3n}
.					
.					
n	—	—	—	$\cdots$	C_{nn}
M_i (Column minimum)					

level and that no inputs occur unless the inventory level has dropped to zero. Let the input quantities be q_i, where $i = 1, \cdots, m$. These inputs occur at the times t_i, where $i = 1, \cdots, m$. Since the process starts with zero inventory level,

$$t_1 = 0 \qquad (5.15)$$

Also define

$$t_{m+1} = T \qquad (5.16)$$

It then follows that

$$q_i = \int_{t_i}^{t_{i+1}} r(t)\, dt \qquad (i = 1, \cdots, m) \qquad (5.17)$$

Clearly, the inventory level at time t, where $t_i \le t \le t_{i+1}$, is given by

$$I(t) = q_i - \int_{t_i}^{t} r(\tau)\, d\tau$$

$$= R(t_{i+1}) - R(t) \qquad (5.18)$$

The inventory cost during the interval $t_i \leq t \leq t_{i+1}$ is proportional to

$$\int_{t_i}^{t_{i+1}} I(t) \, dt = (t_{i+1} - t_i) \, R(t_{i+1}) - \int_{t_i}^{t_{i+1}} R(t) \, dt \qquad (5.19)$$

so that the total inventory cost for the horizon is given by

$$H_m = h \left[\sum_{i=1}^{m} (t_{i+1} - t_i) \, R(t_{i+1}) - \int_0^T R(t) \, dt \right] \qquad (5.20)$$

For the determination of optimal values t_i, we can restrict ourselves to the criterion function

$$(t_2 - t_1) \, R(t_2)$$
$$+ \, (t_3 - t_2) \, R(t_3) \qquad\qquad (5.21)$$
$$+ \, (t_4 - t_3) \, R(t_4)$$
$$+ \, \cdots$$

Differentiating this function with respect to t_2 and setting the partial derivative equal to zero, we obtain

$$R(t_3) = R(t_2) + (t_2 - t_1) \, r(t_2) \qquad (5.22)$$

In general, we have

$$R(t_{i+1}) = R(t_i) + (t_i - t_{i-1}) \, r(t_i) \qquad (i = 1, \cdots, m) \quad (5.23)$$

These relations must be fulfilled by the optimal values $\hat{t}_i$. If we begin with an estimate t'_2, we can conveniently calculate a set of values $t'_3, \cdots, t'_m$ which fulfills all relations of Eq. 5.23 but the last. If the expression on the right-hand side of the last relation is evaluated, the amount of deviation from $R(T)$ can be used to calculate an improved value t'_2 by linear interpolation. Generally, the method converges rapidly, although nonconvergence or convergence to a local minimum may also occur [55].

The relations 5.23 also show that for the optimal solution the area under the curve $r(t)$ taken over the interval $t_i \leq t \leq t_{i+1}$ must equal the area of the rectangle of height $r(t_i)$ over the preceding interval (Fig. 5-1). Consequently, for a not too small number of setups it will be a good approximation to derive the points $\hat{t}_i$ by dividing the area under the curve $r(t)$ into m equal areas:

$$R(t_i) = \frac{i - 1}{m} \, R(T) \qquad (i = 2, \cdots, m) \qquad (5.24)$$

This approximate solution is conveniently obtained in graphical form. Once the $\hat{t}_i$ have been determined, H_m can be calculated from Eq. 5.20. Finally, we vary m and select the over-all optimal policy by choosing

$$\min_m (ms + H_m) \tag{5.25}$$

This inventory problem is a special case of a broader class of problems dealing with "linear inefficiencies" which can be handled by virtually the same mathematical model [23, 55].

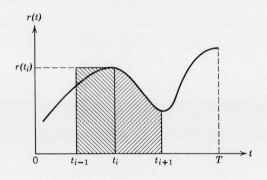

Fig. 5-1.

In an interesting study, McDowell [45] determines the economical planning period for engineering works such as the installation of additional telephone cables when demand for service is increasing. There is a fixed cost (setup cost) associated with each installation of new capacity. On the other hand, idle capacity is also costly. Thus, the problem of finding an optimal expansion policy may be viewed as a dynamic economic-lot-size problem with increasing demand. A rather cumbersome and theoretical approach to the dynamic economic-lot-size problem is found in [58]. The approach is based on a Fourier analysis of the demand function.

GENERALIZED ORDERING MODEL BY DVORETZKY, KIEFER, AND WOLFOWITZ

Dvoretzky, Kiefer, and Wolfowitz have conceptualized the ordering problem for most general conditions [17]. In particular, these authors have considered dynamic single-station models with a finite number of decision intervals. The demand in period i is described by a conditional probability distribution

$$f_i(r \mid B_i) \tag{5.26}$$

where the vector

$$B_i = (x_1, \cdots x_i; y_1, \cdots, y_i; r_1, \cdots, r_{i-1}) \tag{5.27}$$

is a summary description of the history of demands (r) and stock levels before (x) and after ordering (y), including the stock levels x_i and y_i of the present period i. Consequently, the expected cost in period i is a function of the form

$$C_i(x_i, y_i \mid B''_{i-1}) \tag{5.28}$$

where

$$B''_{i-1} = (x_1, \cdots, x_{i-1}; y_1, \cdots, y_{i-1}; r_1, \cdots, r_{i-1}) \tag{5.29}$$

An ordering policy is defined by a set of functions

$$y_i = g_i(x_i \mid B''_{i-1}) \qquad (i = 1, \cdots, n) \tag{5.30}$$

which obey the restrictions

$$y_i \geq x_i \qquad (i = 1, \cdots, n) \tag{5.31}$$

It now is possible to define the expected cost associated with a given policy, and to define an optimal policy accordingly. Starting with the last period, the optimal solution is constructed by a series of one-dimensional minimizations with respect to the y_i; the technique is very similar to dynamic programming which was discussed in the context of the Arrow-Harris-Marschak model. The main difference is that at the ith stage of the process a one-dimensional minimization must be carried out for *each combination* of the initial conditions (B''_{i-1}, x_i), whereas in dynamic programming we were dealing with only *one* initial condition, x_i. The larger the number of initial conditions, the greater is the computational effort. In the case of many initial conditions, the outlined approach is hardly practical so that it reduces to a conceptual construction in the sense of pure mathematics.

THE PRODUCTION SMOOTHING PROBLEM

Of any single dynamic problem, the so-called production smoothing problem has received the most attention in the literature. This problem is concerned with the conflict between the cost of imperfect synchronization of production and demand on one hand (i.e., cost of inventories and shortages), and the cost of changing the production rate and the effect of nonconstant marginal production costs on the other hand. In the following we shall discuss only a selection of the many alternative formulations given in the literature. For more complete coverage, see Bibliography D. Simple graphical solutions of certain smoothing problems are found in [30] and in Bibliography A [10].

Linear Programming Formulations

We first consider the case of fixed labor force [9]. When the planned production for period i exceeds the regular time capacity of the labor force, overtime is used. The marginal production cost is thereby raised from c_r to c_0, where these constants denote unit production costs for regular time and for overtime, respectively. What quantities should be produced in each period in order to satisfy given requirements r_i without occurrence of shortages and with minimum cost of production and inventories? Let h be the unit inventory carrying cost per period. The requirements of period i can be satisfied with units produced in any of the periods $k = 1, \cdots, i$. If a unit is produced in period k and consumed in period i, it gives rise to the total cost

$$c_i + h(i - k) \quad \text{or} \quad c_0 + h(i - k)(i = 1, \cdots, n; k = 1, \cdots, i) \quad (5.32)$$

depending on whether it is produced on regular time or overtime. These costs are exhibited in Table 5-3; the starting inventory Inv(0)

Table 5-3
Unit Costs of Production and Storage

Source of Supply, j \ Consumption Period, i / Demand / Capacity	1 / r_1	2 / r_2	$\cdots$	n / r_n	Inv(n)
Inv (0) / M_1	0	h		nh	
Reg(1) / M_2	c_r	$c_r + h$		$c_r + (n-1)h$	
Ot (1) / M_3	c_0	$c_0 + h$		$c_0 + (n-1)h$	
Reg(2) / M_4	—	c_r		$c_r + (n-2)h$	
Ot (2) / M_5	—	c_0		$c_0 + (n-2)h$	
. / .		—			
.					
.					
Reg(n) / M_{m-1}	—			c_r	
Ot (n) / M_m	—			c_0	

has also been included as a possible source of supply. The maximum amounts M_j which can be obtained from the various sources have been consecutively numbered ($j = 1, \cdots, m$, where $m = 2n + 1$). From the table it is readily seen that our problem may be viewed as one of allocating the available supplies M_j to consumption points (destinations) i. The cost of allocating one unit from source j to destination i is constant and given. A "dummy" column designated by Inv(n) is used to absorb excess capacity. Thus it is seen that our problem is a "transportation problem" in linear programming which may be solved by one of the well-known algorithms.*

We now turn to the more general case where the labor force is also under control. We thus have two sets of decision variables: production quantities q_i and work force levels W_i, where W_i is measured by the number of regular manhours obtainable in period i. Note that for a given pair of values (q_i, W_i) the respective amounts to be produced on regular time and on overtime are determined, if we assume that the total amount of manhours needed to produce the quantity q_i is given by kq_i, where k is a constant. If we let c_r and c_0 be the cost of one labor hour on regular time and on overtime respectively, the cost of overtime in period i is $c_0(kq_i - W_i)^+$ where we have defined

$$a^+ = \begin{cases} a & \text{for } a \geq 0 \\ 0 & \text{for } a < 0 \end{cases}$$

$$a^- = \begin{cases} 0 & \text{for } a \geq 0 \\ |a| & \text{for } a < 0 \end{cases} \tag{5.33}$$

for any real number a. Obviously,

$$a = a^+ - a^- \tag{5.34}$$

The total cost incurred in period i will be composed of the following elements:

Regular payroll	$c_r W_i$
Hiring	$c_h(W_i - W_{i-1})^+$
Layoffs	$c_f(W_i - W_{i-1})^-$
Overtime	$c_0(kq_i - W_i)^+$
Inventory	$h I_i^+$
Shortage	$d I_i^- \qquad (i = 1, \cdots, n)$

where I_i is the closing inventory in month i, and the unit costs c_r, c_h, c_f, c_0, h, d are given.

* See Mathematical Appendix.

The problem of minimizing total costs for a horizon of n periods can now be formulated as one of minimizing the function

$$C(q_1, \cdots, q_n; W_1, \cdots, W_n) = \sum_{i=1}^{n} [c_r W_i + c_h (W_i - W_{i-1})^+$$
$$+ c_f (W_i - W_{i-1})^- + c_0 (kq_i - W_i)^+ + hI_i^+ + dI_i^-] \quad (5.35)$$

subject to the restrictions

$$q_i \geq 0 \tag{5.36}$$

$$W_i \geq 0 \tag{5.37}$$

$$I_i = I_{i-1} + q_i - r_i \qquad (i = 1, \cdots, n) \tag{5.38}$$

where the demands r_i and the initial conditions (I_0, W_0) are given. Minimization is with respect to the decision variables q_i and W_i. Obviously, the cost function is a piecewise linear function of the decision variables. To arrive at a strictly linear cost function, let us introduce the following set of new variables:

$$\begin{aligned}
x_i &= (W_i - W_{i-1})^+ \\
y_i &= (W_i - W_{i-1})^- \\
z_i &= (kq_i - W_i)^+ \\
w_i &= (kq_i - W_i)^- \\
u_i &= I_i^+ \\
v_i &= I_i^- \qquad (i = 1, \cdots, n)
\end{aligned} \tag{5.39}$$

In this notation the variables q_i and W_i can be expressed as follows. From Eqs. 5.38, 5.34, and 5.39 we obtain

$$\begin{aligned}
q_i &= I_i - I_{i-1} + r_i \\
&= (u_i - v_i) - (u_{i-1} - v_{i-1}) + r_i
\end{aligned} \tag{5.40}$$

Similarly, from Eqs. 5.39 and 5.40,

$$kq_i - W_i = z_i - w_i$$

or, equivalently,

$$\begin{aligned}
W_i &= kq_i - (z_i - w_i) \\
&= k[(u_i - v_i) - (u_{i-1} - v_{i-1}) + r_i] - (z_i - w_i)
\end{aligned} \tag{5.41}$$

By Eqs. 5.40 and 5.41, the restrictions of Eqs. 5.36 and 5.37 now take the form of

$$(u_i - v_i) - (u_{i-1} - v_{i-1}) + r_i \geq 0 \tag{5.42}$$

and

$$(u_i - v_i) - (u_{i-1} - v_{i-1}) + r_i - \frac{1}{k}(z_i - w_i) \geq 0 \tag{5.43}$$

It should be noted that the restriction of Eq. 5.38 is already incorporated in Eq. 5.40. The definition of the variables x_i and y_i in Eq. 5.39 gives rise to the following additional restrictions:

$$W_i - W_{i-1} = x_i - y_i \tag{5.44}$$

These restrictions may now be expressed in terms of the new variables. By Eq. 5.41 we have

$$\begin{aligned} W_i - W_{i-1} = k[u_i - v_i - 2(u_{i-1} - v_{i-1}) + u_{i-2} - v_{i-2} \\ + r_i - r_{i-1}] - (z_i - w_i) + z_{i-1} - w_{i-1} \end{aligned} \tag{5.45}$$

Using Eq. 5.44, the set of restrictions introduced by the definitions of the new variables is given by

$$\begin{aligned} k[u_i - v_i - 2(u_{i-1} - v_{i-1}) + u_{i-2} - v_{i-2}] \\ - (z_i - w_i) + (z_{i-1} - w_{i-1}) - (x_i - y_i) = k(r_{i-1} - r_i) \end{aligned} \tag{5.46}$$

The relations of Eq. 5.33 do not give rise to additional restrictions since it is generally known that an optimum solution of a linear programming problem will automatically yield pairs of numbers (x_i, y_i), etc., with the property that either $x_i = 0$ or $y_i = 0$, etc.* It may be observed, however, that these relations require that all variables be nonnegative:

$$x_i, y_i \geq 0$$
$$z_i, w_i \geq 0 \tag{5.47}$$
$$u_i, v_i \geq 0$$

Using Eqs. 5.39 and 5.41, we may write the cost function (Eq. 5.35) in the following form:

$$\begin{aligned} C = \sum_{i=1}^{n} \{ c_h x_i + c_f y_i + c_0 z_i + h u_i + d v_i \\ + c_r k[u_i - v_i - (u_{i-1} - v_{i-1}) + r_i] - c_r(z_i - w_i) \} \end{aligned}$$

---

* This is easily shown by indirect proof.

or, using the relation $I_i = u_i - v_i$,

$$C = \sum_{i=1}^{n} [c_h x_i + c_f y_i + (c_0 - c_r)z_i + c_r w_i + h u_i + d v_i]$$

$$+ c_r k \left(u_n - v_n - I_0 + \sum_{1}^{n} r_i \right) \quad (5.48)$$

Our minimization problem now becomes one of linear programming. It may be stated as follows. Mimimize the cost function Eq. 5.48 subject to the constraints Eqs. 5.42, 5.43, 5.46, 5.47 for $i = 1, \cdot \cdot \cdot, n$.

Each period i of the planning horizon contributes six variables and three significant restrictions. The case study from which this model was developed employed a planning horizon of six months. A linear programming problem of this size can be handled conveniently by a medium-size computer. According to Eqs. 5.42–5.43, the original decision variables q_i and W_i (production rate and work force level) are slack variables of the linear programming problem and can be obtained directly from the final simplex tableau* turned out by the computer.

If demand is probabilistic, a linear programming approach may still be useful. We can replace the r_i by their expected values and obtain an approximate solution. The approximation should not be too bad since the probability distributions of demand enter only into the inventory connected cost. The cost-of-shortage term may, of course, be omitted from the cost equation if a restriction on the amount of shortage is imposed instead [24].

Convex Programming

As a further generalization [11], we introduce general production cost functions $c_i(q_i)$ for period i. We assume that these functions are convex [$c'_i(q_i)$ increasing, $c''_i(q_i) > 0$]. This means that marginal production costs are increasing. There is no cost associated with changes of the production level as such. The demand in period i is probabilistic with density $f_i(r_i)$; the density functions for the different periods are independent. If I_i is the closing inventory level in period i, the inventory carrying cost is assumed proportional to the average inventory level

$$\bar{I}_i = \tfrac{1}{2}(I_i + I_{i-1}) \quad (5.49)$$

---

* A description of the simplex method for the solution of linear programming problems is given in the Mathematical Appendix.

The criterion for optimization is the expected cost

$$E(C) = \int_{r_1} \cdots \int_{r_n} \left\{ \sum_{i=1}^{n} [c_i(q_i) + h\bar{I}_i] \right\} f_1(r_1) \cdots f_n(r_n) \, dr_1 \cdots dr_n$$

$$(5.50)$$

As usual,

$$I_i = I_0 + \sum_{j=1}^{i} (q_j - r_j) \qquad (i = 1, \cdots, n) \qquad (5.51)$$

where I_0 is the starting inventory. Furthermore, let $I_{\min}$ and $I_{\max}$ be the desired minimum and maximum levels of inventory respectively. We then impose the following restrictions, where the symbol "Prob" designates probabilities.

Shortage restriction:

$$\text{Prob} \left\{ I_0 + \sum_{j=1}^{i} (q_j - r_j) \geq I_{\min} \right\} \geq \alpha_i \qquad (5.52)$$

Storage restriction:

$$\text{Prob} \left\{ I_0 + \sum_{j=1}^{i} (q_j - r_j) \leq I_{\max} \right\} = 1 \qquad (i = 1, \cdots, n) \quad (5.53)$$

where α_i is a set of prescribed (usually high) confidence levels. We now seek a set of decision rules of the form

$$\sum_{j=1}^{i} q_j = \sum_{j=1}^{i-1} r_j + \sum_{j=1}^{i} \gamma_j \qquad (5.54)$$

$$q_1 = \gamma_1 \qquad (i = 2, \cdots, n)$$

where γ_j is a set of constants to be determined optimally $(j = 1, \cdots, n)$. The decision rules will be used to determine each production quantity q_i *after* the demands $r_1, \cdots, r_{i-1}$ have materialized and are known. This is a typical example of what we have termed fixed horizon planning. Obviously, the decision rules may also be given the form

$$q_1 = \gamma_1$$

$$q_i = r_{i-1} + \gamma_i \qquad (i = 2, \cdots, n)$$

$$(5.55)$$

Since the q_i must be nonnegative quantities, it is necessary to impose the further restrictions

$$\gamma_1 \geq 0$$
$$\text{Prob } \{r_{i-1} + \gamma_i \geq 0\} = 1 \qquad (i = 2, \cdots, n) \tag{5.56}$$

To determine the γ_i optimally, we substitute the decision rules Eq. 5.55 into the cost equation. The production cost taken by itself becomes

$$c_1(\gamma_1) + \sum_{i=2}^{n} c_i(r_{i-1} + \gamma_i) \tag{5.57}$$

Its expected value is

$$c_1(\gamma_1) + \sum_{i=2}^{n} \int_{r_{i-1}} c_i(r_{i-1} + \gamma_i) f_{i-1}(r_{i-1}) \, dr_{i-1} \tag{5.58}$$

Because of the convexity of the $c_i(q_i)$, each integral also represents a convex function of the corresponding γ_i, and we have a separable convex function of the γ_i. Since the inventory terms which we have omitted depend linearly on the γ_i and the demand rates, the total expected cost is also a separable convex function of the γ_i:

$$E(C) = \sum_{i=1}^{n} g_i(\gamma_i) \tag{5.59}$$

where $g''_i(\gamma_i) > 0$.

We now turn to the restrictions. Substituting the decision rule Eq. 5.54 into 5.52, the shortage restrictions may be rewritten as

$$\text{Prob} \left\{ I_0 + \sum_{j=1}^{i} \gamma_j - r_i \geq I_{\min} \right\} \geq \alpha_i \tag{5.60}$$

Obviously the relation

$$r_i \leq I_0 - I_{\min} + \sum_{j=1}^{i} \gamma_j \tag{5.61}$$

will hold with confidence α_i if

$$F_i \left\{ I_0 - I_{\min} + \sum_{j=1}^{i} \gamma_j \right\} \geq \alpha_i \tag{5.62}$$

where $F_i(r_i)$ is the cumulative function of $f_i(r_i)$.   An equivalent statement is

$$I_0 - I_{\min} + \sum_{j=1}^{i} \gamma_j \geq F_i^{-1}(\alpha_i) \qquad (i = 1, \cdots, n) \quad (5.63)$$

It should be noted that $F_i^{-1}(\alpha_i)$ is a given number.   We thus have a set of linear inequalities which the γ_i must fulfill.   By a similar development, the storage restrictions become

$$I_0 - I_{\max} + \sum_{j=1}^{i} \gamma_j \leq \min r_i \qquad (5.64)$$

and the nonnegativity constraints (Eq. 5.56) become

$$\gamma_1 \geq 0 \qquad (5.65)$$
$$\min r_{i-1} + \gamma_i \geq 0 \qquad (i = 2, \cdots, n)$$

where the min r_i are also given numbers.   We have thus transformed the problem into one of minimizing a separable convex function subject to a set of linear constraints.   This problem of "convex programming" can be solved by an extension of linear programming methods which has been given by Charnes and Lemke (see [11]).

Dynamic Programming

If we consider the same production smoothing problem for deterministic demands r_i, we may impose the shortage restriction in the form

$$I_i = I_0 + \sum_{j=1}^{i} (q_j - r_j) \geq 0 \qquad (i = 1, \cdots, n) \quad (5.66)$$

We further assume that the inventory cost per period is proportional to the (nonnegative) closing inventory level.   Then, the production smoothing problem becomes one of minimizing the cost function

$$C(q_1, \cdots, q_n) = \sum_{1}^{n} c_i(q_i) + h \sum_{1}^{n} I_i \qquad (5.67)$$

subject to Eq. 5.66 and the nonnegativity constraints

$$q_i \geq 0 \qquad (i = 1, \cdots, n) \quad (5.68)$$

By Eq. 5.66, Eq. 5.67 may be rewritten as

$$C = nhI_0 + \sum_1^n [c_i(q_i) + h(n + 1 - i)(q_i - r_i)]$$

$$= nhI_0 + \sum_1^n g_i(q_i) \tag{5.69}$$

where

$$g_i(q_i) = c_i(q_i) + (n + 1 - i)(q_i - r_i) \tag{5.70}$$

Once again, a separable nonlinear function is to be minimized, subject to a set of linear constraints. Bellman [5] has given a dynamic programming formulation of this problem. (The previously treated convex programming problem may also be solved by dynamic programming.) Let us define

$$Q_i = \sum_{j=1}^i q_j \tag{5.71}$$

$$R_i = \sum_{j=1}^i r_j \tag{5.72}$$

$$f_i(Q_{i-1}) = \min_A \sum_{j=i}^n g_j(Q_j - Q_{j-1}) \qquad (i = 1, \cdots, n) \tag{5.73}$$

where A is the area given by

$$Q_j \geq Q_{j-1} \tag{5.74}$$

$$Q_j \geq R_j \qquad (j = i, \cdots, n) \tag{5.75}$$

We also define

$$Q_0 = I_0$$

Clearly, we are interested in finding $f_1(Q_0)$ and the corresponding optimal production decisions $Q_1, \cdots, Q_n$. This function may be derived recursively as follows. Obviously,

$$F_n(Q_{n-1}) = \min_{\substack{Q_n \geq Q_{n-1} \\ Q_n \geq R_n}} g_n(Q_n - Q_{n-1})$$

$$= g_n(\max(0, R_n - Q_{n-1})) \tag{5.76}$$

When the functions $f_{i+1}, \cdots, f_n$ are already known, we may derive the function $f_i(Q_{i-1})$ by the one-dimensional minimization

$$f_i(Q_{i-1}) = \min_{\substack{Q_i \geq Q_{i-1} \\ Q_i \leq R_i}} [g_i(Q_i - Q_{i-1}) + f_{i+1}(Q_i)]$$

$$(i = 1, \cdots, n - 1) \quad (5.77)$$

As the minimizations are carried out, the optimal production decisions Q_i are also obtained. If the input quantities q_i are not produced but purchased in a fluctuating market with known (or forecast) prices p_i in period i, we may retain the model and the method of solution by setting

$$c_i(q_i) = p_i q_i \qquad (5.78)$$

Of course, a linear programming solution then becomes possible, too.

Under certain simple conditions our smoothing problem may also be solved by elementary calculus methods. As an example, consider the two-period problem, assuming $c_i(q_i) = q_i^2$. Of course, $I_2 = 0$ may also be assumed. Thus Eq. 5.69 becomes

$$C = 2hI_0 + q_1^2 + 2h(q_1 - r_1) + q_2^2 + h(q_2 - r_2) \qquad (5.79)$$

This cost function is to be minimized, subject to the restrictions

$$I_0 + q_1 - r_1 \geq 0 \qquad (5.80)$$

$$I_0 + q_1 - r_1 + q_2 - r_2 = 0 \qquad (5.81)$$

$$q_1 \geq 0 \qquad (5.82)$$

$$q_2 \geq 0 \qquad (5.83)$$

Since by Eq. 5.81

$$q_2 = r_1 + r_2 - q_1 - I_0 \qquad (5.84)$$

we have

$$C = C(q_1) = 2hI_0 + q_1^2 + 2h(q_1 - r_1) + (I_0 + q_1 - r_1 - r_2)^2 + h(r_1 - q_1 - I_0) \qquad (5.85)$$

The problem has thus been reduced to minimizing a quadratic function $C(q_1)$ of one variable q_1, subject to the restrictions

$$q_1 \geq r_1 - I_0 \qquad (5.86)$$

$$q_1 \geq 0 \qquad (5.87)$$

$$q_1 \leq r_1 + r_2 - I_0 \qquad (5.88)$$

or, equivalently,

$$\max (0, r_1 - I_0) \leq q_1 \leq r_1 + r_2 - I_0 \qquad (5.89)$$

that is,

$$A \leq q_1 \leq B \tag{5.90}$$

with obvious definitions of the constants A and B. The derivative of the cost function $C(q_1)$ vanishes at

$$q_1^* = \frac{r_1 + r_2 - I_0}{2} - \frac{h}{4} \tag{5.91}$$

Consequently, the optimal production quantity q_1 is given by

$$\hat{q}_1 = \begin{cases} q_1^* & \text{if } A \leq q_1^* \leq B \\ B & \text{if } B \leq q_1^* \\ A & \text{if } \quad q_1^* \leq A \end{cases} \tag{5.92}$$

The solution for q_2 follows from Eq. 5.81.

Returning to the general problem, we now consider the case of probabilistic demand. Let $f_i(R_i)$ be the probability density of the cumulative demand R_i. Then the expected cost becomes

$$E(C) = \sum_{i=1}^{n} \left[c_i(Q_i - Q_{i-1}) + h \int_{-\infty}^{I_0 + Q_i} (I_0 + Q_i - R_i) f_i(R_i)\, dR_i \right]$$

$$= \sum_{i=1}^{n} \phi_i(Q_i, Q_{i-1}) \tag{5.93}$$

with obvious definitions of the functions ϕ_i. As in the deterministic case, we have the constraints

$$Q_i \geq Q_{i-1} \qquad (i = 1, \cdots, n) \tag{5.94}$$

However, suitable shortage restrictions must now be imposed in the form

$$I_0 + Q_i \geq E(R_i) + \lambda\, \sigma(R_i) \tag{5.95}$$

when $E(R_i)$ and $\sigma(R_i)$ denote expected value and standard deviation, respectively, of the random variable R_i, and λ is a suitably chosen constant. In Eq. 5.93 the production cost term may also be interpreted as the expected value of a probabilistic production cost. The dynamic programming solution may proceed as before if we define

$$f_i(Q_{i-1}) = \min_{Q_i, \cdots, Q_n \in R} \sum_{j=i}^{n} \phi_j(Q_j, Q_{j-1}) \tag{5.96}$$

where the region R is defined by Eqs. 5.94 and 5.95. For another example of dynamic programming under uncertainty, see "The Hydroelectric Problem" in this chapter.

Calculus of Variations

The problem of balancing inventory costs and production costs when marginal production costs are increasing may also be formulated in continuous form [2]. A deterministic demand rate $r(t)$ is defined in the planning horizon $0 \leq t \leq T$. Production is also described by a continuous rate $p(t)$ which assumes the role of an unknown function. Let

$I(t)$ = inventory level at time t

I_0 = initial inventory

$Q(t)$ = cumulative production up to time t

$c(p)$ = cost rate for production; this means that the cost of producing the quantity $p(t)\,dt$ is $c(p(t))\,dt$

We wish to minimize total production and holding costs

$$J\{p(t)\} = \int_0^T [c(p(\tau)) + hI(\tau)]\,d\tau \qquad (5.97)$$

where

$$I(t) = I_0 + \int_0^t p(\tau)\,d\tau - \int_0^t r(\tau)\,d\tau \qquad (5.98)$$

The restriction is that there be no shortages:

$$I_0 + \int_0^t p(\tau)\,d\tau \geq \int_0^t r(\tau)\,d\tau \qquad (5.99)$$

or, equivalently,

$$Q(t) \geq \int_0^t r(\tau)\,d\tau - I_0 = S(t) \qquad (5.100)$$

where $S(t)$ is defined by Eq. 5.100. Of course, the boundary condition of zero-closing inventory,

$$Q(T) = S(T) \qquad (5.101)$$

must hold for an optimal solution. The only exception occurs for the trivial case

$$I_0 > \int_0^T r(\tau)\,d\tau \qquad (5.102)$$

Because of the restriction Eq. 5.99 the optimal function $p(t)$ cannot be found by conventional tools of the calculus of variations. Arrow, Karlin, and Scarf have developed a novel method of solution. However, the algorithms are rather tedious from the viewpoint of applications, and we shall not discuss this method further. The interested reader is referred to the literature [2].

Quadratic Programming

We return to the problem of balancing labor costs, costs of changing the labor force, and inventory connected costs, which was previously formulated in linear programming form. Holt, Modigliani, Muth, and Simon [28, 29] have developed a model in which most of these costs are assumed to be quadratic functions of the production quantities q_i and work force levels W_i. Specifically, the cost elements for period i are

Regular payroll	$C_1 W_i$	(5.103)
Hiring and layoff	$C_2(W_i - W_{i-1})^2$	(5.104)
Overtime	$C_3(q_i - C_4 W_i)^2 + C_5 q_i - C_6 W_i$	(5.105)
Inventory and Shortage	$C_7(I_i - C_8 - C_9 r_i)^2$	
	$(i = 1, \cdots, n)$	(5.106)

where the C are constants. W_i is measured by the number of regular labor hours per period which may be obtained from the work force. The initial work force is W_0. The inventory level I_i obeys the rule

$$I_i = I_{i-1} + q_i - r_i \qquad (i = 1, \cdots, n) \qquad (5.107)$$

where I_0 is the starting inventory. We first assume deterministic demands r_i. The cost term Eq. 5.105 is a parabolic approximation to a piecewise linear function of q_i which is equal to zero up to a critical value of q_i (determined by W_i), and then rises linearly with a slope given by the unit cost of overtime production. A justification of the quadratic inventory term will be given in Chapter 7 (see Eq. 7.69); see also [8].

The obvious advantage of quadratic cost functions is that differential calculus may be employed to arrive at a system of linear equations for the optimal quantities q_i, W_i. This system may be solved by a matrix inversion. It is an important property of this linear system that the coefficients of the unknowns q_i, W_i do not contain the demand parameters r_i or the parameters I_0, W_0. Using, say, Cramer's rule for finding the unknowns as quotients of two determinants, it follows that the optimal decisions q_i, W_i are linear functions of the demand parameters r_i and of I_0, W_0. The coefficients depend only on the cost parameters. In particular, q_1 and W_1 are of the form

$$q_1 = \sum_1^n a_i r_i + b W_0 + c I_0 + d \qquad (5.108)$$

$$W_1 = \sum_1^n a'_i r_i + b' W_0 + c' I_0 + d' \qquad (5.109)$$

where all coefficients depend only on the cost parameters and may, therefore, be determined once for all as long as the cost parameters do not change. Since the model is designed for optimization over a shifting horizon, we are only interested in the quantities q_1 and W_1. The linear decision rules Eqs. 5.108–5.109 are all that is needed for sequential decision making. At each decision point, the forecasts for the next n periods are substituted for the r_i.

Finally, consider the case of probabilistic demands r_i. Let $f_i(r_1, \cdots, r_i)$ be the joint probability density of the demands $r_1, \cdots, r_i$, as known at the beginning of period 1, and let $E(r_1), \cdots, E(r_i)$ be the expected demands. In a probabilistic formulation, Eq. 5.106 must be replaced by

$$C_7 \int_{r_1} \cdots \int_{r_i} (I_0 + q_1 + \cdots + q_i - r_1 - \cdots - r_i - C_8 - C_9 r_i)^2$$
$$f_i(r_1, \cdots, r_i)\, dr_1 \cdots dr_i \quad (5.110)$$

All other cost terms remain unaffected. When partial derivatives with respect to $q_1, \cdots, q_i$ are taken, Eq. 5.110 leads to

$$2C_7[I_0 + q_1 + \cdots + q_i - E(r_1) - \cdots - E(r_i)$$
$$- C_8 - C_9\, E(r_i)] \quad (5.111)$$

This result no longer depends on any probability distribution but only on the expected values of the demands. Therefore, the same linear decision rules as in the deterministic case apply if the demands r_i are replaced by their expectations. Estimates of these expectations may be obtained in the form of unbiased forecasts.

THE WAREHOUSING PROBLEM

A warehouse stocks a commodity the selling price and purchasing price of which change in time. Both the input x_i (quantity bought) and the output y_i (quantity sold) in period i are under control. The market is unlimited. The cost of stocking consists of the fixed cost of the warehouse and a variable cost which depends on the average inventory level. It will be assumed that the variable cost is insignificant. (This assumption is not critical.) As a consequence, the cost of stocking need not be considered. Nevertheless, the inventory process plays the central part in the warehousing problem since the upper limit on inventory given by the warehouse capacity places the effective constraints on purchasing and selling decisions.

In period i, the warehouse buys the quantity x_i at unit cost c_i and sells the quantity y_i at unit price p_i. The unit costs and prices are given for all periods $i = 1, \cdots, n$, and are not under the control of the warehouse.   A quantity bought in a given period cannot be sold in the same period.   The initial inventory is A, the warehouse capacity is B.   We are interested in finding the optimal purchasing and selling quantities x_i and y_i, where the criterion is the profit function

$$P = \sum_{i=1}^{n} (p_i y_i - c_i x_i) \tag{5.112}$$

The profit function is to be maximized, subject to the following restrictions:

Buying constraints

$$A + \sum_{j=1}^{i} (x_j - y_j) \leq B \tag{5.113}$$

Selling constraints

$$y_i \leq A + \sum_{j=1}^{i-1} (x_j - y_j) \tag{5.114}$$

Nonnegativity constraints

$$x_i, y_i \geq 0 \qquad (i = 1, \cdots, n) \tag{5.115}$$

This problem may be solved by linear programming techniques.   We shall, however, discuss a dynamic programming solution given by Bellman [6].   Let I_i designate the closing inventory level in period i, and let $f_i(I_{i-1})$ be the profit associated with the optimal policy for periods $i, \cdots, n$, where I_{i-1} is given.   Clearly,

$$f_n(I_{n-1}) = \max_{\substack{y_n \leq I_{n-1} \\ I_{n-1} + (x_n - y_n) \leq B \\ x_n, y_n \geq 0}} (p_n y_n - c_n x_n) \tag{5.116}$$

and

$$f_k(I_{k-1}) = \max_{\substack{y_k \leq I_{k-1} \\ I_{k-1} + x_k - y_k \leq B \\ x_k, y_k \geq 0}} [p_k y_k - c_k x_k + f_{k+1}(I_{k-1} + x_k - y_k)]$$

$$(k = 1, \cdots, n - 1) \quad (5.117)$$

The two-dimensional maximization seems complicated at first glance but can be greatly simplified when we borrow from linear programming the fact that the maximum occurs at a corner point of the maximization region, sketched in Fig. 5-2 (the subscripts have been omitted.)   We can, therefore, restrict ourselves to choosing the maximum from the following four numbers which are obtained by evaluating the profit function at the four corner points.

Corner Point	Value of Function
$(0, 0)$	$f_{k+1}(I)$
$(B - I, 0)$	$-c_k(B - I) + f_{k+1}(B)$
(B, I)	$p_k I - c_k B + f_{k+1}(B)$
$(0, I)$	$p_k I + f_{k+1}(0)$

Proceeding in this way, the function $f_1(A)$ and the corresponding optimal purchasing and selling decisions are readily derived. Further material on the warehousing problem is found in [16, 18].

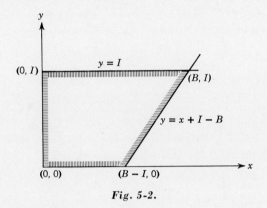

Fig. 5-2.

THE HYDROELECTRIC PROBLEM

Hydroelectric operations which utilize the storage water of large reservoirs for power generation are faced with the problem of optimal water discharge control. The dynamic feature of the problem is the highly seasonal pattern of water input (river flow) into the reservoir. The first treatment of the problem from the viewpoint of inventory theory has been given by Little [43]. The objective of water output control is to minimize the cost of satisfying a given pattern of demand for electric energy. Since hydroelectric energy is assumed to be free, the relevant cost is the cost of supplying electric energy from other sources. In each decision period, management must decide what fraction of the total demand is to be satisfied by hydroelectric energy. Define the following quantities for the ith period of the planning horizon:

I_i = water inventory in reservoir at the beginning of period i
x_i = river flow into reservoir during period i
u_i = water usage (discharge) from reservoir during period i
r_i = given demand for electric energy in period i $(i = 1, \cdots, n)$

The technology of the hydroelectric operation considered by Little is such that the cost incurred in period i has the structure

$$C_i = C_i(u_i, I_i, x_i) \tag{5.118}$$

The inventory level I_i enters because of its effect on the productivity per unit of water discharge; river flow enters since it places restrictions on the amount of water discharge; finally, the decision u_i determines what fraction of the demand r_i is satisfied by hydroelectric energy; hence it determines the cost of shortage. Since river flows in consecutive periods are highly correlated, the density function of x_i is assumed to be of the form $g_i(x_i \mid x_{i-1})$. Consequently, the expected cost in period i is of the form

$$E(C_i) = E_i(u_i, I_i, x_{i-1}) \tag{5.119}$$

Among other factors it depends on the two initial conditions I_i and x_{i-1}. Obviously, we have a special case of the Dvoretzky-Kiefer-Wolfowitz model. If we let $f_i(I_i, x_{i-1})$ be the cost of an optimal policy for periods i through n, the recurrence relations for a dynamic programming solution are given by

$$f_i(I_i, x_{i-1}) = \min_{u_i} \int_{-\infty}^{+\infty} [C_i(u_i, I_i, x_i) + f_{i+1}(I_{i+1}, x_i)] \, g_i(x_i \mid x_{i-1}) \, dx_i$$

$$(i = 1, \cdots, n-1) \tag{5.120}$$

where the connecting relations

$$I_{i+1} = I_{i+1}(u_i, I_i, x_i) \qquad (i = 1, \cdots, n-1) \tag{5.121}$$

are known. It should be noted that at each stage i a one-dimensional minimization is required for each set (I_i, x_{i-1}) of initial conditions. The optimal decision functions are, therefore, obtained in the form

$$u_i = u_i(I_i, x_{i-1}) \tag{5.122}$$

The function f_n is found in the usual way by minimizing the cost for the last period alone.

Gessford and Karlin [2, 22] have treated the hydroelectric problem for a different set of assumptions. The river flows x_i are taken to be independent random variables with known density functions $\phi_i(x_i)$. In case the demand is not fully satisfied by (free) hydroelectric energy, a steam generating plant can supply electric energy at a unit cost c. However, the steam plant has limited capacity K per decision interval. Demand which remains unsatisfied gives rise to a penalty cost $p > c$ per unit of shortage. The productivity of electricity generation in the hydroplant does not depend on reservoir elevation. Therefore, all amounts of energy—in particular the demands r_i—are measured in equivalent amounts of water. Reservoir capacity is infinite. Consequently, consecutive water inventory levels are connected by the relations

$$I_{i+1} = I_i + x_i - u_i \qquad (i = 1, \cdots, n - 1) \qquad (5.123)$$

I_i will serve as the initial condition for a dynamic programming formulation. Let $f_i(I_i)$ be the expected cost of an optimum policy for periods $i, \cdots, n$. We wish to derive the function $f_1(I_1)$. According to our assumptions, the cost in period i is

$$C_i = c \min (K, r_i - u_i) + p \max (0, r_i - u_i - K) \qquad (5.124)$$

where u_i is restricted to the range

$$0 \leq u_i \leq \min (r_i, I_i) \qquad (5.125)$$

The curve given by Eq. 5.124 is pictured in Fig. 5-3 under the assumption that $r_i > K$.

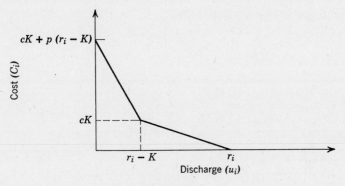

Fig. 5-3.

The recurrence relations for the functions $f_i(I_i)$ may now be written in the form

$$f_i(I_i) = \min_{0 \leq u_i \leq \min (r_i, I_i)} \Big[c \min (K, r_i - u_i) + p \max (0, r_i - u_i - K)$$
$$+ \int_0^\infty f_{i+1}(I_i + x_i - u_i) \, \phi_i(x_i) \, dx_i \Big] \qquad (5.126)$$

The function $f_n(I_n)$ may easily be obtained by observing that the optimum value for u_n is

$$\hat{u}_n = \min (r_n, I_n) \qquad (5.127)$$

because no water need be saved in the last period.   We are especially interested in the optimal decision $\hat{u}_1$ in the first period.   Obviously, $\hat{u}_1$ is a function of the water inventory I_1 at the beginning of the planning horizon.   Gessford and Karlin [2] have shown that this function has the simple form pictured in Fig. 5-4, where I'_1 and I''_1 are constants. Since $I''_1 - I'_1 = K$, only one constant need be calculated in order to draw the graph.

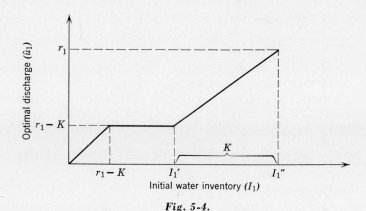

Fig. 5-4.

For additional references on a "Theory of Dams," see [21, 38, 40, 49] and Bibliography A [13].

FEEDBACK BEHAVIOR

A very confusing feature of dynamic models is that, in general, they do not permit an analytical prediction of *long-run* cost (or expected cost).   This is particularly true of models employing a shifting horizon since, here, each sequential decision is based on a new set of forecasts. Obviously, a long-run prediction cannot be made unless the complete mechanism of *forecasting and decision making* for each point of time has been incorporated in the model.   This is trivially true for static models.   For most dynamic models, however, it is out of the question, if not for reasons of analytical complexity, then because the forecasting mechanism cannot be formalized in mathematical terms.   An exception occurs for certain fixed-horizon models which employ a preconceived decision rule for each point in time and a formalized forecasting procedure based on history alone.   An example is given by the general ordering model by Dvoretzky, Kiefer, and Wolfowitz discussed earlier in this chapter. In that model, the demand for the next period is forecast in the form of a conditional probability distribution which depends only on past demands, stock levels, and ordering levels; consequently, the ordering decisions are functions of the same quantities. Certain dynamic programming models are another example. Because of their stringent assumptions, such models are restricted in application. They permit, however, to derive an analytical expression for the expected cost during the horizon. For fixed horizon models which do not fulfill these prerequisites and for shifting horizon models it seems inevitable that their long-run behavior be explored by a simulation. (Hand methods should normally suffice.) This is all the more necessary since certain decision rules derived from dynamic models have very unpleasant instability characteristics which could cause catastrophic oscillations or explosions of the inventory level. Some elementary facts of servomechanism theory will shed light on this peculiar phenomenon and may also help to avoid it. For illustrative purposes, consider a simple production smoothing problem [27] with the cost function

$$C = \sum_{i=2}^{n+1} hI_i^2 + \sum_{i=1}^{n} c(q_i - q_{i-1})^2 \qquad (5.128)$$

where I_i and q_i are the *starting* inventory level and the production quantity in period i, respectively. If we define

$$\Delta q_i = q_{i+1} - q_i \qquad (5.129)$$

$$\Delta I_i = I_{i+1} - I_i \qquad (5.130)$$

we may write the fundamental inventory equation in the form

$$q_i = \Delta I_i + r_i \qquad (5.131)$$

where r_i is the demand in period i. The cost equation now takes the form

$$C = \sum_{i=2}^{n+1} hI_i^2 + \sum_{i=0}^{n-1} c(\Delta q_i)^2 \qquad (5.132)$$

Treating the I_i as independent variables, we can derive an optimal decision rule by taking partial derivatives

$$\frac{\partial C}{\partial I_j} = 2hI_j + 2c \sum_{i=0}^{n-1} \Delta q_i \frac{\partial \Delta q_i}{\partial I_j} \qquad (5.133)$$

By Eq. 5.131,

$$\Delta q_i = \Delta^2 I_i + \Delta r_i$$
$$= I_{i+2} - 2I_{i+1} + I_i + \Delta r_i \qquad (5.134)$$

This shows that most of the partial derivatives in Eq. 5.133 are zero. Nonzero contributions occur only for $i = j,\, j - 1,\, j - 2$. Thus we obtain the following condition of optimality:

$$\frac{\partial C}{\partial I_j} = \frac{h}{c} I_j + \Delta q_j - 2\,\Delta q_{j-1} + \Delta q_{j-2}$$

$$= \frac{h}{c} I_j + \Delta^3 q_{j-2} = 0 \qquad (5.135)$$

By this relation, q_{j+1} may be written as a linear function of q_j, q_{j-1}, q_{j-2}, and I_j. It is tempting to use this linear relationship as a decision rule which yields the next production decision as a function of some simple historical quantities. We shall now show that this decision rule cannot, in fact, be used since it is inherently unstable. In order to do so, we rewrite Eq. 5.135, using Eq. 5.131:

$$\frac{h}{c} I_j + \Delta^4 I_{j-2} + \Delta^3 r_{j-2} = 0 \qquad (5.136)$$

We now have to borrow certain facts from servo theory. Equation 5.136 may be regarded as describing a filter with the input sequence r_i and the output sequence I_i. The behavior of the filter is analyzed with the aid of a transformed equation. Let $\{y_i\}$ be a sequence of real numbers which may be interpreted as the time series of some quantity of interest $(i = 0, \cdots, \infty)$. The subscript i designates points of time. We enlarge the definition by setting

$$y_{-1} = y_{-2} = \cdots = y_{-N} = 0 \qquad (5.137)$$

for a henceforth fixed positive integer N. N may be thought of as large. Along with the sequence $\{y_i\}$, the sequences $\{Y_{i+k}\}$ are defined for the same range of i and any positive integer k. The *power series transform**** of the sequence $\{y_i\}$ may be defined by the following power series in the complex variable z:

$$Y_i(z) = \sum_{i=0}^{\infty} \frac{y_{i-N}}{z^i} \qquad (5.138)$$

---

* There appears to be no uniform definition of the power series transform in the literature. For a different definition resulting in different rules of transformation, see [63].

Consequently, the transform of y_{i+k} is given by

$$Y_{i+k}(z) = \sum_{i=0}^{\infty} \frac{y_{i+k-N}}{z^i}$$

$$= z^k \sum_{j=k}^{\infty} \frac{y_{j-N}}{z^j} \tag{5.139}$$

If we let the summation run from $j = 0$, terms with the coefficients $y_{-N}, \cdots, y_{k-1-N}$ will be added. As long as $k \leq N$, these terms will be zero. For this range of k we have the fundamental relationship

$$Y_{i+k}(z) = z^k \sum_{j=0}^{\infty} \frac{y_{j-N}}{z^j} = z^k Y_i(z) \tag{5.140}$$

We, therefore, obtain the following rules for transformation:
If

$$\{y_i\} \rightarrow Y_i(z) \tag{5.141}$$

then

$$\{y_{i+k}\} \rightarrow z^k \, Y_j(z) \tag{5.142}$$

$$\{\Delta y_i\} \rightarrow (z - 1) \, Y_i(z) \tag{5.143}$$

$$\{\Delta^k y_i\} \rightarrow (z - 1)^k \, Y_i(z) \tag{5.144}$$

where

$$\Delta y_i = y_{i+1} - y_i$$

Returning to the filter equation Eq. 5.136, we introduce the transforms $I(z)$ and $R(z)$ of the sequences I_{j-2} and r_{j-2}, respectively. We may then write the transformed equation

$$\frac{h}{c} z^2 \, I(z) + (z - 1)^4 \, I(z) + (z - 1)^3 \, R(z) = 0 \tag{5.145}$$

which permits us to find the time series $I(z)$ of the inventory level when the time series $R(z)$ of demand is given. The most important quantity in relation to stability is the "transfer function"

$$\frac{I(z)}{R(z)} = - \frac{c(z - 1)^3}{hz^2 + c(z - 1)^4} \tag{5.146}$$

It is well known that the system will be dynamically stable, i.e., the transient response to a random impulse will vanish, if and only if the roots of

$$hz^2 + c(z - 1)^4 = 0 \tag{5.147}$$

have absolute value less than 1. Now define $w = z - 1$. Then Eq. 5.147 is equivalent to

$$cw^4 + h(w + 1)^2 = cw^4 + hw^2 + 2hw + h = 0 \qquad (5.148)$$

If this equation has a root w with positive real part, then there is a corresponding root $z = w + 1$ of Eq. 5.147 with absolute value greater than one (since the real part of this root will be greater than one). But since the cubic term is absent from Eq. 5.148, there is a root w with positive real part. Hence the system is unstable.

It has thus been shown that the deterministic decision rule leads to catastrophic production and inventory fluctuations unless the forecast of demand is perfect. An arbitrarily small deviation of actual demand from the forecast will cause instability. Thus, the actual cost bears no relationship with the cost predicted by the deterministic horizon model. It is obvious that the same tools of servo theory may also be used in a constructive way for the design of stable feedback rules [63, 51]. This may be done by considering a larger class of feedback rules containing damping terms and indefinite coefficients which are then determined in such a way that the stability condition of the transfer function is fulfilled. The original unstable feedback rule may suggest a class of rules to be considered [27, 60]. Despite the helpfulness of servo theory in such special cases, it appears that there is no theory in existence which is broad enough to give general insight into the long-run servomechanism behavior of dynamic decision rules, especially when these rules continuously utilize "outside" forecasting information rather than forecasts based on demand and production history. We are, therefore, forced to conclude the discussion of dynamic models with these statements: (1) There is great need for a more general theory of long-run behavior of dynamic decision rules; and (2) at the present time, the practitioner is forced to explore long-run behavior by simulation.

chapter 6
Applications of Dynamic Models

The principles for applications of static models which were discussed in Chapter 4 are equally valid and important for the application of dynamic models. However, two points deserve special emphasis. To an even greater extent than is the case with static models, the dynamic models of Chapter 5 employ cost notions which are not normally used in present business and accounting practice. Examples are: the cost of hiring and layoffs, production costs as a function of the monthly production quantity, the cost of changing the production level, and many others. Therefore, great care must be exercised in making cost comparisons between current practice and mathematical decision rules. It is essential to not be satisfied with an over-all cost comparison given by a cost model but to make available to the decision maker the time series of the *physical* quantities that are behind the various cost components, for example, production levels, changes in labor force, inventory levels, and order backlogs as functions of time.

If demand is seasonal, and forecasts are to be based on history, historical data for several seasons should be available. The forecasting techniques for seasonal demand are not significantly different from those presented in Chapter 4. In fact, the identical linear techniques can be used with a slight reinterpretation: the quantity to be forecast is no longer the demand itself but the *ratio* of the demand to a "base series"; a base series is a *known* time series which is thought to be characteristic of the seasonality pattern. For example, if the sales of a given product are to be forecast, the base series might be last year's sales of the same product or of a similar group of products, possibly smoothed and adjusted in various ways. Sometimes, the *average* sales per period, taken over longer intervals of time surrounding the various points of time, give a smoother base series than the *actual* sales per period. After a base series has been selected from the historical data, one can set up a ratio forecast as a linear function of the historical values of the same ratio. Exponential smoothing and other linear techniques may be applied (see Chapter 4). The forecast of the demand itself is obtained by multiplying the ratio forecast by the appropriate value of the base series. An interesting graphical method for forecasting seasonal demand is discussed in [25].

In most applications of dynamic models, the system in question is treated as a single station so that only one aggregate forecast is required. Consequently, the traditional methods of business forecasting may also be applicable.

PRODUCTION SMOOTHING IN A PAINT FACTORY

The classical quadratic programming model by Holt et. al. [28, 29] was developed in a case study dealing with the production smoothing problem in a paint factory. The paint business is highly seasonal. As a consequence, the factory had a major problem of backorders on one hand, high inventories on the other hand, and, at the same time, hiring and layoffs occurred with considerable frequency. The natural planning horizon for a seasonal business is one year. The mathematical model was set up for monthly production and employment decisions. After the various cost parameters in Eqs. 5.103–5.106 had been estimated, the linear decision rules Eqs. 5.108–5.109 took the following form:

$$q_1 = \begin{cases} + 0.463r_1 \\ + 0.234r_2 \\ + 0.111r_3 \\ + 0.046r_4 \\ + 0.013r_5 \\ - 0.002r_6 \\ - 0.008r_7 \\ - 0.010r_8 \\ - 0.009r_9 \\ - 0.008r_{10} \\ - 0.007r_{11} \\ - 0.005r_{12} \end{cases} + 0.993W_0 + 153 - 0.464I_0 \qquad (6.1)$$

$$W_1 = 0.743W_0 + 2.09 - 0.010I_0 + \begin{cases} + 0.0101r_1 \\ + 0.0088r_2 \\ + 0.0071r_3 \\ + 0.0054r_4 \\ + 0.0042r_5 \\ + 0.0031r_6 \\ + 0.0023r_7 \\ + 0.0016r_8 \\ + 0.0012r_9 \\ + 0.0009r_{10} \\ + 0.0006r_{11} \\ + 0.0005r_{12} \end{cases} \qquad (6.2)$$

It is interesting to note the decreasing weight of forecasts of the distant future. The performance of these rules was tested in retrospect for a period of several years. At the beginning of each month, forecasts for the next twelve months were obtained by a simple moving-average method based on last year's seasonality pattern. The mathematical rules yielded a cost reduction of 8% in comparison with a reconstruction of actual performance. At the same time, the amount of back-orders was substantially reduced. A second test using the same decision rules under the assumption of *perfect* forecasts led to the interesting result that the additional gain from perfect forecasts was slight. Thus, the decision rule itself carried more importance than the quality of the forecast. This suggests that accurate forecasts may not be as essential to good decisions as many production people think. The real problem seems to be the optimal use of relatively crude forecasts.

OTHER SMOOTHING PROBLEMS

Similar studies of smoothing problems have been made in various industries. Charnes and Cooper [11] have applied their fixed-horizon model with linear decision rule to refinery operations. Here, the production of heating oil poses a smoothing problem. The relevant costs were inventory costs on one hand and the consolidated transportation and refining costs on the other hand. The latter were found to be a convex function of the monthly production quantity, i.e., marginal costs were increasing. Thus, the previously discussed convex programming approach was applicable (see Eq. 5.50). Demand for heating oil is strongly weather dependent. With the aid of weather forecasts, probability distributions of demand could be established.

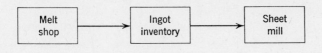

Fig. 6-1.

Hanssmann and Hess [24] have used a linear programming model in the metal fabricating industry. In this application, the production smoothing problem arose in a rather unusual way. Originally, the operation worked as a job shop. *No* ingot inventory was maintained between melt shop and sheet mill (Fig. 6-1). In an earlier phase of the study the possibilities of reducing delivery time had been considered. One way of achieving a reduction is to maintain an inventory of ingots and start the processing of incoming orders at the ingot stage. Thus, the considerable production lead time through the melt shop can be saved. At the same time, the existence of an inventory permits the fluctuations of ingot demand to be absorbed so that production smoothing in the melt shop becomes possible. A retrospective solution of the melt shop production smoothing problem led to the interesting result that the savings attributable to smoother production patterns were greater than the cost of inventory. Consequently, it was not necessary to justify the inventory carrying cost by the intangible value of reduced delivery time alone. In fact, the inventory seemed justifiable even if no sales increase was expected as a consequence of the reduction in delivery time.

PURCHASING RAW MATERIALS
IN A FLUCTUATING MARKET

A manufacturing company uses a raw material the price of which is subject to considerable fluctuation [19]. Clearly, the company wishes to purchase at minimum prices. On the other hand, a strict minimization of purchasing costs would tend to produce very high inventory levels. Therefore, the problem is to develop a purchasing strategy which balances inventory costs and purchasing costs. Purchasing decisions are made monthly. Since reliable forecasts of monthly (average) prices could be obtained only for the next four months, a (shifting) planning horizon of four months was chosen. Let q_i and r_i be the monthly purchasing quantities and internal requirements, respectively, and let I_0 be the inventory level at the beginning of the horizon. Because of limited storage possibilities, an upper limit I_{max} had to be imposed on all inventory levels. Similarly, a lower limit I_{min} was imposed to ensure sufficient protection against shortages. Thus, we have the restrictions

$$I_{min} \leq I_0 + \sum_{j=1}^{i} (q_j - r_j) \leq I_{max} \qquad (i = 1, \cdots, 4) \quad (6.3)$$

If p_i is the price in month i and h is the inventory carrying cost per month per unit of closing inventory, the total purchasing and inventory cost for the planning interval will be

$$C = \sum_{1}^{4} p_i q_i + h \sum_{i=1}^{4} \left[I_0 + \sum_{j=1}^{4} (q_j - r_j) \right]$$

$$= \sum_{1}^{4} c_i q_i + \text{const} \qquad (6.4)$$

where the coefficients c_i depend only on the prices and the holding cost h. Considering both the prices and the requirements as known, the optimal purchasing plan for the horizon may be found by solving the linear programming problem of minimizing the function in Eq. 6.4 with respect to the q_i, subject to the restrictions of Eq. 6.3. Fortunately, this problem can be solved by inspection once the coefficients c_i have been computed. Knowledge of the rank ordering of the c_i is sufficient for solution. For example, if

$$c_1 < c_2 < c_3 < c_4 \tag{6.5}$$

it is clear that we shall always buy up to $I_{\max}$ in the first month. A table has been drawn up which gives similar simple buying rules for all 24 possible relationships between the c_i. With the aid of this table, purchasing decisions can be made very quickly. Since prices are not in fact known, a probabilistic formulation of the problem seems more natural. This possibility was considered. However, the introduction of probability distributions of prices complicated the solution so much that it would have required a high-speed computer. This possibility had to be ruled out. Hence, the simple deterministic model was adopted.

We now turn to the problem of forecasting prices. The company belongs to an industry which is the major user of the raw material in question. Industry demand for the raw material was, therefore, expected to be the major factor in price formation. Industry demand, in turn, depends on the level of activity in the industry. The company had reason to believe that its own level of activity was representative of the industry's. Consequently, price history was analyzed in its relationship to company shipments and the amount of prebooked capacity. The latter was expected to be indicative of *future* activity. After some trial and error, the following quantities were found to be of particular interest:

$$x_i = \frac{V_i + V_{i-1}}{2} - \frac{\theta_{(i+1)/(i-1)} + \theta_{(i+2)/i}}{2} \tag{6.6}$$

$$x_2 = \theta_{i/i-1} - \theta_{(i+1)/(i-1)} \tag{6.7}$$

where $V_i =$ shipments in month i

$\theta_{a/b} =$ amount of orders for month a which was already booked in month b

A regression analysis yielded the following relationships between x_1 and x_2 on one hand and the price increases over the present price p_i

on the other hand (prices are measured in dollars per physical unit):

$$p_{i+1} - p_i = 15.6 - 0.090x_1 - 0.044x_2$$
$$p_{i+2} - p_i = 29.9 - 0.229x_1 \qquad (6.8)$$
$$p_{i+3} - p_i = 36.4 - 0.262x_1$$

These equations were used for the forecasting of prices. Of course, all required information (see Eqs. 6.6 and 6.7) must be made available before the end of month i. It was assumed that this could be done by the middle of the month so that the purchasing decision for month i can be adjusted in accordance with the optimal plan. To appraise the merit of the proposed method, it was applied retrospectively for a period of one year. Comparison was made with a "buy for need" policy which was thought to come reasonably close to the actual company policy. (Actual purchasing history could not be reconstructed.) The results of the test are given in Table 6-1 (all figures are in dollars per physical unit and were changed for reasons of industrial security).

Table 6-1
Costs of Alternative Policies

Policy	Purchasing cost per unit, dollars	Inventory cost per unit, dollars	Total cost per unit, dollars
"Buy for need"	60.60	0.40	61.00
Proposed policy	56.90	1.10	58.00

Because of the high annual purchasing volume, the cost difference between the two policies is of the order of millions per year. Although it cannot be guaranteed that the same savings will be realized in the future, there is undoubtedly a high potential for savings.

THE HYDROELECTRIC PROBLEM
AT THE GRAND COULEE DAM

Little [43] has specialized his hydroelectric model (Eq. 5.118) for the situation at the Grand Coulee Dam. The amount of electricity generated by discharging an amount u_i of water through the turbines may be approximated by

$$e_i = \rho u_i[I_0 + \tfrac{1}{2}(I_i + I_{i+1})] \qquad (6.9)$$

where ρ and I_0 are constants, and I_i is the water inventory at the beginning of month i. Let r_i be the demand for electricity in period i. The cost in month i of supplying electric energy from other than hydroelectric sources is assumed to be of the form

$$C_i = a_0 + a_1(r_i - e_i) + a_2(r_i - e_i)^2 \qquad (6.10)$$

Hydroelectric energy is assumed to be free. For technological reasons, there is an upper limit u_{max} for the discharge. In addition, discharge is limited by the total water supply $I_i + x_i$, where x_i is the river flow in month i. As long as the water supply permits, it is also desired to keep the discharge above a given minimum u_{min}. In summary, we have the discharge restrictions

$$\min (u_{min}, I_i + x_i) \leq u_i \leq \min (u_{max}, I_i + x_i) \qquad (6.11)$$

The water inventory itself obeys the restriction

$$0 \leq I_i \leq I_{max} \qquad (6.12)$$

where I_{max} is the capacity of the reservoir. Consecutive inventory levels are, therefore, connected by the relation

$$I_{i+1} = \begin{cases} I_i + x_i - u_i & \text{for } I_i + x_i - u_i \leq I_{max} \\ I_{max} & \text{for } I_i + x_i - u_i > I_{max} \end{cases} \qquad (6.13)$$

By these relations, the cost function $C_i(u_i, I_i, x_i)$ in Eq. 5.118 is completely specified. Note that the river flow enters both directly and through the restrictions.

A planning horizon of one year is suggested in a natural way by the periodicity of river flow. The horizon was divided into 26 periods of 2 weeks each. A 39-year historical record of riverflows of the Columbia river was used for determining probability density functions $g_i(x_i \mid x_{i-1})$ for all periods i. The dynamic programming solution of the problem was carried out on the Whirlwind I computer at M.I.T. The one-dimensional minimizations were handled by direct evaluation of the cost functions in question. The calculation of a complete solution in the form of 26 tabulated decision functions took from 5 minutes to an hour depending on the mesh size chosen for the tables.

Current rules for controlling water output are given by a "rule curve" which specifies lower limits for reservoir elevation as a function of the time in the year. The existence of such a formal rule made it possible to reconstruct operations under current rules and under the mathematically derived rules for the 39 years of historical flows. The cost comparison was made on the basis of the quadratic cost function (Eq. 6.10); on the average, the mathematical rules yielded a 1% cost savings per year (roughly $70,000 per year). The significance of these savings is debatable because of the nature of the cost function. However, it is remarkable that the mathematical solution is computationally feasible and approximates actual performance very well. An important factor which was not considered in this study is the interaction between various power plants along the same river.   This more general problem involves series of inventory stations.

BIBLIOGRAPHY D

Dynamic Single Station Models and Their Applications

1. Antosiewiez, H., Hoffman, A., "A Remark on the Smoothing Problem," *Management Science*, **1**, No. 1 (Oct. 1954), 92–95.
2. Arrow, K. J., Karlin, S., Scarf, H., *Studies in the Mathematical Theory of Inventory and Production*, Stanford, Calif.: Stanford University Press, 1958.
3. Bellman, R., *Dynamic Programming*, Princeton, New Jersey: Princeton University Press, 1957.
4. Bellman, R., "On a Dynamic Programming Approach to the Caterer Problem—I," *Management Science*, **3**, No. 3 (Apr. 1957), 270–278.
5. Bellman, R., "Dynamic Programming and the Smoothing Problem," *Management Science*, **3**, No. 1 (Oct. 1956), 111–113.
6. Bellman, R., "On the Theory of Dynamic Programming—A Warehousing Problem," *Management Science*, **2**, No. 3 (Apr. 1956), 272–275.
7. Bishop, G. T., "On a Problem of Production Scheduling," *Operations Research*, **5**, No. 1 (Feb. 1957), 97–103.
8. Bonini, C. P., "Decision Rules for Buffer Inventories," *Management Science*, **4**, No. 4 (July 1958), 457–471.
9. Bowman, E. H., "Production Scheduling by the Transportation Method of Linear Programming," *Operations Research*, **4**, No. 1 (Feb. 1956), 100–103.
10. Charnes, A., Cooper, W. W., Mellon, B., "A Model for Optimizing Production by Reference to Cost Surrogates," *Econometrica*, **23**, No. 3 (July 1955), 307–323.
11. Charnes, A., Cooper, W. W., Symonds, G. H., "Cost Horizons and Certainty Equivalents: An Approach to Stochastic Programming of Heating Oil," *Management Science*, **4**, No. 3 (Apr. 1958), 235–263.
12. Dannerstedt, G., "Production Scheduling for an Arbitrary Number of Periods Given the Sales Forecast in the Form of a Probability Distribution," *Operations Research*, **3**, No. 3 (Aug. 1955), 300–318.
13. Danskin, J. M., "Mathematical Treatment of a Stockpiling Problem," *Naval Research Logistics Quarterly*, **2**, Nos. 1 and 2 (Mar.–June 1955), 99–110.
14. Dantzig, G., Johnson, S., "A Production Smoothing Problem," *Proceedings of the Second Symposium on Linear Programming*, Washington, D.C. (Jan. 1955).
15. Dreyfus, S. E., "Computational Aspects of Dynamic Programming," *Operations Research*, **5**, No. 3 (June 1957), 409–415.
16. Dreyfus, S. E., "An Analytic Solution of the Warehouse Problem," *Management Science*, **4**, No. 1 (Oct. 1957), 99–104.
17. Dvoretzky, A., Kiefer, J., Wolfowitz, J., "The Inventory Problem," *Econometrica*, **20**, No. 2 (Apr. 1952), 187–222; *ibid.*, No. 3 (July 1952), 450–466.
18. Eastman, W. L., "A Note on the Multi-Commodity Warehouse Problem," *Management Science*, **5**, No. 3 (Apr. 1959), 327–331.

19. Fabian, T., Fisher, J. L., Sasieni, M. W., Yardeni, A., "Purchasing Raw Material on a Fluctuating Market," *Operations Research*, **7**, No. 1 (Jan.–Feb. 1959), 107–122.

20. Gaddum, J. W., Hoffman, A. J., Sokolowsky, D., "On the Solution of the Caterer Problem," *Naval Research Logistics Quarterly*, **1**, No. 3 (Sept. 1954), 223–229.

21. Gani, J., "Problems in the Probability Theory of Storage Systems," *Journal of the Royal Statistical Society*, **19**, Series B (1957).

22. Gessford, J., "Scheduling the Use of Water Power," *Management Science*, **5**, No. 2 (Jan. 1959), 179–191.

23. Hanssmann, F., "Determination of Optimal Capacities of Service for Facilities With a Linear Measure of Inefficiency," *Operations Research*, **5**, No. 5 (Oct. 1957), 713–717.

24. Hanssmann, F., Hess, S. W., "A Linear Programming Approach to Production and Employment Scheduling," *Management Technology*, Monograph of the Institute of Management Sciences (Jan. 1960), 46–51.

25. Hertz, D. B., Schaffir, K. H., "A Forecasting Method for Management of Seasonal Style-Goods Inventories," *Operations Research*, **8**, No. 1 (Jan.–Feb. 1960), 45–52.

26. Hoffman, A. J., Jacobs, W., "Smooth Patterns of Production," *Management Science*, **1**, No. 1 (Oct. 1954), 86–91.

27. Holt, C. C., Simon, H. A., "Optimal Decision Rules for Production and Inventory Control," in *Proceedings of the Conference on Operations Research in Production and Inventory Control*, Cleveland, Ohio: Case Institute of Technology (Jan. 1954), 73–89.

28. Holt, C. C., Modigliani, F., Simon, H. A., "Linear Decision Rule for Production and Employment Scheduling," *Management Science*, **2**, No. 1 (Oct. 1955), 1–30.

29. Holt, C. C., Modigliani, F., Muth, J. F., "Derivation of a Linear Decision Rule for Production and Employment Scheduling," *Management Science*, **2**, No. 2 (Jan. 1956), 159–177.

30. Hu, T. C., Prager, W., "Network Analysis of Production Smoothing," *Naval Research Logistics Quarterly*, **6**, No. 1 (Mar. 1959), 17–24.

31. Jewel, W. S., "Warehousing and Distribution of a Seasonal Product," *Naval Research Logistics Quarterly*, **4**, No. 1 (Mar. 1957), 29–34.

32. Johnson, S. M., "Sequential Production Planning Over Time at Minimum Cost," *Management Science*, **3**, No. 4 (July 1957), 435–437.

33. Karlin S., "The Structure of Dynamic Programming Models," *Naval Research Logistics Quarterly*, **2** (1955), 285–294.

34. Karlin, S., "Dynamic Inventory Policy with Varying Stochastic Demands," *Management Science*, **6**, No. 3 (Apr. 1960), 231–258.

35. Karush, W., "On a Class of Minimum Cost Problems," *Management Science*, **4**, No. 2 (Jan. 1958), 136–155.

36. Karush, W., Vazsonyi, A., "Mathematical Programming and Employment Scheduling," *Naval Research Logistics Quarterly*, **4**, No. 4 (Dec. 1957), 297–320.

37. Karush, W., Vazsonyi, A., "Mathematical Programming and Service Scheduling," *Management Science*, **3**, No. 2 (Jan. 1957), 140–148.

38. Kendall, D. G., "Some Problems in the Theory of Dams," *Journal of the Royal Statistical Society*, **19**, Series B (1957).

39. Klein, M., "Some Production Planning Problems," *Naval Research Logistics Quarterly*, **4**, No. 4 (Dec. 1957), 269–286.

40. Koopmans, T. C., "Water Storage Policy in a Simplified Hydroelectric System," in *Proceedings of the First International Conference on Operational Research*, Bristol, England: John Wright and Sons, 1958, 193–227.

41. Laderman, J., Littauer, S. B., Weiss, L., "The Inventory Problem," *Journal of the American Statistical Association*, **48** (Dec. 1953), 717–732.

42. Levy, J., "Optimal Inventory Policy When Demand is Increasing," *Operations Research*, **8**, No. 6 (Nov.–Dec. 1960), 861–863.

43. Little, J. D. C., "The Use of Storage Water in a Hydroelectric System," *Operations Research*, **3**, No. 2 (May 1955), 187–197.

44. Manne, A. S., "A Note on the Modigliani-Hohn Production Smoothing Model," *Management Science*, **3**, No. 4 (July 1957), 371–379.

45. McDowell, Ian, "The Economical Planning Period for Engineering Works," *Operations Research*, **8**, No. 4 (July–Aug. 1960), 533–542.

46. Mills, E. S., "The Theory of Inventory Decisions," *Econometrica*, **25**, No. 2 (Apr. 1957), 222–238.

47. Mills, E. S., "A Note on the Asymptotic Behavior of an Optimal Procurement Policy," *Management Science*, **5**, No. 2 (Jan. 1959), 204–209.

48. Modigliani, F., Hohn, F. E., "Production Planning Over Time and the Nature of the Expectation and Planning Horizon," *Econometrica*, **23**, No. 1 (Jan. 1955), 46–66.

49. Moran, P. A. P., "A Probability Theory of a Dam with a Continuous Release," *The Quarterly Journal of Mathematics*, **VII** (1956), 130–137.

50. Morin, F., "Note on an Inventory Problem Discussed by Modigliani and Hohn," *Econometrica*, **23**, No. 4 (Oct. 1955), 447–50.

51. Oliver, Robert M., "The Design and Error Analysis of a Sampled-Data Production and Inventory Control System," *Proceedings of the First International Conference on Operational Research*, Bristol, England: John Wright and Sons, 1958, 228–242.

52. Prager, W., "On the Caterer Problem," *Management Science*, **3**, No. 1 (Oct. 1956), 15–23.

53. Reiter, St., "A Note on Surrogates for Uncertain Decision Problems," *Econometrica*, **25**, No. 2 (Apr. 1957), 339–345.

54. Rosenblatt, M., "An Inventory Problem," *Econometrica*, **22**, No. 2 (Apr. 1954), 244–247.

55. Sadowski, W., "A Few Remarks on the Assortment Problem," *Management Science*, **6**, No. 1 (Oct. 1959), 13–24.

56. Schild, A., "On Inventory, Production, and Employment Scheduling," *Management Science*, **5**, No. 2 (Jan. 1959), 157–168.

57. Schneider, E., "Absatz, Produktion und Lagerhaltung bei einfacher Produktion," *Archiv fuer mathematische Wirtschafts- und Sozialforschung*, **4**, No. 1 (1938).

58. Schupack, M. B., "Economic-Lot Sizes with Seasonal Demand," *Operations Research*, **7**, No. 1 (Jan.–Feb. 1959), 45–57.

59. Sherman, S., "Comment on Smooth Patterns of Production," *Management Science*, **1**, No. 3–4 (Apr.–July 1955), 271.

60. Simon, H. A., "On the Application of Servomechanism Theory in the Study of Production Control," *Econometrica*, **20**, No. 2 (Apr. 1952), 247–268.

61. Simon, H. A., "Dynamic Programming Under Uncertainty with a Quadratic Criterion Function," *Econometrica*, **24**, No. 1 (Jan. 1956), 74–81.

62. Theil, H., "A Note on Certainty Equivalence in Dynamic Planning," *Econometrica*, **25**, No. 2 (Apr. 1957), 346–349.

63. Vassian, H. J., "Application of Discrete Variable Servo Theory to Inventory Control," *Operations Research*, **3**, No. 3 (Aug. 1955), 272–282.

64. Wagner, H. M., "A Postscript to 'Dynamic Problems in the Theory of the Firm,'" *Naval Research Logistics Quarterly*, **7**, No. 1 (Mar. 1960), 7–12.

65. Wagner, H. M., Whitin, T. M., "Dynamic Problems in the Theory of the Firm," *Naval Research Logistics Quarterly*, **5**, No. 1 (Mar. 1958), 53–74.

66. Wagner, H. M., Whitin, T. M., "Dynamic Version of the Economic-Lot-Size Model," *Management Science*, **5**, No. 1 (Oct. 1958), 89–96.

67. Whitin, T. M., "Erich Schneider's Inventory Control Analysis," *Operations Research*, **2**, No. 3 (Aug. 1954), 329–334.

part III

PARALLEL STATIONS

chapter 7
Models of Parallel Stations

Problems involving parallel inventory stations would represent little more than a set of independent single-station problems unless there were interactions between the parallel inputs, outputs, and inventories. These interactions often take the form of restrictions on the state variables of the whole system and may significantly complicate the mathematical treatment of the decision problem. The newsboy problem furnishes a typical example.

GENERALIZATION OF THE NEWSBOY PROBLEM

The single-station newsboy problem may be viewed as one of finding the optimal inventory investment when a one-time probabilistic demand is anticipated and the total cost of overage and shortage (lost profit) is to be minimized. Now consider the more general situation where the newsboy can stock several kinds $i = 1, \cdot \cdot \cdot, m$ of newspapers but has limited total funds c for inventory investment. Which amount x_i should he allocate to the ith newspaper?

Clearly, the expected profit derived from the ith paper is of the form $f_i(x_i)$. The allocated amounts x_i must be determined such that

$$F(x_1, \cdot \cdot \cdot, x_m) = \sum_{i=1}^{m} f_i(x_i) \qquad (7.1)$$

is maximized subject to the restriction

$$\sum_{i=1}^{m} x_i = c \qquad (7.2)$$

The solution may proceed as shown in Table 7-1. In the first column, possible levels of investment with constant increments a are listed. For each newspaper i the marginal return from investing an additional amount a is given by the first difference of the return function $f_i(x_i)$. One may begin with an arbitrary allocation of the total sum c and mark the corresponding cells in the Δ columns.   One of these cells will show the smallest marginal loss.   If investment in the corresponding column is reduced by the amount a, and the amount a is transferred to the column with the greatest marginal gain, an improved allocation results.   If the return functions are concave $[f_i'(x_i)$ decreasing], repeated application of this method of improvement will lead to an optimal allocation.   The process ends when the smallest marginal loss is greater than or equal to the greatest marginal gain.   The accuracy of the solution depends, of course, on the size of increment a.   The

Table 7-1
Returns as a Function of Investment

Investment Levels	Returns and Marginal Returns						
x	$f_1(x_1)$	Δf_1	$f_2(x_2)$	Δf_2	$\cdots$	$f_n(x_n)$	Δf_n
0							
a							
$2a$							
$3a$							
.							
.							
.							

smaller a, the closer the solution will come to an allocation with equal marginal gains for all investments.   We have made the tacit assumption that the amount c is not sufficient to achieve the maximum profit for each single investment.   If this assumption does not hold, the solution is, of course, obvious.

An alternative method of solution, which is especially powerful when c is to be parametrized, proceeds as follows.   Compute the "marginal utilities"

$$u_{ji} = \frac{\Delta f_i(ja)}{a} \qquad (i = 1, \cdots, m; j = 0, 1, 2, \cdots) \qquad (7.3)$$

and redesignate them by u_k in decreasing order of their amounts $(k = 1, 2, \cdots)$.   The division by the constant a is not necessary for this ranking process but we wish to be more general for later applications.   If a total amount $c = \lambda a$ is available for investment, then all investments with marginal utilities

$$u_k \geq u_\lambda \qquad (7.4)$$

should be made—in other words, the investments with the marginal utilities $u_1, \cdots, u_\lambda$. It is clear that the return is maximized in this way.

Furthermore, the concavity of the return functions which may be expressed by the relations

$$u_{ji} \leq u_{j-1,i} \tag{7.5}$$

for all j and i, ensures that no level j of investment will be chosen unless all lower levels $1, \cdots, j - 1$ have already been chosen. Thus, there will be no "gaps" between investments. Table 7-2 conveniently exhibits the procedure of calculation. The last two columns give the optimal return as a function of the total investment. This method has obvious generalizations for indivisible investments (machines, parts, projects) which cannot meaningfully be broken down into constant small increments a.

Table 7-2
Marginal Utilities in Order of Rank

Rank	Marginal Utility	Average Utility*	Total Investment	Total Utility
k	u_k	$\dfrac{1}{k} \sum u_k$	ka	$a \sum u_k$
1			a	
2			$2a$	
3			$3a$	
.			.	
.			.	
.			.	

* The average utility for the first k investments is defined as the ratio of total utility (return) to total investment.

In this section we have presented a somewhat general model for resource allocation. A theory referring specifically to the allocation of stocks to warehouses is given in [31].

ALLOCATION OF AIRCRAFT TO ROUTES

In the generalized newsboy problem we assumed several categories i of demand, each of which could be satisfied by exactly one stock item. We now admit the possibility that the customer will accept any of several alternative items. As a prototype example, consider air traffic: the demand for transportation on a given route j may be satisfied by using any one of several types i of aircraft. Given the total numbers of aircraft of each type which are available in an operation, and given the probability distributions of demand for all routes, how many airplanes of each type should be allocated to each route [6, 7]?   In this inventory problem, the cost of unused carrying capacity plays the role of overage cost; the penalty for a shortage of capacity is the loss of potential profit.

Using a planning interval of one month, let:

c_{ij} = monthly cost per aircraft of type i assigned to route j

k_{ij} = monthly passenger carrying capacity per aircraft of type i assigned to route j

x_{ij} = number of aircraft of type i assigned to route j

p_j = revenue per unit of satisfied demand on route j

a_i = total number of aircraft of type i available in the operation

$$(i = 1, \cdots, m; j = 1, \cdots, n)$$

The demand on route j is assumed to be given by a discrete probability distribution, as shown in Table 7-3.

Table 7-3
Demand for Service on Route j

Level of Demand	Probability of Reaching or Exceeding This Level	Increment of Demand
0	1	—
r_{1j}	α_{1j}	b_{1j}
r_{2j}	α_{2j}	b_{2j}
.	.	.
.	.	.
.	.	.
r_{dj}	α_{dj}	b_{dj}

Now let Y_j be the total capacity assigned to route j. Since Y_j may be viewed as the maximum demand which can be satisfied, we may write

$$Y_j = \sum_{h=1}^{d} y_{hj} \tag{7.6}$$

where the y_{hj} correspond to the d ranges (and probability levels) of demand given in Table 7.3. By definition, the variables y_{hj} fulfill the restrictions

$$0 \leq y_{1j} \leq b_{1j} \tag{7.7}$$

$$\vdots$$

$$0 \leq y_{dj} \leq b_{dj} \qquad (j = 1, \cdots, n)$$

A further (definitional) restriction of each quantity y_{hj} is that it cannot assume a nonzero value unless the quantities $y_{1j}, \cdots, y_{h-1,j}$ are at their upper bounds (no "gaps" occur). Obviously, the expected value of satisfied demand, given the capacity Y_j, may now be written

$$\sum_{h=1}^{d} \alpha_{hj} y_{hj} \qquad (7.8)$$

Thus, the expected profit for the total system takes the form

$$E(P) = \sum_{j=1}^{n} p_j \sum_{h=1}^{d} \alpha_{hj} y_{hj} - \sum_{i=1}^{m} \sum_{j=1}^{n} c_{ij} x_{ij} \qquad (7.9)$$

Since all aircraft must be assigned, we have

$$\sum_{j=1}^{n} x_{ij} = a_i \qquad (i = 1, \cdots, m) \qquad (7.10)$$

Setting the total capacity assigned to route j equal to the maximum demand which can be satisfied, we obtain the further relations

$$\sum_{i=1}^{m} k_{ij} x_{ij} = \sum_{h=1}^{d} y_{hd} \qquad (j = 1, \cdots, n) \qquad (7.11)$$

If we solve the linear programming problem of maximizing $E(P)$ in Eq. 7.9 subject to the restrictions of Eqs. 7.7, 7.10, 7.11, and the non-negativity constraints

$$x_{ij} \geq 0 \qquad (i = 1, \cdots, m; j = 1, \cdots, n) \qquad (7.12)$$

we shall obtain a usable answer *provided* that the further restrictions of the y_{hj} mentioned after Eq. 7.7 are satisfied by the solution. As long as the α_{hj} are nonincreasing for $h = 1, 2, \cdots$, it is easy to see that these restrictions will be fulfilled automatically. For, otherwise, $E(P)$ could be increased without violation of the restrictons by simply closing the "gaps" in the sequence of the y_{hj}. Another study dealing with the allocation of transport equipment is found in [30].

THE ECONOMIC-LOT SCHEDULING PROBLEM

Very critical difficulties can arise when the elementary single-station models are applied to a set of parallel stations. For example, when economic production lots are established independently for a number of products, it is a common phenomenon that unfeasible production schedules result, particularly by overloading of facilities. One is thus faced with the economic-lot scheduling problem. The more general approaches to this problem lead to rather unwieldy mathematics [28, 23] and do not hold much promise of being helpful in practical situations. In the following we confine ourselves to certain simplified versions of the problem.

Feasible Schedules

The economic-lot scheduling problem may be viewed as one of minimizing total setup cost and inventory carrying cost for a large number of products during a given planning horizon, subject to restrictions on shortages and available machine time. In the following model, we admit dynamic demand patterns [37]. The planning horizon comprises n production periods. Let

r_{ij} = requirements of product i in period j

R_{ij} = cumulative requirements of product i up to and including period j

x_{ij} = amount of product i produced in period j

X_{ij} = cumulative production of product i up to and including period j

a_{ik} = setup time for product i on machine k (equal to zero if machine k is not used in the production process of product i)

b_{ik} = unit run time for product i on machine k

s_{ik} = setup cost for product i on machine k

h_i = holding cost for product i per period per unit of closing inventory

L_{kj} = capacity of machine k in period j (in hours)

$$i = 1, \cdots, m \text{ (products)}$$
$$j = 1, \cdots, n \text{ (periods)}$$
$$k = 1, \cdots, d \text{ (machines)}$$

We also define the "unit function"

$$u(x) = \begin{cases} 0 & \text{for } x = 0 \\ 1 & \text{for } x > 0 \end{cases} \tag{7.13}$$

The shortage restriction is given by

$$X_{ij} - R_{ij} \geq 0 \tag{7.14}$$

for all i and j. Consequently, the closing inventories at the end of each period are nonnegative. Since the holding cost is proportional to the closing inventories, the total cost of inventories and setups during the planning horizon becomes

$$C = \sum_{i,j} h_i (X_{ij} - R_{ij}) + \sum_{i,j,k} s_{ik}\, u(x_{ij}) \qquad (7.15)$$

To remain within machine capacities, we have to observe the restrictions

$$\sum_i a_{ik}\, u(x_{ij}) + \sum_i b_{ik} x_{ij} \leq L_{kj} \qquad (7.16)$$

for all k and j. We thus have a nonlinear programming problem: the x_{ij} are to be determined so that C in Eq. 7.15 is minimized, subject to the restrictions of Eqs. 7.14 and 7.16. Unfortunately, the solution is beyond the present capabilities of high-speed computers for realistic assumptions about the number of products. Nevertheless, the formulation of the problem may serve as a guide to approximate solutions. Also, the problem of finding feasible schedules (i.e., schedules which fulfill the restrictions of our formulation) without consideration of cost is legitimate in itself. We shall concentrate on the latter aspect.

Construction of a feasible schedule may begin by considering the first product alone. In the last period, we produce either the total requirements of the last period or the maximum amount possible with available machine time, whichever the smaller; in other words,

$$x_{1n} = \min \left(r_{1n};\ \min_k \frac{L_{kn}}{b_{1k}} \right) \qquad (7.17)$$

For simplicity's sake, we have ignored setup times. Their inclusion is an obvious generalization. If $x_{1n} < r_{1n}$, the demand balance $r_{1n} - x_{1n}$ is added to the previous period's requirements. Then $x_{1,n-1}$ is determined in analogous fashion. The last step of this procedure yields x_{11}. If any unsatisfied demand is left over, an initial inventory is needed to avoid shortages. If capacities are adequate this should not happen. This scheduling procedure tends to minimize inventory costs for product 1. It seems, therefore, reasonable to begin with the most expensive product. After product 1 has been scheduled, the same procedure is repeated for product 2 with adjusted machine capacities allowing for the machine time already reserved for product 1; and so on for all products. The final result will be a schedule which fulfills shortage and capacity restrictions. Without going into further ramifications, it is clear that the method may be refined so that the solution comes closer to minimizing the total cost of inventories and setups.

Optimization of Cycle Length

We now return to the deterministic classical lot-size problem with finite production rate, assuming that m different products $i = 1$, $\cdots$, m with demand rates r_i must be manufactured, one at a time, on the same facility. What should be the lot sizes for these products, and how should they be scheduled in order to minimize total cost of inventories and setups? As in the classical model for a single station, shortages are not permitted. Let s_i and h_i be the setup cost and inventory carrying cost for product i respectively. Furthermore, let T_i be the cycle length (time between production runs) and t_i the time spent

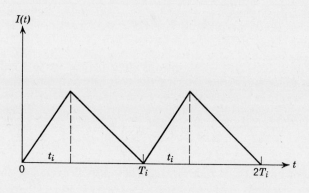

Fig. 7-1.

in production during one cycle (Fig. 7.1). The lot size is, of course, given by

$$q_i = p_i t_i = r_i T_i \tag{7.18}$$

where p_i is the production rate. We shall keep cycle lengths and lot sizes q_i constant in time. Schedules of this type result in the familiar inventory pattern pictured in Fig. 7-1. Interference of the various products may be avoided by imposing the restriction of equal cycle length T for all products. By so doing, we restrict ourselves to a subset of all feasible production policies. But we are rewarded by the simplicity of the solution. (Usually, the cumbersome search for a more nearly optimal solution yields little improvement anyway. This can often be shown by bounding the cost of the optimal policy: obviously, it must lie between the cost of the approximate solution and the cost associated with the unrestricted classical lot sizes).

Starting with the assumption of equal cycle times T, we have

$$q_i = p_i t_i = r_i T \qquad (7.19)$$

or

$$t_i = \frac{r_i}{p_i} T = \beta_i T \qquad (7.20)$$

where

$$\beta_i = \frac{r_i}{p_i} \qquad (7.21)$$

The total cost per cycle may now be written

$$\sum_{i=1}^{m} \left[s_i + T \frac{h_i}{2} (p_i - r_i) t_i \right] \qquad (7.22)$$

Substituting t_i from Eq. 7.20 and dividing by the cycle length T, we obtain the following expression for the cost per unit time:

$$C = \sum_{i=1}^{n} \left[\frac{s_i}{T} + T \frac{h_i r_i}{2} \left(1 - \frac{r_i}{p_i} \right) \right] \qquad (7.23)$$

By standard methods, it follows that the optimal cycle length and the optimal lot sizes are given by

$$\hat{T} = \sqrt{\frac{2 \sum_{i=1}^{n} s_i}{\sum_{i=1}^{n} h_i r_i [1 - (r_i/p_i)]}} \qquad (7.24)$$

and

$$\hat{q}_j = r_j \sqrt{\frac{2 \sum_{i=1}^{n} s_i}{\sum_{i=1}^{n} h_i r_i [1 - (r_i/p_i)]}} \qquad (7.25)$$

respectively.   If total capacity is sufficient—which we assume—the relation

$$\sum_{i=1}^{n} \frac{r_i}{p_i} \leq 1 \qquad (7.26)$$

holds. By Eq. 7.20 it follows that, for any cycle length,

$$\sum_{i=1}^{n} t_i \leq T \tag{7.27}$$

Since the production sequence does not enter into Eq. 7.27, the n products may be scheduled in an arbitrary sequence and with an arbitrary distribution of idle time between production runs. Of course, this holds only as long as the setup time is not greater than the amount of idle time available in a cycle. The fact that schedule feasibility is not affected by the production sequence may be exploited when the setup times are not constants but depend on the production sequence. Then, the production sequence may be chosen beforehand in such a way that Σs_i is minimized. This may be done by solving a so-called traveling-salesman problem [5] which we do not further discuss here. The cost per unit time of the inventory policy Eq. 7.24 is given by

$$\hat{C} = \sqrt{2 \left(\sum_{1}^{n} s_i \right) \left[\sum_{1}^{n} h_i r_i \left(1 - \frac{r_i}{p_i} \right) \right]} \tag{7.28}$$

Consequently, the minimization of Σs_i also leads to minimum cost.

In this approach we have not considered setup *times*. If the optimal cycle (Eq. 7.24) does not contain sufficient slack time for setups, the cycle must be lengthened accordingly. It should be noted that the amount of slack time per cycle is proportional to the cycle length, whereas the total setup time per cycle (for a given production sequence) does *not* depend on the cycle length. For a similar treatment of the problem, see [12]. Alternatively, one may take advantage of the fact that the cost curves of the individual products are quite flat in the neighborhood of the economic-lot size. If each lot size is restricted to an "economic-lot range"[34], the scheduling problem can often be solved without serious increase in cost.

LAGRANGIAN MULTIPLIERS

If the interactions between products may be stated by a small number of restrictions, the technique of Lagrangian multipliers may be used in the derivation of optimal lot sizes [5]. As an example, consider a storage space limitation, assuming that the space requirements for product i are proportional to the lot size q_i. We then have a restriction of the form

$$\sum_{i=1}^{m} a_i q_i \leq A \qquad (7.29)$$

where the a_i are given constants and A is the total available space. Further assume that the cost equation is of the familiar form

$$C(q_1, \cdots, q_n) = \sum_{i=1}^{m} \left(\frac{s_i r_i}{q_i} + \frac{h_i}{2} q_i \right) \qquad (7.30)$$

If the unrestricted lot sizes lead to a space requirement $> A$, the space restriction may be stated with the equality sign. Introducing a Lagrangian multiplier λ, the problem becomes one of minimizing

$$\sum_{i=1}^{m} \left(\frac{s_i r_i}{q_i} + \frac{h_i}{2} q_i \right) + \lambda \left(\sum_{i=1}^{m} a_i q_i - A \right) \qquad (7.31)$$

with respect to $q_1, \cdots, q_m$ and λ. Taking partials with respect to these variables and setting them equal to zero, we are led to the following system of $m + 1$ equations for $m + 1$ unknowns:

$$q_i = \sqrt{\frac{2 s_i r_i}{h_i + 2\lambda a_i}} \qquad (i = 1, \cdots, m) \qquad (7.32)$$

$$\sum_{i=1}^{m} a_i q_i = A \qquad (7.33)$$

In this particular case, the system may be solved iteratively by trying different values of λ. By analogy with Eqs. 7.1 and 7.2, the problem may also be viewed as a generalized newsboy problem. The only difference is that the scarce resource is space rather than total funds. The same methods of solution are applicable.

SIMULTANEOUS ORDERING OF SEVERAL ITEMS

Consider an inventory system with m stock items $i = 1, \cdots, m$ which are all purchased from the same supplier, e.g., a central warehouse [26]. When a particular item i must be replenished, a purchasing requisition is filed with a central ordering agency (purchasing department). For each requisition sent to the central agency, a fixed charge s_i is incurred. For each order sent to the supplier by the central agency, a fixed charge s_0 is incurred. Consequently, the central agency should try to combine several requisitions into one order. However, the restriction is imposed that requisitions cannot be accumulated; they must be changed into orders without delay. Furthermore, orders must be placed at checking points t time units apart, and requisitions for item i must be placed at checking points t_i time units apart. This is possible only when all cycles t_i are multiples of the ordering cycle t:

$$\frac{t_i}{t} = k_i \tag{7.34}$$

where k_i is an integer ≥ 1. If we remain within the framework of the classical model with instantaneous input, the ordering quantities are

$$q_i = r_i t_i \tag{7.35}$$

where r_i is the demand rate for item i. Let h_i be the inventory carrying cost for item i. Then, the total system cost per unit time is given by

$$C = \sum_{i=1}^{m} \left(\frac{h_i}{2} q_i + \frac{s_i}{t_i} \right) + \frac{s_0}{t} \tag{7.36}$$

or, in terms of the cycle times,

$$C(t_1, \cdots, t_m \mid t) = \sum_{i=1}^{m} \left(\frac{h_i r_i}{2} t_i + \frac{s_i}{t_i} \right) + \frac{s_0}{t} \tag{7.37}$$

The cost function Eq. 7.37 is to be minimized with respect to all cycle times, subject to the restriction of Eq. 7.34. It is clear that, for each value of t, we are interested only in the minimum cost contribution $M_i(t)$ for each item i. The functions $M_i(t)$ may be established as follows. Define

$$C_i(t_i) = \frac{h_i r_i}{2} t_i + \frac{s_i}{t_i} \tag{7.38}$$

Furthermore, let $\hat{t}_i$ be the (unrestricted) optimal cycle time for item i, and $\hat{C}_i$ the associated minimum cost

$$\hat{C}_i = C_i(\hat{t}_i) \tag{7.39}$$

It is clear that for $t \geq \hat{t}_i$ the lowest achievable cost for item i is $C_i(t)$. Because of the flatness of the cost curve $C_i(t_i)$ in the neighborhood of the minimum, the lowest achievable cost for $t \leq \hat{t}_i$ may be approximated by $\hat{C}_i$. If necessary, this approximation can easily be refined. We thus have

$$M_i(t) = \begin{cases} \hat{C}_i & \text{for } t \leq \hat{t}_i \\ C_i(t) & \text{for } t > \hat{t}_i \end{cases} \tag{7.40}$$

The problem then reduces to minimizing the function

$$M(t) = \sum_{i=1}^{m} M_i(t) \tag{7.41}$$

with respect to t. This may be done by direct evaluation. Once the optimal value t_0 has been determined, the optimal value of each t_i is found as the particular multiple of t_0 which comes closest to t_i.

A somewhat related problem arises in manufacturing when many parts are simultaneously assembled into finished products. An interesting model and case study along these lines are found in [24].

SELECTION OF WAREHOUSES

Consider a distribution system consisting of factories i, warehouses j, and retail outlets k [2]. Factories and retail outlets are company owned whereas warehouse space is rented. Hence, we have a problem of warehouse selection from a set of available warehouses j. Suppose it is decided to channel an annual amount z_j of product through a given warehouse j. We assume that warehouse charges will be proportional to the average inventory level and that the total volume z_j will be ordered in economic-lot sizes. According to the classical model Eq. 2.6, the warehousing and ordering costs per year will be of the form

$$\sum_j b_j \sqrt{z_j} \tag{7.42}$$

where the b_j are known constants. The annual demands r_k at the retail outlets are given. Let

c_{ij} = unit transportation cost from factory i to warehouse j
d_{jk} = unit transportation cost from warehouse j to retailer k
x_{ijk} = annual volume shipped from factory i to retailer k via warehouse j

The x_{ijk} are to be chosen so that the annual cost of transportation, warehousing, and ordering (for replenishment of warehouse inventories) is minimized.   This cost is given by

$$C = \sum_{i,j,k} (c_{ij} + d_{jk})x_{ijk} + \sum_j b_j z_j^{\lambda} \tag{7.43}$$

where

$$z_j = \sum_{i,k} x_{ijk} \tag{7.44}$$

and $\lambda = \frac{1}{2}$.   The algorithm for solution which will be presented is, however, valid for all λ with $0 < \lambda < 1$.   If factory i can supply an annual amount A_i, where the relation

$$\sum_i A_i = \sum_k r_k \tag{7.45}$$

is assumed to hold, we have the following obvious restrictions:

$$\sum_{j,k} x_{ijk} = A_i \tag{7.46}$$

$$\sum_{i,j} x_{ijk} = r_k \tag{7.47}$$

We thus have the nonlinear programming problem of minimizing C in Eq. 7.43 subject to the constraints of Eqs. 7.44, 7.46, and 7.47. Exact solutions are difficult to obtain, especially when the number of variables is large.   Baumol and Wolfe [2] have given the following simple algorithm which leads to a local minimum, if not the exact solution:

Step 1

Select the minimum transportation cost between factory i and retailer k, i.e.,

$$a'_{ik} = \min_j (c_{ij} + d_{jk}) \tag{7.48}$$

Using the cost coefficients a'_{ik}, solve the ordinary transportation problem between factories and retailers, i.e., minimize

$$\sum_{i,k} a'_{ik} x'_{ik}$$

with respect to the quantities x'_{ik} shipped from source i to destination k.

Step 2

Compute the warehouse loadings z'_j associated with the solution obtained under step 1.   (Note that each x'_{ik} corresponds to a well-determined warehouse j by Eq. 7.48.) Define new "transportation costs"

$$c_{ij} + d_{jk} + \lambda b_j z_j'^{\lambda-1} \qquad (7.49)$$

and again choose the minimum

$$a_{ik}'' = \min_j (c_{ij} + d_{jk} + \lambda b_j z_j'^{\lambda-1}) \qquad (7.50)$$

Then proceed as in step 1 to the second approximate solution, and so on.

Equation 7.49 may be interpreted as the marginal cost of shipping another unit of product from i to k via j when the warehouse loadings are z_j'. Based on these marginal costs, the second approximation leads to a new allocation z_j'' which reduces total cost.

THE PRODUCTION SMOOTHING PROBLEM FOR MANY PRODUCTS

We have previously discussed the production smoothing problem for a single station (Chapter 5). In this section we shall show that systems with many parallel stations may, under certain conditions, be treated as single stations [3]. The inventory term in the cost equation will then refer to the aggregate inventory level which may be measured by its dollar value or in meaningful physical units. Production and inventory decisions will be made in terms of the aggregate. To make such an approach meaningful, we must carry out these steps:

1. Given the cost characteristics of the individual products, derive the cost function for the whole system. Prove that it depends only on aggregate quantities.

2. Given an over-all decision in terms of aggregate production and inventory, translate this decision into decisions for the individual products.

We assume that unfilled demand can be backlogged and that probability distributions of demand are given for all products $i = 1, \cdots, m$ and all periods of the planning horizon. Thus, the inventory level I_i of product i at the end of a given period will be a random variable whose mean $\bar{I}_i$ depends on earlier production decisions, whereas all other parameters of its probability distribution are fixed by the probability distributions of demand and, hence, are not under control. We may, therefore, introduce $\bar{I}_i$ as the decision variable and write

$$I_i = \bar{I}_i + \Delta_i \qquad (7.51)$$

where the random variable Δ_i has a known probability density function $f_i(\Delta_i)$. Now assume that the inventory-connected costs attributable to the inventory level I_i are of the familiar form

$$C_i = h_i \int_0^\infty I_i\, g_i(I_i)\, dI_i - d_i \int_{-\infty}^0 I_i\, g_i(I_i)\, dI_i \qquad (7.52)$$

where h_i and d_i are given cost parameters and

$$g_i(I_i) = f_i(I_i - \bar I_i) \qquad (7.53)$$

is the probability density function of I_i. Clearly,

$$C_i(\bar I_i) = h_i \bar I_i - (h_i + d_i) \int_{-\infty}^0 I_i\, g_i(I_i)\, dI_i \qquad (7.54)$$

The inventory levels I_i are measured in physical units. Let c_i be the unit dollar value of product i. We can then introduce the (expected) aggregate inventory level, measured by its dollar value:

$$\bar I = \sum_{i=1}^m c_i \bar I_i \qquad (7.55)$$

We now make the assumption that for any level of the aggregate inventory $\bar I$ we shall always maintain the optimal inventory mix which minimizes total inventory connected costs. By this important assumption, a basic functional relationship between $\bar I$ and the $\bar I_i$ is established. It may be obtained by minimizing $\sum_i C_i(\bar I_i)$ with respect to the $\bar I_i$, subject to the restriction of Eq. 7.55. One of our earlier methods for optimal allocation of inventory investment or the technique of Lagrangian multipliers may be employed for solving this minimization problem. However, these methods do not usually lead to explicit relationships between $\bar I$ and $\bar I_i$. We, therefore, take the preliminary step of approximating each function $C_i(\bar I_i)$ by the first three terms of its Taylor expansion about the minimum point $\{\hat I_i,\ C_i(\hat I_i)\}$. A quadratic approximation seems reasonable for a wide class of probability distributions. To obtain the coefficients of the Taylor expansion, we take the derivatives of $C_i(\bar I_i)$.

Since

$$C_i(\bar I_i) = h_i \bar I_i - (h_i + d_i) \int_{-\infty}^{-\bar I_i} (\bar I_i + \Delta) f_i(\Delta)\, d\Delta \qquad (7.56)$$

we have

$$C'_i(\bar I_i) = h_i - (h_i + d_i)\, F_i(-\bar I_i) \qquad (7.57)$$

$$C''_i(\bar I_i) = (h_i + d_i)\, F_i(-\bar I_i) \qquad (7.58)$$

where $F_i(\Delta)$ is the cumulative function of $f_i(\Delta)$. Since $\{\hat{I}_i, C_i(\hat{I}_i)\}$ is the minimum point, $C'_i(\hat{I}_i) = 0$. We now introduce the abbreviations

$$a_i = C_i(\hat{I}_i) = -(h_i + d_i) \int_{-\infty}^{-I_i} \Delta f_i(\Delta) \, d\Delta \qquad (7.59)$$

$$2b_i = C''_i(\hat{I}_i) = (h_i + d_i) f_i(-\hat{I}_i) \qquad (7.60)$$

Thus, the desired approximation is given by

$$C_i(\bar{I}_i) = a_i + b_i(\bar{I}_i - \hat{I}_i)^2 \qquad (7.61)$$

To find the optimal inventory mix for a given aggregate inventory $\bar{I}$, we set up the Lagrangian function

$$L = \sum_{i=1}^{m} [a_i + b_i(\bar{I}_i - \hat{I}_i)^2] + \lambda \left(\bar{I} - \sum_{i=1}^{m} c_i \bar{I}_i \right) \qquad (7.62)$$

Equating the partials to zero, we obtain

$$\frac{\partial L}{\partial \bar{I}_i} = 2b_i(\bar{I}_i - \hat{I}_i) - \lambda c_i = 0 \qquad (7.63)$$

or equivalently

$$\bar{I}_i = \hat{I}_i + \frac{\lambda c_i}{2b_i} \qquad (7.64)$$

$$= \hat{I}_i + \lambda \alpha_i$$

where

$$\alpha_i = \frac{c_i}{2b_i} \qquad (7.65)$$

It follows from Eq. 7.64 that

$$\bar{I} = \sum_i c_i \bar{I}_i = \sum_i c_i \hat{I}_i + \lambda \Sigma \alpha_i c_i \qquad (7.66)$$

so that

$$\lambda = \frac{\bar{I} - \Sigma c_i \hat{I}_i}{\Sigma \alpha_i c_i} \qquad (7.67)$$

Substitution of this expression in Eq. 7.64 leads to

$$\bar{I}_i = \hat{I}_i + \alpha_i \frac{\bar{I} - \Sigma c_i \hat{I}_i}{\Sigma \alpha_i c_i} \qquad (7.68)$$

We have thus arrived at a remarkably simple (linear) relationship between the aggregate inventory and the inventory levels of individual products.   Substitution of Eq. 7.67 in Eq. 7.61 shows that the total inventory connected cost

$$\sum_i C_i(\bar{I}_i) = \sum_i a_i + \left(\sum_i \alpha_i b_i\right)\left(\frac{\bar{I} - \Sigma c_i \hat{I}_i}{\Sigma \alpha_i c_i}\right)^2 \qquad (7.69)$$

indeed depends only on the aggregate inventory level.   Furthermore, it is linearly related to the square of the deviation of the aggregate inventory level from its optimal value $\Sigma c_i \hat{I}_i$.   This is a justification and interpretation of the inventory term used in quadratic programming.   (It is not difficult to see that the optimal inventory level $\Sigma c_i \hat{I}_i$ may be approximated by a linear function of expected aggregate demand as is done in quadratic programming, see Eq. 5.106.)

We have shown that the multiproduct smoothing problem may be handled by use of single-station models employing an aggregate inventory term of the form of Eq. 7.69.   After aggregate production decisions have been made, these are translated into decisions for individual products by the rules of Eq. 7.68.

chapter 8
Applications Involving Parallel Stations

Problems involving parallel stations often arise when alternative inventory locations with differing characteristics exist at the same level of a distribution system. As a first example, consider a set of warehouses with differing storage cost characteristics.

INVENTORY ALLOCATION AND INVENTORY BUDGETS

A study dealing with the optimal use of a warehousing system was conducted for the Hawaiian Pineapple Company [10]. This company is faced with the problem of allocating its highly seasonal production of canned pineapple to a number of warehouses scattered over the continental United States. Each warehouse serves a given geographical area and hence has a well-defined demand rate. Company policy excludes transshipments from warehouse to warehouse and carry-over of inventories from one season to the next. Warehouses differ in storage costs per case of goods per month as well as the dates on which warehouse inventories are taxed. When a shipment of canned goods is sent to the continent, allocation to warehouses is to be made in such a manner that total storage costs and taxes attributable to the shipped quantity are minimized. Since the total future storage cost attributable to a certain stock in a warehouse is proportional to the square of the stock level, it follows that the marginal storage cost at the warehouse is a linear function of the stock level. Figure 8-1 shows this relationship. Since the stock level is measured in months' supply, the jumps of marginal cost because of taxation on given dates can be incorporated in the figure as long as it is kept in mind that the figure refers to a given date. With curves of this kind available for all warehouses, it is easy to find the optimal allocation of the total available quantity by making marginal costs equal at all warehouses. Retrospective simulation of this method demonstrated a potential for substantial

169

savings. The company adopted the method and put a company officer in charge of its implementation. Similar problems arising in the allocation of vehicle and equipment inventories are discussed in [30, 36].

Many military and industrial supply systems must operate with a limited budget imposed by management policy. The budgetary restriction may be stated in terms of total inventory investment or total stock purchases during a given period of time. The question arises how the available budget should be allocated to items or groups of

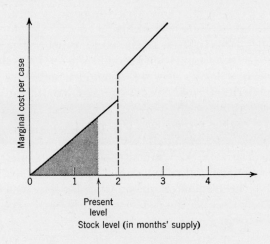

Fig. 8-1. (Next taxation in two months.)

items that might be stocked. This problem is, in principle, a generalized newsboy problem (see Eq. 7.1), where the function to be minimized is total cost and the control variables are the amounts allocated to the various items. In fact, the contribution of an item to total cost depends largely on the amount of funds allocated to it. If this amount is zero (no purchases for stock), the cost contribution should include a charge for delays in filling demands and possibly a cost for special purchasing procedures and special prices. If a positive amount is allocated, one must decide on a reasonable, if not optimal inventory policy in order to make the cost contribution of the item a function of the allocated amount alone. To make such an approach practical, one would have to work with larger classes of items rather than individual items (compare the simplified stocking rules, Eq. 2.43). With proper simplifications of the problem, the technique of

Lagrangian multipliers as applied in Eqs. 7.31 and 7.62 may offer a feasible alternative to the newsboy solution. Another simplified but efficient approach is to use a stocking rule of the type of Eq. 2.43, where an (unrestricted) optimal inventory policy is adopted for all stock items. The cutoff point j can then be chosen in such a way that the budgetary restriction is fulfilled.

COMPETITIVE BIDDING

The newsboy problem with limited resources has found numerous applications. Consider the following competitive bidding situation. A specific amount of money is available to a bidder for submitting closed bids on n objects such as contracts, property rights, and the like [13, 18]. In each case, the highest bid wins. The submitted bids assume the role of stock levels where demand is measured by the highest bid of competition. Obviously, the demand is probabilistic and depends on the value of the object. If demand is higher than the "stock level," a rather serious cost of shortage is incurred: the object is lost. If the bid is successful, a cost of overage is incurred which is a function of the excess of the winning bid over the second highest bid. Competitive bidding models for industrial applications have been constructed for the purpose of maximizing the expected gain to the bidder. Mathematically, this leads to the problem of maximizing a function of the form

$$F(x_1, \cdot \cdot \cdot, x_n) = \sum_{i=1}^{n} f_i(x_i) \tag{8.1}$$

subject to the restriction

$$\sum_{i=1}^{n} x_i = c \tag{8.2}$$

where x_i is the bid on object i, and c is the total available amount of money. Clearly, this problem is mathematically identical with the generalized newsboy problem (see Eqs. 7.1 and 7.2), which deals with the optimal allocation of limited inventory investment to stock items. A large amount of work in practical bidding studies goes into establishing a measure of the value of the objects in question. After this has been accomplished, probability distributions of "demand" for objects of different value may be derived by a statistical analysis of historical data. Then, the cumulative probability distribution of demand for object i, taken at the level x_i, measures the proability of winning object i with a bid of amount x_i.   Given the probabilities of winning as functions of the amounts bid, the return function in Eq. 8.1 is easily established.   The optimal set of bids may then be calculated by one of the methods of solution for the generalized newsboy problem (Chapter 7).   Such solutions have proved successful in industrial applications.   Needless to say, many complications arise in the construction of the critical probability distributions of demand.   One of them is the existence of price trends which are caused by general economic conditions as well as by the changing supply of the objects in question.

OPTIMAL MOBILITY PACKAGES

In the area of military aircraft maintenance, the problem of optimal mobility packages has received attention.   Mobility packages contain spare parts for aircraft and are limited in weight since, in cases of emergency, they must be airlifted to air bases all over the world.   It is obviously important that the parts for a package be selected in such a manner that the expected number of part shortages* during a given maintenance period is minimized within the weight limitation of the package.

A solution of this problem presupposes knowledge of the probability distributions of demand for all eligible parts i.   Given these, it is possible to tabulate usage probabilities, as shown in Table 8-1.

Table 8-1
Usage Probabilities for Part i

Number of Parts in Package j	Probability That All j Parts Will Be Used p_{ij}
0	1
1	p_{i1}
2	p_{i2}
.	.
.	.
.	.

If w_i is the weight of the ith type of part, then the quantity

$$u_{ij} = \frac{p_{ij}}{w_i} \qquad (8.3)$$

---

* Some authors also consider the *essentiality* of parts; for example, see [21] and [8].

plays the role of a "marginal utility" [22] associated with the addition of the jth part of the ith type. These marginal utilities can be listed in decreasing order. To find the best parts selection for a given weight of the package, one need only keep a running total of parts weights corresponding to the decreasing sequence of the u_{ij}. At the prescribed weight, the sequence is cut off, and all parts corresponding to the u_{ij} above the cutoff point are included in the package. Packages constructed in this way performed better than the existing packages when tested in a simulation of emergency situations. As usual, the most critical part of the analysis is the derivation of probability distributions of parts usage from historical data and engineering estimates. The great interest in this problem is reflected by a rather large number of similar publications [15, 16, 17, 21, 22, 27, 32, 35].

BIBLIOGRAPHY E

Parallel Stations

1. Allen, S. G., "Redistribution of Total Stock Over Several User Locations," *Naval Research Logistics Quarterly*, **5**, No. 4 (Dec. 1958), 337–356.
2. Baumol, W. J., Wolfe, Ph., "A Warehouse Location Problem," *Operations Research*, **6**, No. 2 (Mar.–Apr. 1958), 252–263.
3. Bonini, C. P., "Decision Rules for Buffer Inventories," *Management Science*, **4**, No. 4 (July 1958), 457–471.
4. Busby, J. C., "Comments on the Morgenstern Model," *Naval Research Logistics Quarterly*, **2**, No. 4 (Dec. 1955), 225–236.
5. Churchman, C. W., Ackoff, R. L., Arnoff, E. L., *Introduction to Operations Research*, New York: John Wiley & Sons, 1957.
6. Dantzig, G. B., "Linear Programming Under Uncertainty," *Management Science*, **1**, No. 3–4 (Apr.–July 1955), 197–206.
7. Dantzig, G. B., Ferguson, A. R., "The Allocation of Aircraft to Routes—An Example of Linear Programming Under Uncertain Demand," *Management Science*, **3**, No. 1 (Oct. 1956), 45–73.
8. Denicoff, M., Fennel, J. P., Solomon, H., "Summary of a Method for Determining the Military Worth of Spare Parts," *Naval Research Logistics Quarterly*, **7**, No. 3 (Sept. 1960), 221–234.
9. Derman, C., "A Simple Allocation Problem," *Management Science*, **5**, No. 4 (July 1959), 453–459.
10. Eagle, A. R., "Distribution of Seasonal Inventory of the Hawaiian Pineapple Company," *Operations Research*, **5**, No. 3 (June 1957), 382–396.
11. Eastman, W. L., "A Note on the Multi-Commodity Warehouse Problem," *Management Science*, **5**, No. 3 (Apr. 1959), 327–331.
12. Eilon, Samuel, "Economic Batch-Size Determination for Multi-Product Scheduling," *Operational Research Quarterly*, **9**, No. 4 (Dec. 1958), 217–227.
13. Friedman, L., "A Competitive Bidding Strategy," *Operations Research*, **4**, No. 1 (Feb. 1956), 104–112.
14. Geisler, M. A., "A First Experiment in Logistics System Simulation," *Naval Research Logistics Quarterly*, **7**, No. 1 (Mar. 1960), 21–44.

15. Geisler, M. A., Karr, H. W., "The Design of Military Supply Tables for Spare Parts," *Operations Research*, **4**, No. 4 (Aug. 1956), 431–442.
16. Gourary, M. H., "An Optimum Allowance List Model," *Naval Research Logistics Quarterly*, **3**, No. 3 (Sept. 1956), 177–191.
17. Gourary, M. H., "A Simple Rule for the Consolidation of Allowance Lists," *Naval Research Logistics Quarterly*, **5**, No. 1 (Mar. 1958), 1–16.
18. Hanssmann, F., Rivett, B. H. P., "Competitive Bidding," *Operational Research Quarterly*, **10**, No. 1 (Mar. 1959), 49–55.
19. Henn, C. L., Jr., "Multinational Logistics in the Nuclear Age," *Naval Research Logistics Quarterly*, **4**, No. 2 (June 1957), 117–129.
20. Jewel, W. S., "Warehousing and Distribution of a Seasonal Product," *Naval Research Logistics Quarterly*, **4**, No. 1 (Mar. 1957), 29–34.
21. Karr, H. W., "A Method of Estimating Spare Parts Essentiality," *Naval Research Logistics Quarterly*, **5**, No. 1 (Mar. 1958), 29–42.
22. Karr, H. W., Geisler, M. A., "A Fruitful Application of Static Marginal Analysis," *Management Science*, **2**, No. 4 (July 1956), 313–326.
23. Manne, A. S., "Programming of Economic Lot Sizes," *Management Science*, **4**, No. 2 (Jan. 1958), 115–135.
24. Mills, E. S., McClain, H. G., "A Study of Optimum Assembly Runs," *Operations Research*, **9**, No. 1 (Jan.–Feb. 1961), 30–38.
25. Morgenstern, O., "Consistency Problems in the Military Supply System," *Naval Research Logistics Quarterly*, **1**, No. 4 (Dec. 1954), 265–281.
26. Naddor, E., Saltzman, S., "Optimal Reorder Periods for an Inventory System with Variable Costs of Ordering," *Operations Research*, **6**, No. 5 (Sept.–Oct. 1958), 676–685.
27. Okun, B., "Design, Test, and Evaluation of an Experimental Flyaway Kit," *Naval Research Logistics Quarterly*, **7**, No. 2 (June 1960), 109–136.
28. Rogers, J., "A Computational Approach to the Economic Lot Scheduling Problem," *Management Science*, **4**, No. 3 (Apr. 1958), 264–291.
29. Salveson, M. E., "A Problem in Optimal Machine Loading," *Management Science*, **2**, No. 3 (Apr. 1956), 232–260.
30. Saposnik, R., Smith, V. L., "Allocation of a Resource to Alternative Probabilistic Demands: Transport-Equipment Pool Assignments," *Naval Research Logistics Quarterly*, **6**, No. 3 (Sept. 1959), 193–207.
31. Simpson, K. F., Jr., "A Theory of Allocation of Stocks to Warehouses," *Operations Research*, **7**, No. 6 (Nov.–Dec. 1959), 797–805.
32. Solomon, H., Denicoff, M., "Simulations of Alternative Allowance List Policies," *Naval Research Logistics Quarterly*, **7**, No. 2 (June 1960), 137–150.
33. Solomon, M. J., "Optimum Operation of a Complex Activity Under Conditions of Uncertainty," *Operations Research*, **2**, No. 4 (Nov. 1954), 419–432.
34. Solomon, M. J., "The Use of an Economic-Lot Range in Scheduling Production," *Management Science*, **5**, No. 4 (July 1959), 434–442.
35. Sutherland, W. H., "Graphical Selection of Military Supply Tables," *Operations Research*, **6**, No. 5 (Sept.–Oct. 1958), 775–777.
36. Suzuki, G., "Procurement and Allocation of Naval Electronic Equipments," *Naval Research Logistics Quarterly*, **4**, No. 1 (Mar. 1957), 1–7.
37. Vazsonyi, A., "Economic-Lot-Size Formulas in Manufacturing," *Operations Research*, **5**, No. 1 (Feb. 1957), 28–44.

part IV

SERIES OF STATIONS

chapter 9
Models of Series of Stations

In a series of inventory stations, all stations work together to produce a common result which is the delivery of the end product of the process to the customer. Performance at the last level of the series is, therefore, of central interest. Inventories at earlier stages perform only auxiliary functions. Thus, the inventory problem presents itself in the form of two questions:

1. Should there be an inventory at a given stage?
2. If so, what should be the inventory policy at that stage?

We thus have the problem of inventory location and control. The various inventory stations in a series are often spatially separated. Since inventory control requires communication between stations, the transmission time for messages—especially orders—becomes significant. The effect of transmission time is essentially a lengthening of the lead time between stations. Problems of communication also exist for the single station, for example, when there is a time lag in the reporting of inventory levels; here, too, the problem can be handled by adjusting the lead time accordingly. Of course, increased lead time means more costly inventory policies and more difficult forecasting problems. This must be kept in mind when control rules for serial systems are designed. It may pay to provide for rapid feedback from station to station. After these remarks, we can assume without loss of generality that the transmission time between stations is zero. Most of the mathematical models in the present chapter are based on this assumption. In accordance with the philosophy of this book, a number of somewhat specific models will be presented. For a more general theoretical treatment of some multistage problems, the reader is referred to [3] and [6].

STOCK LOCATION FOR A ONE-TIME DEMAND

Consider the following generalization of the newsboy problem. A one-time demand r with probability density $f(r)$ for a finished good is anticipated. Fabrication of the finished good involves three distinct processes, and there is no barrier to maintaining inventories in the form of raw materials (which we shall designate as stage 3), semifinished goods (stages 2 and 1), or finished goods (stage 0). The unit liquidation losses h_i $(i = 0, \cdots, 3)$, for unused inventories increase for more advanced production stages. On the other hand, each order which can be filled out of finished goods represents a sale with unit profit p (not considering liquidation losses from unused inventories); but in the case of a shortage, only a certain percentage of the customers will wait for goods to be brought up from stage 1, a smaller percentage will await processing from stage 2, and so on. More precisely, it is assumed that the fraction z_1 of the unsatisfied demand for finished goods may be carried over to stage 1. When the inventory at stage 1 has been exhausted, a fraction z_2 of the still unsatisfied demand may be carried over to stage 2; similarly, z_3 is defined. Demand not satisfied at stage 3 is lost. What quantities q_i $(i = 0, \cdots, 3)$ should be stocked at the various stages to maximize expected profit [2]?

If demand r exceeds the amount q_0, a fraction z_1 of the excess may be carried over to stage 1. Consequently, the inventory q_1 will not be exhausted as long as the excess demand is less than q_1/z_1, or as long as the demand r falls in the range $q_0 \leq r \leq q_0 + q_1/z_1$ (see the second row in Table 9-1). In that case, the actual amount sold from stage 1 is obviously equal to the excess of r over its lower limit q_0, times the factor z_1. Therefore, the total number of units sold is $q_0 + z_1 (r - q_0)$. The number of units liquidated at stage 1 is given by q_1 minus the number sold from stage 1, that is, $q_1 - z_1 (r - q_0)$. All earlier inventories must be completely liquidated. This explains the remainder of the second row in Table 9-1. The results listed in the other rows may be obtained in analagous fashion. The profit functions $P_i(r)$ in the last column are defined as the differences between the corresponding expressions in the two preceding columns. For convenience, let

$$x_0 = 0$$

$$x_1 = q_0$$

$$x_2 = x_1 + \frac{q_1}{z_1}$$

$$x_3 = x_2 + \frac{q_2}{z_2} \tag{9.1}$$

$$x_4 = x_3 + \frac{q_3}{z_3}$$

$$x_5 = \infty$$

Table 9-1
Derivation of Profit Function

Demand Will Reach Stage	If it Falls in the Range	Profit Excluding Liquidation Losses	Liquidation Losses	Profit
0	$0 \leq r \leq q_0$	pr	$h_0(q_0 - r) + \sum_1^3 h_i q_i$	$P_0(r)$
1	$q_0 \leq r \leq q_0 + \frac{q_1}{z_1}$	$p[q_0 + z_1(r - q_0)]$	$h_1[q_1 - z_1(r - q_0)] + \sum_2^3 h_i q_i$	$P_1(r)$
2	$q_0 + \frac{q_1}{z_1} \leq r \leq q_0 + \frac{q_1}{z_1} + \frac{q_2}{z_2}$	$p\left[q_0 + q_1 + z_2\left(r - q_0 - \frac{q_1}{z_1}\right)\right]$	$h_2\left[q_2 - z_2\left(r - q_0 - \frac{q_1}{z_1}\right)\right] + h_3 q_3$	$P_2(r)$
3	$q_0 + \frac{q_1}{z_1} + \frac{q_2}{z_2} \leq r \leq q_0 + \frac{q_1}{z_1} + \frac{q_2}{z_2} + \frac{q_3}{z_3}$	$p\left[q_0 + q_1 + q_2 + z_3\left(r - q_0 - \frac{q_1}{z_1} - \frac{q_2}{z_2}\right)\right]$	$h_3\left[q_3 - z_3\left(r - q_0 - \frac{q_1}{z_1} - \frac{q_2}{z_2}\right)\right]$	$P_3(r)$
—	$r \geq q_0 + \frac{q_1}{z_1} + \frac{q_2}{z_2} + \frac{q_3}{z_3}$	$p[q_0 + q_1 + q_2 + q_3]$	—	$P_4(r)$

The expected profit can now be written as

$$E(P) = \sum_{i=0}^{4} \int_{x_i}^{x_{i+1}} P_i(r)\, f(r)\, dr \qquad (9.2)$$

The partial derivative with respect to the control variable q_0 is

$$\frac{\partial E(P)}{\partial q_0} = \sum_{i=0}^{4} \int_{x_i}^{x_{i+1}} \frac{\partial P_i(r)}{\partial q_0} f(r)\, dr$$

$$+ \sum_{i=1}^{4} [P_{i-1}(x_i) - P_i(x_i)]\, f(x_i)\, \frac{\partial x_i}{\partial q_0} \qquad (9.3)$$

Because of the continuity of the profit function, we have

$$P_{i-1}(x_i) = P_i(x_i) \qquad (9.4)$$

so that the second summation in Eq. 9.3 gives no contribution. In the first summation, the partial derivatives under the integrals are constants A_i:

$$A_i = \frac{\partial P_i}{\partial q_0} \qquad (i = 0, \cdots, 4) \qquad (9.5)$$

By the definition of the P_i we have

$$A_0 = -h_0$$
$$A_4 = p \qquad (9.6)$$
$$A_i = pz_i(h_i + p) \qquad (i = 1, 2, 3)$$

If we further define

$$y_i = \int_{x_i}^{x_{i+1}} f(r)\, dr \qquad (i = 0, \cdots, 4) \qquad (9.7)$$

then Eq. 9.3 may be rewritten as

$$\frac{\partial E(P)}{\partial q_0} = \sum_{i=0}^{4} A_i y_i \qquad (9.8)$$

But since, by Eq. 9.7,

$$y_4 = 1 - y_0 - y_1 - y_2 - y_3 \qquad (9.9)$$

Eq. 9.8 takes the form

$$\frac{\partial E(P)}{\partial q_0} = A_0 y_0 + A_1 y_1 + A_2 y_2 + A_3 y_3 + A_4(1 - y_0 - y_1 - y_2 - y_3)$$

$$= \sum_{i=0}^{3} (A_i - A_4) y_i + A_4$$

$$= -A_4 \left[\sum_{i=0}^{3} \left(1 - \frac{A_i}{A_4}\right) y_i - 1 \right] \quad (9.10)$$

We now define the abbreviations

$$B_0 = 1 - \frac{A_0}{A_4}$$

$$B_i = \frac{1}{z_i} \left(1 - \frac{A_i}{A_4}\right) \qquad (i = 1, 2, 3) \quad (9.11)$$

Setting the partial derivative Eq. 9.10 equal to zero leads to the following linear equation in the unknowns $y_0, \cdots, y_3$:

$$B_0 y_0 + z_1 B_1 y_1 + z_2 B_2 y_2 + z_3 B_3 y_3 = 1 \quad (9.12)$$

By complete analogy, the other partial derivatives of the expected profit function give rise to the three additional equations

$$B_1 y_0 + B_1 y_1 + \frac{z_2}{z_1} B_2 y_2 + \frac{z_3}{z_1} B_3 y_3 = 1 \quad (9.13)$$

$$B_2 y_0 + B_2 y_1 + B_2 y_2 + \frac{z_3}{z_2} B_3 y_3 = 1 \quad (9.14)$$

$$B_3 y_0 + B_3 y_1 + B_3 y_2 + B_3 y_3 = 1 \quad (9.15)$$

The linear system Eqs. 9.12–9.15 may be solved by standard methods. This leads to the following solutions:

$$y_0 = \frac{1 - z_1}{B_0 - z_1 B_1} \quad (9.16)$$

$$y_1 = \frac{z_1 - z_2}{z_1 B_1 - z_2 B_2} - y_0 \quad (9.17)$$

$$y_2 = \frac{z_2 - z_3}{z_2 B_2 - z_3 B_3} - y_0 - y_1 \quad (9.18)$$

$$y_3 = \frac{1}{B_3} - y_0 - y_1 - y_2 \quad (9.19)$$

These solutions may also be obtained directly by equating the marginal profits of stocking for all pairs of adjacent stages. An admissible solution must yield nonnegative values for all quantities y_i. The presence of a negative value would imply that inventory should not be carried at all four stages. In that case, the model breaks down, and it becomes necessary to try reduced models, leaving out first one storage point and then another. The process, however, follows the same outline as before. Having determined the quantities y_i it is possible to determine the quantities x_i and the optimal stock levels q_i by reference to the probability distribution of demand. The generalization of the model for an arbitrary number of stages is obvious.

STOCK LOCATION UNDER A BASE-STOCK SYSTEM

Simpson [15] has constructed a multistage model which employs the base-stock system of reordering. When an order is received at one of the stages, $i = 1, \cdot \cdot \cdot, n$, it is either filled immediately or (in the

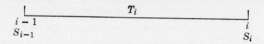

Fig. 9-1.

case of a stockout) placed into a backorder file; in either case a replacement order is placed with the preceding stage $i - 1$. Thus, when one unit is withdrawn from the finished stage $i = n$, a process of "explosion" throughout the system is released. Performance at a given inventory stage i can be characterized by a service time S_i. By definition of S_i, an order placed against inventory i is *always* filled within S_i time units. More precisely, this is true as long as demand per time unit does not exceed a "reasonable maximum" set by policy decision. Delivery to the customer as well as the fulfillment of raw material requisitions is to take place without delay, that is,

$$S_n = S_1 = 0 \tag{9.20}$$

All other parameters S_i are decision variables which are manipulated by choosing alternative inventory policies. If T_i is the production lead time between stages $i - 1$ and i (see Fig. 9-1), it is clear that S_i fulfills the inequality

$$0 \leq S_i \leq T_i + S_{i-1} \tag{9.21}$$

The upper limit corresponds to an "empty inventory" at stage i (no orders are filled immediately), the lower limit to a "full inventory" (all orders are filled immediately). If the base stock at stage i is set at B_i, then the inventory level is a random variable $B_i - r(L_i)$, where $r(L_i)$ is the demand during the replenishment lead time L_i (see Eq. 3.109). Obviously, the lead time L_i into stage i is given by

$$L_i = T_i + S_{i-1} \qquad (9.22)$$

Let $M_i(L_i)$ be the (finite) maximum demand during a time span L_i which we wish to be protected against. Then a base stock of $M_i(L_i)$ units will be sufficient to avoid shortages with the desired confidence. But since we allow a service time S_i within which orders may be filled, the required base stock is in fact lower. If we set the base stock at the level $M_i(L_i - S_i)$, the maximum demand during a time span $L_i - S_i$, all orders will be filled within S_i time units. (The delivery of a demanded unit may be postponed by S_i time units; however, the reorder is placed immediately when the demand arrives. Consequently, the system may be treated as if the lead time L_i had been reduced to $L_i - S_i$.)

We now assume that the demand per unit time comes from independent, identical probability distributions with mean μ and standard deviation σ. Demand during a time span $L_i - S_i$ may then be approximated by a random variable with mean $\mu(L_i - S_i)$ and standard deviation $\sigma \sqrt{L_i - S_i}$. The "reasonable maximum demand" is assumed to be fixed at k_i standard deviations above the mean, that is,

$$M_i(L_i - S_i) = \mu(L_i - S_i) + k_i \sigma \sqrt{L_i - S_i} \qquad (9.23)$$

where k_i is a constant. Keeping in mind that we may treat the problem as if the lead time were $L_i - S_i$, the actual inventory level will be a random variable

$$M_i(L_i - S_i) - r(L_i - S_i)$$

with mean

$$\bar{I}_i = k_i \sigma \sqrt{L_i - S_i} \qquad (9.24)$$

Assuming that the expected inventory charge per unit time is $h_i \bar{I}_i$, where h_i is a constant, the total relevant cost is given by (see Eq. 9.22)

$$E(C) = \sum_i h_i k_i \sigma \sqrt{T_i + S_{i-1} - S_i} \qquad (9.25)$$

Thus, the expected cost becomes a function of the service times S_i alone. After the service times have been determined optimally, the optimal base stocks are given by

$$B_i = M_i(L_i - S_i)$$
$$= \mu(T_i + S_{i-1} - S_i) + k_i\sigma \sqrt{T_i + S_{i-1} - S_i} \qquad (9.26)$$

The mathematical problem is the minimization of $E(C)$ in Eq. 9.25 with respect to the variables S_i, subject to the restrictions of Eqs. 9.20–9.21. Since the cost function is "concave downward," we take it as intuitive that the minimum occurs at a vertex of the region defined by Eqs. 9.20–9.21. (For a proof, see [15]). This means that in the optimal solution either $S_i = 0$ or $S_i = T_i + S_{i-1}$, that is, all inventories are either "full" or "empty." Altogether, 2^{n-1} vertices must be examined. This is a manageable number for a small number of production stages. If $S_i = T_i + S_{i-1}$ in the optimal solution, then the ith inventory should be eliminated. No complications arise when there are several parallel stations at each stage; the parameter σ in Eq. 9.25 must then be replaced by the standard deviation σ_i of the total demand exerted upon stage i, measured in an appropriate unit.

PRODUCTION CONTROL AND INVENTORY LOCATION WHEN SALES ARE SENSITIVE TO DELIVERY TIME

In the model just discussed, the delivery time to the customer had been fixed. In other instances, however, changes of delivery time may be the major consideration in the location of inventories [8]. As in the corresponding single-station model (Eq. 3.81), we assume that reordering can be done at equidistant checking points, and that no setup cost is involved. One may think of a continuous production process where production levels are set weekly. The expected number of units sold per week is a given function $s(t) = \alpha(t)s$ of the average delivery time t; the constant s represents maximum possible sales, and $0 \le \alpha(t) \le 1$. The multistage models that will be discussed in this section recognize two important factors of inventory costs: (1) The rising intrinsic value of products at more advanced stages; and (2) the increasing fluctuations (coefficient of variation) of inventories at more advanced stages. We begin with a single inventory which is to be optimally located in a multistage process. The finished products are designated by $i = 1, \cdots, n$.

Optimal Production Stage for Application of Orders

Consider a production process with raw material, semifinished, and finished stages (stages R, S, F in Fig. 9-2). Delivery time to the customer as well as inventory carrying costs can be manipulated by selecting any one of these stages for setting up an inventory to which incoming orders are "applied" for further processing or, in the case of the finished stage, for immediate delivery to the customer. (It is intended to maintain inventories at only one stage.) Which is the optimal stage for inventory location?

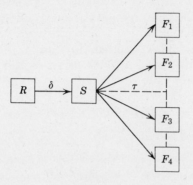

Fig. 9-2.

Suppose that the demand per week for the n end items is given by a set of independent normal distributions with means

$$s_i(t) = \alpha_i(t)s_i \tag{9.27}$$

and standard deviations

$$\sigma_i(t) = \alpha_i(t)\sigma_i \qquad (i = 1, \cdots, n) \tag{9.28}$$

Both sets of parameters are functions of average delivery time t to the customer. Let the average processing time be τ between stages S and F, δ between stages R and S; also let the unit holding cost per period be h_i for product i at stage F, and h_s for stage S. Given these constants, consider the problem of finding the optimal stage to which orders should be applied, as well as the optimal inventory level(s) to be maintained at that stage. The criterion is expected profit. Specifically, we shall consider the following three alternatives:

1. Orders are applied to the raw material stage for initiation of the production process ('production to order').
2. Orders are applied to the semifinished stage for further processing of the semifinished material.
3. Orders are applied to the finished stage for immediate shipment.

We shall assume that the cost of maintaining a sufficiently high raw-material inventory is the same for all three policies. Thus, we have the problem of finding the maximum of the following three numbers where R, S, F designate the respective stages to which orders are applied:

Expected revenue (R) $\qquad\qquad\qquad = R_R$

Expected revenue (S) − expected holding cost (S) $= R_S - H_S$

Expected revenue (F) − expected holding cost (F) $= R_F - H_F$

Let p_i be the unit sale price* for product i. Clearly,

$$R_R = \sum_{i=1}^{n} p_i s_i(\delta + \tau) = R(\delta + \tau) \qquad (9.29)$$

where $R(t)$ is defined as follows:

$$R(t) = \sum_{i=1}^{n} p_i\, s_i(t) \qquad (9.30)$$

Let us also define $\sigma(t)$ by

$$\sigma^2(t) = \sum_{i=1}^{n} \sigma_i{}^2\, \alpha_i{}^2(t) \qquad (9.31)$$

Next, consider the possibility of locating the inventory at S.

Suppose that the inventory target (see Eq. 3.78) is J_0, and that the average delivery time for product i resulting from this inventory policy is

$$t_i = \tau + \Delta t_i \qquad (9.32)$$

By analogy with Eq. 3.78, the inventory level will be normally distributed with parameters

$$\left\{ J_0; \sqrt{(\delta + 1) \sum_{i=1}^{n} \sigma_i{}^2\, \alpha_i{}^2(t_i)} \right\} \qquad (9.33)$$

A certain expected shortage B will be associated with this inventory fluctuation (see Eq. 3.70). It is reasonable to assume that this shortage can be allocated to the individual products on the basis of their respective shares in total output. Thus, the expected shortage for

---

* More precisely, we should be concerned with expected profit, not considering holding costs, and p_i should be the unit profit, not considering holding costs. It is only for simplicity's sake that we use the terms of expected revenue and unit sale price.

product i becomes

$$B_i = \frac{B \, s_i(t_i)}{\sum\limits_{i=1}^{n} s_i(t_i)} \tag{9.34}$$

This relation is equivalent to

$$\frac{B}{\sum\limits_{i=1}^{n} s_i(t_i)} = \frac{B_i}{s_i(t_i)} = -\Delta t_i \tag{9.35}$$

since the average delay Δt_i is, as in Eq. 3.79, obtained as the quotient of the expected amount of shortage and the output rate. We conclude that the delays Δt_i and, consequently, the delivery times t_i are independent of the product i. We, therefore, write

$$\Delta t_i = \Delta t \tag{9.36}$$

$$t_i = t \tag{9.37}$$

Thus, it follows from Eq. 9.33 that the parameters of the inventory level are

$$\{J_0; \ \sqrt{\delta + 1}\, \sigma(t)\} \tag{9.38}$$

and that the expected revenue is

$$R_S = \sum\limits_{i=1}^{n} p_i \, s_i(t) = R(t) \tag{9.39}$$

Obviously, the expected profit now becomes

$$E(P) = R_S(t) - H_S(t)$$
$$= R(t) - h_s \sqrt{\delta + 1}\, \sigma(t) \, A_n \, B_n^{-1} \left(-\frac{\Delta t \, s(t)}{\sqrt{\delta + 1}\, \sigma(t)} \right) \tag{9.40}$$

applying the rule that the known function $A_n B_n^{-1}$ measures the normalized overage as a function of the normalized shortage (see Eq. 3.75). The permissible range for t is

$$\tau \le t < \tau + \delta \tag{9.41}$$

The particular value $\hat{t}$ which maximizes $E(P)$ subject to the restriction of Eq. 9.41 can now be found, and the quantity

$$R_S(\hat{t}) - H_S(\hat{t}) \tag{9.42}$$

can be computed. This expression represents the expected profit, associated with the optimal inventory policy at stage S.

Finally, consider the finished stage F as a possible inventory location. In this case there are n separate inventories. For each of these we can find the optimal delivery time $\hat{t}_i$ which maximizes the expected profit

$$E_i(t) = p_i \, s_i(t) - h_i \sqrt{\tau + \delta + 1} \; \sigma_i(t) A_n B_n^{-1} \left(- \frac{ts_i}{\sqrt{\tau + \delta + 1} \, \sigma_i} \right)$$

(9.43)

subject to the restriction

$$0 \leq t \leq \tau \tag{9.44}$$

The expected profit associated with the optimal inventory policy at stage F is obtained as

$$\hat{R}_F - \hat{H}_F = \sum_{i=1}^{n} E_i(\hat{t}_i) \tag{9.45}$$

At this stage select (see Eqs. 9.29, 9.42, and 9.45):

$$\max \left[R(\delta + \tau), \; R_S(\hat{t}) - H_S(\hat{t}), \; \hat{R}_F - \hat{H}_F \right] \tag{9.46}$$

The production stage corresponding to the maximum is the optimal inventory location.

In summary, we have considered a branching production flow resulting in n different products at the finished stage. If inventories are to be carried only at a single stage, the choice of the optimal stage is guided by two considerations: by selecting an earlier stage in the process, delivery time is prolonged and sales revenue is reduced; on the other hand, the demands for certain groups of finished products are consolidated. Assuming independence of the demands for the individual products, the consolidated demand exerted upon an inventory at an earlier stage has a lower coefficient of variation. Thus, the inventory cost is also reduced. To find the particular stage with the best balance between sales revenue and inventory costs, we have examined all stages. For each stage we have derived the parameters of consolidated demands and the (sub) optimal inventory policy. The optimal stage is found by selecting the most profitable policy from these suboptimal policies.

Multilevel Production Control for One Product

We now consider the more general case where inventories can be maintained simultaneously at several stages. The target levels of the various inventories now represent *several* variables by which delivery time to the customer can be controlled.   At the same time, holding costs are incurred at several locations.   Which set of target levels will maximize the total expected profit?

Consider the case of one intermediate (semifinished) inventory and one product (see Fig. 9-3).   Before the problem can be formulated more precisely, it is necessary to state the ordering mechanism for the system.   Let I_0 and J_0 be a specified pair of target levels for the finished and the semifinished inventories respectively.   Both targets refer to the closing inventory levels at the end of given decision periods.   Let the *actual* inventory levels at the end of period zero be V_0 and W_0 respectively, and let the production quantities in the production pipeline be designated as in Fig. 9-3.   Generally speaking,

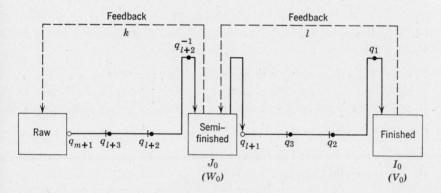

Fig. 9-3. ($k + l = m.$)

the quantity q_i arrives at the finished stage at the beginning of period i where $i = 1, \cdots, m + 1$.   At the beginning of period 1, the quantities q_{l+2}^{-1} and q_1 arrive at the semifinished and finished stages respectively.   At the same point of time, the input quantities q_{l+1} and q_{m+1} are to be chosen.   We shall specify order rules for their determination.

The general ordering mechanism is as follows.   Given the quantities q_i in the pipeline and the inventory level V_0 at stage F, a quantity x is computed and transmitted to stage S as an order calling for the release of an amount x of semifinished product.   All such orders are charged against the semifinished inventory, and are served in the sequence of their arrival.   Thus, the semifinished inventory level at the end of period 1 becomes

$$W_1 = W_0 + q_{l+2}^{-1} - x \qquad (9.47)$$

Given W_1 and $q_{l+2}, \cdot \cdot \cdot, q_m$, a quantity q_{m+1} is computed and transmitted to stage R as an order calling for the input of an amount q_{m+1} into the production process. We assume that the raw material inventory is sufficiently high so that the amount q_{m+1} is always released without delay. At stage S, shortages may exist; that is, it may not always be possible to release the full amount x. The actual input q_{l+1} into the second phase of the production process is equal to the total supply on hand or equal to total unfilled orders, whichever the smaller.

To write down specific order rules for the computation of x and q_{m+1} consider the question of when an order x will affect the finished inventory level. Obviously this depends on the amount of shortage prevailing at stage S. This shortage can be characterized by the average time k' which it takes to release an order x. Choose as time unit one period, and assume for the moment that k' is an integer. Clearly, the first finished inventory level which we can control is $V_{l+k'+1}$ where

$$V_{l+k'+1} = V_0 + q_1 + \cdot \cdot \cdot + q_l + q_{l+2}^{-1} + q_{l+2} + \cdot \cdot \cdot$$
$$+ q_{l+k'} + x - (s_1 + \cdot \cdot \cdot + s_{l+k'+1}) \quad (9.48)$$

Hence, we choose the order rule such that the expected value of this inventory level is equal to the target I_0:

$$E(V_{l+k'+1}) = I_0 \quad (9.49)$$

By Eq. 9.48, this may be written as

$$V_0 + \sum_{i=1}^{l} q_i + q_{l+2}^{-1} + q_{l+2} + \cdot \cdot \cdot q_{l+k'} + x$$
$$- (l + k' + 1) s(t) = I_0 \quad (9.50)$$

where t is the average delivery time maintained at the finished stage, and $s(t)$ designates the expected sales per period. After x has been determined from the order rule Eq. 9.50, W_1 (and q_{l+1}) can be computed by Eq. 9.47. Finally, q_{m+1} is determined by the order rule

$$W_1 + q_{l+2} + \cdot \cdot \cdot + q_{m+1} - (k + 1) s(t) = J_0 \quad (9.51)$$

Next, consider the behavior of the inventory levels, given the target levels I_0 and J_0. From Eqs. 9.48 and 9.50, it follows that the finished inventory level will be normally distributed with parameters

$$\{I_0; \sqrt{l + k' + 1}\, \sigma(t)\} \quad (9.52)$$

where $\sigma(t)$ is the standard deviation of sales per period. As in Eqs.

9.27–9.28, we assume that

$$\sigma(t) = \alpha(t)\sigma \tag{9.53}$$

$$s(t) = \alpha(t)s \tag{9.54}$$

where $\alpha(t)$ is a fraction and σ and s are constants. Since the weekly output from the system (at stage F) is a normally distributed random variable with parameters $\{s(t); \sigma(t)\}$, we further assume that the output q_{l+1} from stage S can be approximated reasonably well by the same normal random variable. Thus, it follows from Eq. 9.51 that the semifinished inventory level is normally distributed with parameters

$$\{J_0; \sqrt{k+1}\,\sigma(t)\} \tag{9.55}$$

The expected shortages at the finished and semifinished stages are given by the respective quantities

$$-t\,s(t) \quad \text{and} \quad -k'\,s(t) \tag{9.56}$$

Applying the rule that the function $A_n B_n^{-1}$ measures the expected overage in standard deviations as a function of the expected shortage in standard deviations, we can write the following expression for the expected profit per period:

$$E(P) = p\,s(t) - h_f\,\sqrt{l+k'+1}\,\sigma(t) A_n B_n^{-1}\left(-\frac{ts}{\sqrt{l+k'+1}\,\sigma}\right)$$
$$- h_s\,\sqrt{k+1}\,\sigma(t) A_n B_n^{-1}\left(-\frac{k's}{\sqrt{k+1}\,\sigma}\right) \tag{9.57}$$

where h_f and h_s are the unit holding costs per period at stages F and S respectively. The problem of finding the optimal inventory policy can now be stated as the mathematical problem of maximizing $E(P)$ with respect to the variables t and k', subject to the restrictions

$$t \geq 0 \qquad k' \geq 0 \qquad 0 \leq t \leq m \qquad t - l \leq k' \leq k \tag{9.58}$$

The last restriction may be derived as follows. If k' could drop below $t - l$, then $t > l + k'$ would follow. This is impossible. The extreme case $t = m$ implies $k' = k$ and is equivalent to production to order. A method of solution will be discussed in the context of a more general problem in the next section.

Equation 9.57 gives insight into the role of the semifinished inventory. Suppose that t is kept constant and k' is decreased. This is equivalent to an increase of the semifinished inventory level. As k' decreases, the standard deviation of the finished inventory level also decreases.   Since the expected shortage (Eq. 9.56) at stage F has not changed, the expected overage is reduced.   The response of the finished inventory level to demand has improved.   The price that must be paid for this improvement is a higher carrying cost at stage S. For each given value of t, one can find an optimal balance between the two inventories by selecting the profit-maximizing value of k'.

The Multiproduct Case of the Multilevel Control Problem

In this section the multilevel inventory problem considered in the previous section will be generalized for an arbitrary number of production stages S_i and an arbitrary number of inventories at each stage. Let the pair (i, j) designate the jth inventory at the ith stage ($i = 1$, $\cdots$, $m; j = 1, \cdots, k_i$).   The stages are numbered in reverse so that S_1 is the finished stage.   The totality of finished products that can be derived from the inventory (i, j) will be referred to as the product group G_{ij}.   It is then possible to define the two functions

$$\sigma_{ij}^2(t_1) = \sum_{G_{ij}} \sigma_h^2(t_1) \qquad (9.59)$$

$$s_{ij}(t_1) = \sum_{G_{ij}} s_h(t_1) \qquad (9.60)$$

where the subscript h designates the finished products ($h = 1, \cdots, n$). Clearly, these quantities represent variance and mean, respectively, of the demand exerted upon the inventory (i, j) when a delivery time of t_1 is maintained at the finished stage.   To simplify the search for an optimum, we shall examine only policies with equal delivery delays for all inventories at a given stage.   Thus, let t_i be the average delay at stage S_i and let l_i be the production lead time between S_{i+1} and S_i (see Fig. 9-4).

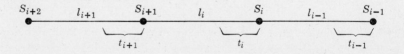

Fig. 9-4.

Note that the average replenishment time for inventories at stage S_i is $l_i + t_{i+1}$, and that t_1 is the average delivery time to the customer. As before, we exclude the raw material inventory at stage S_m from consideration and assume $t_m = 0$.   Thus, if I_{ij} is the target level for the inventory (i, j) where $i = 1, \cdots, m - 1$, it follows that the actual inventory level is a normally distributed random variable with parameters

$$\{I_{ij}; \sqrt{l_i + t_{i+1} + 1}\, \sigma_{ij}(t_1)\} \qquad (i = 1, \cdots, m - 1) \quad (9.61)$$

The expected shortage associated with this fluctuation is

$$B_{ij} = -t_i\, s_{ij}(t_1) \tag{9.62}$$

By analogy with earlier considerations we can now write the following expression for the total expected profit per period:

$$E(P) = \sum_{h=1}^{n} p_h s_h(t_1) - \sum_{i=1}^{m-1} \sum_{j=1}^{k_i} h_{ij} \sqrt{l_i + t_{i+1} + 1}\, \sigma_{ij}(t_1)$$

$$A_n B_n^{-1}\left(- \frac{t_i\, s_{ij}(t_1)}{\sqrt{l_i + t_{i+1} + 1}\, \sigma_{ij}(t_1)}\right) \tag{9.63}$$

To somewhat reduce the mathematical complexity, we shall assume that the decay function $\alpha(t)$ is the same for all finished products. Thus,

$$\begin{aligned} s_h(t_1) &= \alpha(t_1)s_h & s_{ij}(t_1) &= \alpha(t_1)s_{ij} \\ \sigma_h(t_1) &= \alpha(t_1)\sigma_h & \sigma_{ij}(t_1) &= \alpha(t_1)\sigma_{ij} \end{aligned} \tag{9.64}$$

with appropriate constants s_h, σ_h, s_{ij}, σ_{ij}. With this assumption, we may rewrite Eq. 9.63 in the following form:

$$E(P) = \alpha(t_1)\left[\sum_{h=1}^{n} p_h s_h - \sum_{i=1}^{m-1} C_i(t_i, t_{i+1})\right] \tag{9.65}$$

where

$$C_i(t_i, t_{i+1}) = \sum_{j=1}^{k_i} h_{ij} \sqrt{l_i + t_{i+1} + 1}\, \sigma_{ij}$$

$$A_n B_n^{-1}\left(- \frac{t_i s_{ij}}{\sqrt{l_i + t_{i+1} + 1}\, \sigma_{ij}}\right) \tag{9.66}$$

The mathematical problem is to maximize $E(P)$ in Eq. 9.65 with respect to the delay times t_i subject to the following restrictions (see Fig. 9-4):

$$\max (0, t_{i-1} - l_{i-1}) \le t_i \le m - \sum_{\lambda=1}^{i-1} l_\lambda \qquad (i = 1, \cdots, m - 1)$$

$$(9.67)$$

The solution may be obtained in two steps. First, find the function

$$f(t_1) = \min_{t_2, \ldots, t_{m-1}} \sum_{i=1}^{m-1} C_i(t_i, t_{i+1}) \tag{9.68}$$

by dynamic programming. Second, find the maximum expected profit by the following one-dimensional maximization

$$\max E(P) = \max_{0 \le t_1 \le m} \alpha(t_1) \left[\sum_{h=1}^{n} p_h s_h - f(t_1) \right] \tag{9.69}$$

It is interesting to note that the problem falls into two relatively independent parts:

1. How can a given average delivery time t_1 to the customer be achieved with minimum inventory costs? This question is answered by the functon $f(t_1)$.

2. Given the optimum inventory policy for each value t_1 of the average delivery time, what is the best compromise between inventory costs and sales? This question is answered by the maximization of $E(P)$ in Eq. 9.69.

Because of this structure of the problem, the solution can also be used to find an optimum inventory policy when no changes in delivery time to the customer are contemplated.

In the last two sections we have considered multistage processes where inventories are maintained simultaneously at all stages. Each stage S_i places orders with the preceding stage S_{i+1}. It has been shown that the inventory control conducted at stage S_{i+1} determines the standard deviation of the inventory level at S_i as long as delivery time at the finished stage is held constant. More precisely, the standard deviation at S_i is proportional to $\sqrt{l_i + t_{i+1} + 1}$, where l_i is the production lead time between stages $i + 1$ and i, and t_{i+1} is the average delay at stage $i + 1$. This linkage between stages suggests the use of dynamic programming for finding the optimal set of delay times t_i. Given the optimal delay times, the corresponding rules are easily established by routine calculations of target levels.

PIPELINE INVENTORY

It is sometimes of interest to know the total monetary value of resources—say, materials—*between* two stages R and F of an inventory network, excluding the inventories *at* R and F (see Fig. 9-5). Materials between R and F consist of materials at nodes (ordinary inventories) and materials in channels (materials on which an operation is being performed). Resources in channels are not inventories by our original definition since they are not idle in the strict sense. However, they are idle with respect to their end use and with respect to alternative uses of the capital tied up in them. We, therefore, generalize our definition of inventory to include resources in network channels (operations).

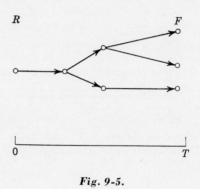

Fig. 9-5.

These resources will be referred to as "in-process inventories." It should be noted that this definition differs from the ordinary, somewhat ambiguous, notion of in-process inventory which often includes ordinary inventories at intermediate stages. The total amount of resources between R and F will be referred to as "pipeline inventory." Thus we have the definitional equation:

Pipeline inventory = ordinary (idle) inventories

+ in-process inventories

If we view the channels of an inventory network as "pseudo stations," then the pipeline inventory may be considered as the sum of all inventories in a series of inventory stations.   Each channel may be broken down into arbitrarily small segments (pseudo stations).   The average throughput rate a of the "pipeline" between stages R and F may be expressed in physical units or in monetary units, where monetary value refers to, say, the final stage F.   For illustrative purposes, assume physical units.   Let T be the average traveling time between the two stages, and let intermediate stages be designated by the continuous variable t where $0 \leq t \leq T$.   The monetary value $v(t)$ of a physical unit at stage t will normally be a function of the kind pictured in Fig. 9-6.   The horizontal segments correspond to nodes, the slanted

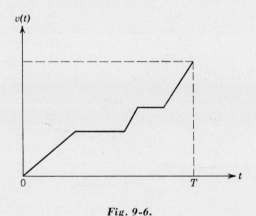

Fig. 9-6.

segments to channels.   In the long run, the average throughput rate must be the same at all stages t.   Consequently, the average value of the pipeline inventory between stages t and $t + dt$ is given by $a\,v(t)\,dt$. The total value of the pipeline inventory is, therefore,

$$V(T) \;=\; a \int_0^T v(t)\,dt \;=\; aT\bar{v} \tag{9.70}$$

where the average value $\bar{v}$ is defined by

$$\bar{v} \;=\; \frac{1}{T} \int_0^T v(t)\,dt \tag{9.71}$$

If the function $v(t)$ can be approximated by a linear function,

$$\bar{v} \;\approx\; \frac{v(0) + v(T)}{2} \tag{9.72}$$

The average number of physical units in the pipeline is given by the following formula*:

$$I(T) = aT = \frac{V(T)}{\bar{v}}$$
(9.73)

As one would expect, the average traveling time T is the controlling factor for the pipeline inventory.   It follows that all methods and techniques aimed at changes of the traveling time are pertinent to pipeline inventory control.   Technological changes, scheduling theory, and queuing theory can only be mentioned in this context.   It is useful to observe that T may be broken down in the following fashion:

$$T = \sum_i t_i + \sum_j \tau_j = T_1 + T_2$$
(9.74)

where t_i is the traveling time through node i, that is, the average time a unit spends in inventory i, and τ_j is the traveling time through channel j. T_2 usually plays the role of a technological constant whereas T_1 may be more readily controllable.

* This formula is also useful in marketing research.   For example, consider a machine that is being sold in a virtually stationary market (replacement market). The total number of machines in use may be estimated by Eq. 9.73, where a is the sales rate and T is the average life of the machine.   Such estimates are especially important when a new product is considered that might supersede the machines currently in use.

chapter 10
Applications Involving Series of Stations

Almost every real operation consists of serial processes and contains serial inventories of one form or another. Nevertheless it is often possible to treat serial inventories as separate, independent stations. Most published case studies of serial systems make this simplification. How serious this simplification is depends on the degree of interaction between the different stations—a point that must be investigated in each individual case. Typical examples of serial inventories are found in the distribution systems of larger companies and in the complex multiechelon supply and procurement systems of the military. But for the reasons mentioned, most case studies conducted in such systems do not represent applications of serial models. We shall, therefore, begin by discussing some cases in a different area. Examples of inventory networks with series of stations are often found in transporation systems. Vehicles, passengers, and cargo traveling between geographically separated locations are conveniently viewed as resources traveling through a series of inventory stations linked by a chain of input-output processes. Thus, many studies of transport problems may be placed into an inventory context.

THE HUB OPERATION SCHEDULING PROBLEM

An interesting two-level inventory allocation problem with dynamic features poses itself in the scheduling of a trucking fleet which operates mostly between a central terminal (the hub) and a number of outlying terminals [14]. Let the outlying terminals be numbered by $i = 1, \cdots, m$ (see Fig. 10-1). The state of the system at a given point of time may be described by the following state variables:

I_i = number of vehicles at location i

I_0 = number of vehicles at the hub (vehicles in transit are properly allocated)

r_i = amount of freight (in carloads) ready to be shipped from location i to the hub

R_i = amount of freight (in carloads) ready to be shipped from the hub to location i

At the beginning of each scheduling period, trucks at the central terminal must be dispatched to the outlying terminals and, at the same

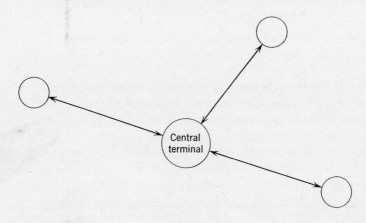

Fig. 10-1.

time, empty trucks not presently needed at the outlying terminals may be ordered back to the central terminal.   Thus, the following variables are under control:

x_i = number of loaded trucks to be dispatched from the hub to terminal i

y_i = number of loaded trucks to be dispatched from terminal i to the hub

z_i = number of empty trucks to be dispatched from terminal i to the hub

These decisions affect the match between demand for service and supply of service at:

1. The central terminal now;
2. the outlying terminals one period hence;
3. the central terminal one period hence.

Imperfect match of supply and demand on a route means either a cost of delay of shipments (cost of shortage) or a cost of running empty vehicles (cost of overage)—a typical inventory situation. The problem has dynamic features in that the demand changes significantly over time and each decision sets initial conditions for future decisions. Since the outputs from vehicle inventories become inputs to other vehicle inventories, we are dealing with a series of inventory stations. The objective is to minimize total expected cost of shortage and overage. In this problem the demands changed significantly from day to day, but forecasts could only be obtained for one day ahead of time. This meant that at scheduling time (evenings) the waiting cargoes r_i, R_i were pretty well established whereas the corresponding quantities for the next evening were only known in terms of probability distributions. Consequently, a planning horizon of two days was used. Before considering costs, it is necessary to introduce certain restrictions imposed by company policy. As long as the vehicle inventory I_0 permits, no shortages are tolerated at the central terminal. This means that

$$\sum_{i=1}^{n} x_i = \min \left(\sum_{i=1}^{n} R_i, I_0 \right) \tag{10.1}$$

Thus, a nontrivial problem of allocating vehicles to routes arises only when $I_0 < \Sigma R_i$. Similarly, we require that

$$y_i = \min (r_i, I_i) \tag{10.2}$$

It follows that the cost of shortage incurred at outlying terminals on the first day is not under control. Hence, it need not be considered. The cost of shortage incurred at the hub on the first day depends somewhat on the routes on which the shortages occur. It is, therefore, a function $f(x_1, \cdots, x_n)$ of the chosen allocation of vehicles. The cost of bringing back empty vehicles on the first day is of the form $\Sigma_{i=1}^{n} a_i z_i$, where the a_i are constants. Turning to the second day, the vehicle inventories will be $I_i + x_i - y_i - z_i$ at the outlying terminals and $I_0 + \Sigma_{i=1}^{n} (y_i + z_i - x_i)$ at the hub. Assuming known probability distributions of demand on the second day, the expected cost of shortage at location i depends only on the vehicle inventory $I_i + x_i - y_i - z_i$ on the second day (see Eq. 10.2); it is therefore a known function $g_i(I_i + x_i - y_i - z_i)$. The expected cost of shortage at the hub depends on the vehicle allocation which will be made on the second day. This allocation will be made after new forecasts have become available. Hence, there is no way of anticipating it, and we can only approximate the expected cost of shortage by the product of the expected amount of shortage and an average cost per unit short (averaged over the different routes i). By this method the expected cost of shortage becomes a known function $g_0[I_0 + \Sigma_{i=1}^n (y_i + z_i - x_i)]$ of the projected inventory level at the hub. Finally, we make the simplifying assumption that no empty vehicles will be brought back on the second day. In summary, we have the following expression for the expected cost during the planning horizon:

$$E(C) = f(x_1, \cdots, x_n) + \sum_{i=1}^{n} a_i z_i + g_0 \left[I_0 + \sum_{1}^{n} (y_i + z_i - x_i) \right]$$
$$+ \sum_{i=1}^{n} g_i(I_i + x_i - y_i - z_i) \quad (10.3)$$

The variables y_i are determined by Eq. 10.2. The variables x_i and z_i must be determined so that $E(C)$ is minimized subject to the restriction of Eq. 10.1 and the nonnegativity constraints

$$x_i, z_i \geq 0 \quad (10.4)$$

Numerical methods for the solution are found in [14].

RAILROAD PROBLEMS

In the previous application, the role of inventory level was assumed by the transportation *facilities*. In other cases the *demand* for transport services plays a typical inventory role. The various geographical locations in a transport system may be viewed as inventory stations where customer demand arrives and is "stored" for some time. These "demand inventories" may be paralleled by physical inventories of cargo. Outputs from the demand inventories occur when service is rendered. Thus, outputs are controlled by the management of the transport system. Turning to railroads in particular, it becomes readily apparent that the problem of output control is essentially an economic-lot-size problem in a complex inventory system with serial and parallel stations. Locomotives and crews give rise to a fixed cost (setup cost) associated with running a train. Demand must, therefore, be accumulated for some time in order to warrant an economical train. On the other hand, too infrequent service leads to high inventories of unfilled demand. These are costly since they "obsolete" in an obvious way: demand may be lost to competing transport systems.   We have a typical balancing problem.   Conventional approaches to the problem of economic train length are often entirely based on internal cost considerations.   This is dangerously one-sided. A broader approach is needed which gives consideration to the effect of train length on customer demand, the required pipeline inventory of freight cars, and other internal cost factors.   G. D. Camp has done some unpublished work in this challenging area of strategic importance to the railroads.

As already mentioned, the freight car fleet in a railroad system may be viewed as a pipeline inventory.   The carrying cost for this pipeline inventory is of such magnitude that it becomes an important factor in almost all major system changes.   For example, Mansfield and Wein [13] have investigated the problem of locating an additional classification yard in an existing railroad system.   The optimal location was defined as the location that minimizes the sum of the following costs:

C_1 = cost per day of hauling trains
C_2 = inventory carrying cost per day for freight car fleet
C_3 = cost per day of classification of freight cars in yards

The problem is to estimate these costs for alternative hypothetical locations of the new yard.   This task is extremely complicated in practice.   Among other things, a large set of operating procedures and restrictions on train routes and car routes must be observed.   A discussion of these ramifications is outside the scope of this book. However, the mathematical model that was used to conceptualize the problem is of interest from the viewpoint of inventory theory.   We shall not concern ourselves with C_3.   Let:

n_r = number of trains per day on train route r
a_r = "normal" hauling cost per train on route r
δ_{ri} = number of cars per day hauled above capacity of the ith leg of train route r
M_{ri} = mileage of the ith leg of train route r
α = cost per car mile above capacity
N_s = number of cars hauled per day over car route s
θ_{rs} = fraction of N_s hauled by trains on train route r
t_{rs} = average time en route for a car on route s hauled by a train on route r
h = inventory carrying cost per car per day (the railroad industry uses \$2.50 per car per day)

With these notations, the hauling cost becomes

$$C_1 = \sum_r a_r n_r + \alpha \sum_{r,i} M_{ri}\, \delta_{ri} \tag{10.5}$$

The inventory carrying cost for the car fleet was written in the following form:

$$C_2 = h \sum_s N_s \left[\sum_r \theta_{rs} t_{rs} + b_s + c \sum_{r \supset s} n_r + d \left(\sum_{r \supset s} n_r \right)^2 \right] \tag{10.6}$$

where b_s, c, and d are constants. This expression requires some explanation. The terms $N_s \theta_{rs} t_{rs}$ represent what we have called in-process inventories. The average traveling time t_{rs} of cars on route s is multiplied with the through-put rate $N_s \theta_{rs}$ (see Eq. 9.73). Consequently, these terms measure the average number of cars en route. The remaining terms represent the inventories of cars in classification yards. The waiting and classification time of a car in the origin yard of its car route s is a function of the total number $\sum_{r \supset s} n_r$ of trains whose routes r "dominate" car route s (symbolically: $r \supset s$). Empirical studies showed that this (decreasing) function may be approximated by a quadratic (see the last three terms in Eq. 10.6). Note in Eq. 10.6 that differences between classification yards enter only through the constants b_s. To complete the inventory expression, the average time spent in the yard is multiplied by the through-put rate N_s of car route s. This inventory may also be looked upon as an in-process inventory where the process is classification and waiting. The remaining part of the study, which is not discussed here, is concerned mainly with the determination of the quantities n_r, δ_{ri}, N_s, and θ_{rs} for different hypothetical locations of the additional classification yard. Once this has been accomplished, the desired cost comparisons can be made. For other studies dealing with problems of the freight car inventory, see [10] and [5].

Similar problems of pipeline inventories may arise in air traffic. Suppose an airline intends to carry a monthly passenger volume V in each direction between two geographical locations d miles apart. One airplane of a given type will on the average carry l passengers. Obviously, the through-put rate of airplanes at either endpoint is V/l and the average traveling time between the two endpoints is d/c where c is the effective average velocity of the airplane. By Eq. 9.73, the required pipeline inventory of airplanes for both directions is

$$I = 2 \frac{V}{l} \frac{d}{c} \tag{10.7}$$

Formulas of this sort may be used for crude estimates of the total investment required for different types of airplanes. The formula shows that the pipeline inventory is very sensitive to speed.

THE CONTROL OF PIPELINE INVENTORIES AND LEAD TIMES IN MANUFACTURING PROCESSES

The pipeline inventory in many manufacturing processes may be broken down into materials being processed (in-process inventory) and materials waiting to be processed (waiting-line inventory). According to Eq. 9.74, the total traveling time T of a production lot or other identifiable quantity of product through the manufacturing process may be written as

$$T = T_1 + T_2 \tag{10.8}$$

where T_1 is the time spent waiting and T_2 is the time spent in process. It is a frequent experience that the productive time T_2 is a rather small fraction of the total production lead time T, sometimes less than 10%. In specific cases, this may be checked by a statistical analysis of arrival dates of orders, shipment dates, and machine time reports.   In general, it is safe to assume that the control of pipeline inventories and production lead times is concerned with waiting-line inventories rather than in-process inventories.   This is all the more true since the time T_2 spent in process is usually fixed by the technology.   But even when changes in technology are possible, a reduction of waiting-line inventories may be a cheaper and more efficient way of reducing lead time. For example, automation of mail-sorting operations in the post office cannot be expected to yield significant improvements in service as long as the major portion of the time the mail spends in the post office is waiting time.   Of course, savings in labor are another consideration.

In the present discussion we shall consider the technology as fixed and concern ourselves only with the control of waiting-line inventories. These inventories are partially intended by management as a protection against work stoppages, but mostly they develop in an uncontrolled fashion as a consequence of machine breakdowns, operator behavior, and fluctuations of arrival rates and service rates for individual jobs.   The lack of formal control of waiting lines is a reason for high pipeline inventory.   Assuming that machine breakdowns and operator behavior are not under control, waiting lines can be influenced only by manipulations of arrival rates and service rates.   The most obvious way of changing the service rate is the use of overtime when inventories become too large.   Often this measure is not taken until

there is no space for further growth of inventories.   Arrival rates may
be influenced to a certain extent by scheduling.   The conflicting considerations in controlling waiting-line inventories are the cost of overtime as well as idle time of men and machines, on one hand, and customer lead time on the other hand.   As in many inventory problems,
the critical factor is the amount of fluctuation of the inventory levels
(see Fig. 10-2).   When the various waiting lines are observed in time,

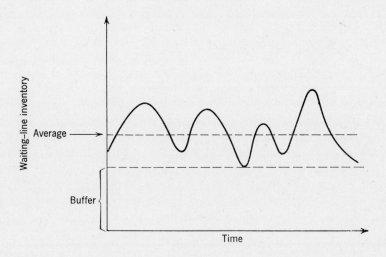

Fig. 10-2.

it will be found that they contain buffer inventories which are lower
limits of the inventory fluctuation.   Sometimes the fluctuations are so
small that the average level and the buffer level are not very different.
This suggests that the operator tries to stabilize the waiting-line by
maintaining a feedback between the length of the line and his rate of
work.   When left to himself, the operator will decide on the average
level at which he wishes to stabilize.   But there is no reason why he
could not stabilize at a lower level, say at the average level minus the
amount of the buffer.   Obviously, elimination of the buffer does not
cause any idle time.   Hence the average output rate remains the same.
On the other hand, lead time is reduced.   We get, so-to-speak, something for nothing.   Whether this trick can be performed depends on
the willingness of the operator to exchange his self-chosen level of
stabilization for one that is prescribed to him.   The elimination of
buffers requires a temporary stepup of the output rate.   Since this

can normally be accomplished only by using overtime, the reduction of lead time requires a one-time investment. The lead time T before and after the reduction can be computed by Eq. 9.73.

Further reduction of lead time—which is equivalent to further reduction of waiting-line inventories—can be accomplished only by accepting occasional idle time of men and machines (see Fig. 10-2). This means a decrease of the output rate. Since the input rate of jobs remains constant, waiting-line inventories have a tendency to grow and can only be kept at the intended levels by recurring use of overtime. Statistical control chart techniques may be used to signal the need for inventory reduction. To minimize the use of overtime, it is desirable to distinguish a systematic growth of inventory from a purely random one. This can be accomplished by a forecast of the work load for the various facilities. Such forecasts are based on orders in the house and the corresponding scheduling decisions. Finally, the occurrence of idle time as well as overtime can be minimized through proper scheduling. The purpose of scheduling is to avoid overloading and underloading of facilities within the restriction of meeting delivery dates. For example, consider a job shop with operations or machine centers $i = 1, \cdots, n$. To simplify the situation, assume that all orders have to be processed through center 1 first. For each order h the sequence of operations is given, and the machine time requirements are specified by a vector t_{ih}. Schedules are made daily by releasing a number of orders to center 1, which is sufficient to raise the waiting-line at center 1 to the equivalent of one day's work. Let $\bar{I}_i$ be the long-range inventory target for the waiting line at center i. With a reasonably stable product mix, the targets $\bar{I}_i$ can be translated into equivalent targets $\bar{J}_i$ for the *total* inventory in the shop destined for center i. Both inventories are measured by their processing time through center i. Let the corresponding *actual* inventory levels at the time of scheduling be $I_i{}^0$ and $J_i{}^0$ respectively. Assume that there are m orders on hand from which the next day's schedule must be made up. We define a binary variable

$$x_h = \begin{cases} 1 & \text{if order } h \text{ is included in schedule} \\ 0 & \text{otherwise} \end{cases} \qquad (h = 1, \cdots, m)$$

If the constants t_{ih} are measured in days, then a schedule must fulfill the condition

$$J_1{}^0 + \sum_{h=1}^{m} t_{1h} x_h = 1 \qquad (10.9)$$

Furthermore, it should as nearly as possible fulfill the relations

$$J_i{}^0 + \sum_{h=1}^{m} t_{ih}x_h \approx J_i \qquad (i = 2, \cdots, n) \qquad (10.10)$$

Various approximate methods for the solution of this scheduling problem suggest themselves. Usually these will rely on ranking ideas and be flexible enough to handle restrictions on delivery dates. Before this type of scheduling and the resulting stabilization of waiting lines can be implemented, it is necessary to have a data-processing system that furnishes the numbers $J_i{}^0$. Also, the time constants t_{ih} must be made available by a reliable standard time system. The preceding discussion of the scheduling problem has been simplified but it still contains the essential points.

MULTISTAGE INVENTORY CONTROL
IN MANUFACTURING PROCESSES

An application of a multistage inventory model in a manufacturing operation is reported by Simpson [15]. The mathematical aspects of the model were developed in Chapter 9 (see Eq. 9.25). The question posed by management was whether two particular operations of the manufacturing process should be separated by an inventory or whether they should be coupled tightly together and considered as a single stage. An inventory seemed highly desirable to management. Plausible qualitative arguments supported this view: "Larger inventories earlier in the process would permit reductions in more expensive finished goods inventories, more flexibility in meeting varying mixes of finished products," and so on. The mathematical model showed that in this case the intuitive feelings were quite wrong; operation with the proposed inventory, instead of being considerably less costly, would have been slightly more costly than operation without it.

Ackoff [1] reports a study of a chemical process involving one intermediate and one finished inventory. The operations connecting the inventory stages are controlled by a set of complex loading and recycling decisions. These decisions also influence production costs. Thus, the total cost of production and inventory became a very complex function of the controllable variables. No practical decision rules could be derived from the cost function, and the use of the model was abandoned in favor of a simple operating scheduling rule. The study is enlightening as to the practical difficulties that may arise in an analytical approach to multistage problems. It is also interesting to see how these difficulties can be circumvented by sacrificing "optimality" of production plans in order to gain feasibility. Of course, this means that one has come closer to a truly optimal operation which must always fulfill the restriction of feasibility. After all, the cost of violating the feasibility restriction is practically infinite. Some problems of reserve inventories in assembly lines are reviewed in [11].

THE CONTROL OF LEAD TIME IN A MAIL ORDER BUSINESS

In Chapter 9 we have discussed a number of multistage models based on the assumption that sales are sensitive to the average delivery time to the customer (see Eq. 9.27). Levinson [12] reports an interesting study of a mail order business where a relationship between sales and delivery time was empirically established. This was accomplished by a statistical analysis of customer returns as a function of the lead time elapsing between receipt of the order and shipment. The analysis showed that the probability of a customer return, that is, the probability of losing a sale, was a sharply increasing function of lead time. In perfect analogy with Eq. 9.27, the functional form varied for different classes of orders, depending mainly on the dollar value of the order. Total orders on hand but not yet shipped may be viewed as a pipeline inventory. Various methods for reducing pipeline inventories have been discussed in previous sections. All of these methods are costly, especially when the capacity for performing certain operations is increased. In Levinson's study the cost of maintaining shorter lead times was investigated for various possible values of average lead time. The functional relationships between lead time and cost, on one hand, and lead time and sales on the other hand became the basis for arriving at an over-all optimum policy which maximized expected profit.

BIBLIOGRAPHY F

Series of Stations

1. Ackoff, R. L., "Production and Inventory Control in a Chemical Process," *Operations Research*, **3**, No. 3 (Aug. 1955), 319–338.
2. Bryan, J. G., Wadsworth, G. P., Whitin, T. M., "A Multi-Stage Inventory Model," *Naval Research Logistics Quarterly*, **2**, Nos. 1 and 2 (Mar.–June 1955), 25–38.
3. Clark, A. J., Scarf, H., "Optimal Policies for a Multi-Echelon Inventory Problem," *Management Science*, **6**, No. 4 (July 1960), 475–490.
4. Dillon, J. D., "Geographical Distribution of Production in Multiple Plant Operations," *Management Science*, **2**, No. 4 (July 1956), 353–365.

5. Feeney, G. J., "The Empty Boxcar Distribution Problem," *Proceedings of the First International Conference on Operational Research*, Bristol, England: John Wright and Sons, 1958, 250–263.
6. Gluss, B., "An Optimal Inventory Solution for Some Specific Demand Distribution," *Naval Research Logistics Quarterly*, **7**, No. 1 (Mar. 1960), 45–48.
7. Gradwohl, A. J., "Case Studies on the Multi-Echelon Inventory Problem," *PRC R-133*, Los Angeles, California: Planning Research Corporation, Dec. 1959.
8. Hanssmann, F., "Optimal Inventory Location and Control in Production and Distribution Networks," *Operations Research*, **7**, No. 4 (July–Aug. 1959), 483–498.
9. Karreman, H. F., "Programming the Supply of a Strategic Material—Part I. A Nonstochastic Model," *Naval Research Logistics Quarterly*, **7**, No. 3 (Sept. 1960), 261–280.
10. Kawata, T., "Standing Time of a Freight Car in a Marshalling Yard," *Proceedings of the First International Conference on Operational Research*, Bristol, England: John Wright and Sons, 1958, pp. 243–250.
11. Koenigsberg, E., "Production Lines and Internal Storage—A Review," *Management Science*, **5**, No. 4 (July 1959), 410–433.
12. Levinson, H. C., "Experiences in Commercial Operations Research," *Operations Research*, **1**, No. 4 (Aug. 1953), 220–239.
13. Mansfield, E., Wein, H. H., "A Model for the Location of a Railroad Classification Yard," *Management Science*, **4**, No. 3 (Apr. 1958), 292–313.
14. Minas, J. G., Mitten, L. G., "The Hub Operation Scheduling Problem," *Operations Research*, **6**, No. 3 (May–June 1958), 329–345.
15. Simpson, K. F., Jr., "In-Process Inventories," *Operations Research*, **6**, No. 6 (Nov.–Dec. 1958), 863–873.

part V

APPENDICES

chapter 11
Mathematical Appendix

In this appendix we give, without proof, some basic mathematical facts frequently used in the main body of this book, and some standard techniques and algorithms for the solution of mathematical problems encountered in the text. For more detailed study, the reader is referred to the literature which is plentiful.

SOME ELEMENTS OF STATISTICS

A variable x that assumes given values with given probabilities is called a random variable. If there is a discrete set x_i of possible values with associated probabilities p_i $(i = 1, 2, \cdot \cdot \cdot)$, then the random variable is said to have a discrete probability distribution. In this case,

$$\sum_i p_i = 1 \tag{11.1}$$

If x is a continuous variable, it is common to define a probability density function $f(x)$ such that the product $f(x)\, dx$ is the probability of the random variable assuming a value between x and $x + dx$. [In the case of several random variables $x_1, \cdot \cdot \cdot, x_n$, a joint density function $f(x_1, \cdot \cdot \cdot, x_n)$ can be defined in analogous fashion]. The density function $f(x)$ is defined for all real values of its argument. If the random variable is restricted to a finite interval, we define $f(x) \equiv 0$ outside that interval. It should be noted that the probability of the random variable assuming any given value is zero. It follows from the definition of $f(x)$ that

$$\int_{-\infty}^{\infty} f(x)\, dx = 1 \tag{11.2}$$

The behavior of discrete and continuous probability distributions is quite analogous in many ways; we shall, therefore, restrict ourselves to the continuous case. The cumulative probability distribution

213

associated with the density function $f(x)$ is defined by

$$F(x) = \int_{-\infty}^{x} f(u)\, du \tag{11.3}$$

Obviously, $F(x)$ measures the probability of the random variable assuming a value less than or equal to x. The relations

$$F'(x) = f(x) \tag{11.4}$$

and

$$F(-\infty) = 0 \qquad F(\infty) = 1 \tag{11.5}$$

follow directly from the definition of $F(x)$. The expected value of a function $g(x)$ relative to the density function $f(x)$ is defined by

$$E(g(x)) = \int_{-\infty}^{\infty} g(x)\, f(x)\, dx \tag{11.6}$$

Important special cases are

$$E(x) = \mu = \int_{-\infty}^{\infty} x\, f(x)\, dx \tag{11.7}$$

and

$$E[(x - \mu)^2] = \sigma^2 = \int_{-\infty}^{\infty} (x - \mu)^2\, f(x)\, dx \tag{11.8}$$

The parameters μ and σ^2 are known as the mean and variance, respectively, of the random variable defined by the density function $f(x)$. The parameter σ is called the standard deviation and may be regarded as a measure of the spread of the random variable. In practical problems, the parameters of probability distributions must usually be estimated from a sample of values of the random variable x (sampling and estimation theory).

In applications it is often necessary to combine certain random variables with known density functions into new random variables, for example, by addition or multiplication. It is important to have some knowledge of the properties of the new probability distribution. Particularly useful statements can be made when the random variables in question are independent. Consider two independent random variables x_1 and x_2 with parameters $\{\mu_1, \sigma_1\}$ and $\{\mu_2, \sigma_2\}$ respectively. Then,

$$E(x_1 + x_2) = \mu_1 + \mu_2 \tag{11.9}$$

$$E(x_1 x_2) = \mu_1 \mu_2 \tag{11.10}$$

If in addition, both variables are normally distributed, that is, their density functions are of the form

$$f(x) = \frac{1}{\sqrt{2\pi}\sigma} e^{-(x-\mu)^2/2\sigma^2} \qquad (11.11)$$

then the following theorem for the variances holds:

$$\text{var}(x_1 + x_2) = \text{var } x_1 + \text{var } x_2$$
$$= \sigma_1{}^2 + \sigma_2{}^2 \qquad (11.12)$$

Furthermore, the variable $x_1 + x_2$ is also normally distributed. As a corollary, the sum of n independent normal random variables with identical probability distributions is a normal random variable with mean $n\mu$ and variance $n\sigma^2$ (or standard deviation $\sqrt{n}\sigma$), where μ and σ^2 are mean and variance, respectively, of each one of the n random variables.

In many applications, for example, in forecasting and in quality control of manufacturing operations, it is desired to discover quickly changes of the mean of random variables. For this purpose, statistical control charts are often used. Assume that initially a random variable x has a known (or estimated) mean μ and standard deviation σ, and is normally distributed. It is a property of the normal distribution that the random variable will assume values inside the interval

$$\mu - 2\sigma \leq x \leq \mu + 2\sigma \qquad (11.13)$$

with a probability of roughly 0.95. If actual values fall outside the "2σ band," then it is likely that the mean has changed, especially when several such cases occur in short succession. The variable is then considered out of control, and an investigation is made or corrective action taken. Although there are many variants, this is the basic concept of the statistical control chart. In practice, the random variable in question is often measured at equidistant points of time, and the measured values are plotted relative to the 2σ band (or another suitable band). Such charts make possible a quick visual discovery of loss of control (see Fig. 11-1.)

In forecasting and other applications, it is often necessary to study the correlation between a random variable y and a (random or nonrandom) variable x. In a trend analysis, time assumes the role of the variable x. A case of special interest is that of linear correlation; it may be said to exist when the expected value of y is a linear function of x. If a sample of n pairs of values (x_i, y_i) is available ($i = 1, \cdots, n$), then the extent to which the two variables are linearly correlated may be measured by the following estimate of their "correlation coefficient":

$$\rho = \frac{\Sigma x_i y_i - n\bar{x}\bar{y}}{\sqrt{(\Sigma x_i^2 - n\bar{x}^2)(\Sigma y_i^2 - n\bar{y}^2)}} \qquad (11.14)$$

where $\bar{x}$ and $\bar{y}$ are the averages, respectively, of the x_i and y_i. The quantity ρ can only assume values in the interval

$$0 \leq \rho \leq 1 \qquad (11.15)$$

If the points (x_i, y_i) fall exactly on a straight line in the (x, y) plane, then $\rho = 1$. This is the highest degree of linear correlation. If

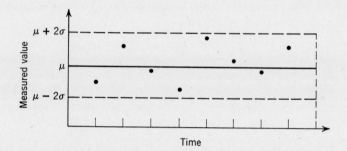

Fig. 11-1. Statistical control chart.

there is scatter, ρ will be less than one. But in the case of a "perfect" nonlinear relationship, the correlation coefficient may also be quite low.

The linear relationship between the expected value of y and the variable x may be estimated by the so-called regression equation

$$\eta = \alpha x + \beta \qquad (11.16)$$

where η is an estimate of the expected value of y. The coefficients of the regression equation are given by

$$\alpha = \frac{\sum_{1}^{n} (x_i - \bar{x})y_i}{\sum_{1}^{n} (x_i - \bar{x})^2} \qquad (11.17)$$

$$\beta = \bar{y} \qquad (11.18)$$

where $\bar{x}$ and $\bar{y}$ are the averages, respectively, of the x_i and y_i. These values of α and β minimize the expression

$$\sum_{i=1}^{n} [y_i - (\alpha x_i + \beta)]^2 \tag{11.19}$$

with respect to α and β. Because of this property, the straight line given by (Eq. 11.16) is referred to as the least-squares fit to the set of sample points (x_i, y_i).

DIFFERENTIATION OF INTEGRALS

If an integral is to be differentiated with respect to a variable x which occurs both in the integrand and the limits of integration, the following rule holds under certain conditions:

$$\frac{d}{dx} \int_{\phi(x)}^{\psi(x)} f(x, t)\, dt = \psi'(x) f(x, \psi(x)) - \phi'(x) f(x, \phi(x))$$
$$+ \int_{\phi(x)}^{\psi(x)} \frac{\partial}{\partial x} f(x, t)\, dt \tag{11.20}$$

where the prime designates the derivative of a function of one variable. The rule is valid in an interval $\alpha < x < \beta$ if the function $f(x, t)$ has a continuous partial derivative with respect to x in the region $\alpha \le x \le \beta$, $\phi(x) \le t \le \psi(x)$. In the case of singular integrals, there is the additional condition that both integrals occurring in the formula must be uniformly convergent in the interval $\alpha \le x \le \beta$.

Important special cases are:

$$\frac{d}{dx} \int_{a}^{x} f(t)\, dt = - \frac{d}{dx} \int_{x}^{a} f(t)\, dt = f(x) \tag{11.21}$$

and

$$\frac{d}{dx} \int_{a}^{b} f(x, t)\, dt = \int_{a}^{b} \frac{\partial}{\partial x} f(x, t)\, dt \tag{11.22}$$

where a and b are constants.

LAGRANGIAN MULTIPLIERS

Consider the problem of finding the extremal value (maximum or minimum) of a function $f(x_1, \cdots, x_n)$ of n variables subject to the side conditions

$$g_j(x_1, \cdots, x_n) = 0 \qquad (j = 1, \cdots, m) \tag{11.23}$$

where $m < n$. If the extremal point $(x_1, \cdots, x_n)$ lies inside the region defined by the side conditions, and if all functions have continuous partial derivatives inside this region, then the extremal point will be among the solutions of the following system of $n + m$ equations for the unknowns $x_1, \cdots, x_n; \lambda_1, \cdots, \lambda_m$:

$$\frac{\partial}{\partial x_i} \left[f(x_1, \cdots, x_n) + \sum_{j=1}^{m} \lambda_j \, g_j(x_1, \cdots, x_n) \right] = 0 \qquad (11.24)$$

$$g_j(x_1, \cdots, x_n) = 0$$

$$(i = 1, \cdots, n; \, j = 1, \cdots, m)$$

The unknowns $\lambda_1, \cdots, \lambda_m$ are called Lagrangian multipliers. In applications they usually have important interpretations. If we define the Lagrangian function

$$L(x_1, \cdots, x_n; \lambda_1, \cdots, \lambda_m) = f(x_1, \cdots, x_n)$$
$$+ \sum_{j=1}^{m} \lambda_j g_j(x_1, \cdots, x_n) \qquad (11.25)$$

then the system of Eqs. 11.24 may be obtained by setting all $m + n$ partial derivatives of the Lagrangian function equal to zero.

FINITE DIFFERENCES

By definition, the first difference of a function $f(x)$ is the function

$$\Delta f(x) = f(x + h) - f(x) \qquad (11.26)$$

where $h > 0$ is a constant. It should be noted that the function $\Delta f(x)$ contains the mesh size h as a parameter. The second difference of $f(x)$ is defined as the first difference of $\Delta f(x)$, and is designated $\Delta^2 f(x)$; all higher differences are analogously defined. The rules for differencing are quite analogous to the rules of differentiation. In particular

$$\Delta[f(x) + g(x)] = \Delta f(x) + \Delta g(x) \qquad (11.27)$$

$$\Delta[a \, f(x)] = a \, \Delta f(x) \qquad (11.28)$$

$$\Delta[f(x) \, g(x)] = [\Delta f(x)] \, g(x) + f(x + h) \, \Delta g(x) \qquad (11.29)$$

$$\Delta \frac{f(x)}{g(x)} = \frac{[\Delta f(x)] \, g(x) - f(x) \, \Delta g(x)}{[g(x + h)] \, g(x)} \qquad (11.30)$$

where a is a constant. Dividing these equations by h and letting $h \to 0$ yields the corresponding rules of differentiation.

THE TRANSPORTATION TECHNIQUE

The transportation problem may be stated as follows. Find a set of nonnegative integers x_{ij} $(i = 1, \cdots, m;\ j = 1, \cdots, n)$ which minimizes the linear function

$$C = \sum_{i,j} c_{ij} x_{ij} \tag{11.31}$$

subject to the constraints

$$\sum_{j=1}^{n} x_{ij} = a_i \qquad (i = 1, \cdots, m, \tag{11.32}$$

$$\sum_{i=1}^{m} x_{ij} = b_j \qquad (j = 1, \cdots, n) \tag{11.33}$$

where the a_i and b_j are given positive integers and the c_{ij} are given real numbers. The problem derives its name from the following interpretation:

a_i = number of units (of a certain commodity) available at "source i"

b_j = number of units required at "destination j"

c_{ij} = unit cost of transshipment from source i to destination j

Any set of nonnegative integers x_{ij} which satisfies the restrictions will be called a solution. The optimal solution of transportation problems may usually be obtained by the method which we are about to discuss. However, there are certain degenerate cases such as the "assignment problem" for which this method fails. The assignment problem will be discussed in a separate section. The solution of the general transportation problem may be carried out in the following steps:

1. Find an initial solution x_{ij} by the "northwest corner rule": Allocate the supply at source 1 to destinations $1, 2, \cdots$ in this sequence by fully satisfying the demand of each destination, until the supply is exhausted; similarly, allocate the supply at source 2 beginning with the first destination whose requirements were not completely satisfied by source 1; and so on.

2. Write all non-zero values x_{ij} in the appropriate cells of an m by n matrix (see Table 11-1), and circle these cells.

3. "Evaluate" the non-occupied cells (ij) according to the following rules:

a. For a given cell (ij), proceed to the nearest occupied cell (ik) in the same row that has another occupied cell in its column k (see Table 11-1).

b. Return to cell (ij) in a closed path, using only vertical and horizontal moves, and using only occupied cells as "stepping stones."

c. Form the alternating sum of the unit costs c_{ij} corresponding to the stepping stones used, beginning with the plus sign for cell (ik). Enter the value of the sum as evaluation e_{ij} into cell (ij).

Table 11-1
Transportation Matrix*

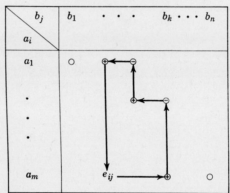

* Circles (○) designate occupied cells.

4. If all evaluations are nonnegative, the solution is optimal. If there is one or more negative numbers, the solution can be improved. In the latter case, select any negative evaluation, say, $e_{ij} = -N$. Retrace the evaluation path of this cell, and consider only those stepping stones whose unit costs entered with the positive sign into the evaluation. From these, select the cell (hr) with the lowest occupancy $x_{hr} = \alpha$. For an improved solution x'_{ij}, set

$$x'_{hr} = 0 \qquad (11.34)$$

$$x'_{ij} = \alpha \qquad (11.35)$$

All other occupied cells of the initial solution remain occupied, and their occupancies are recomputed on the basis of the restrictions of Eqs. 11.32–11.33. The cost reduction effected by the improved solution is αN.

5. Repeat the procedure from step 2 on until all evaluations of non-occupied cells are nonnegative.

THE GENERAL LINEAR PROGRAMMING PROBLEM

The general linear programming problem of maximizing or minimizing a linear function subject to a number of linear inequality constraints may be solved by hand or on a computer by the so-called simplex algorithm. We shall first discuss the mechanics of the rather complex algorithm without reference to the linear programming problem.

The Simplex Algorithm

Suppose that the positive integers n and $m < n$ and a set of real numbers c_j $(j = 0, 1, \cdots, n + m)$ are given. We then define a "simplex tableau" as follows. Its major part is a matrix with rows $i = 1, \cdots, m + 2$ and columns $j = 0, 1, \cdots, n + m$ arranged as shown in Table 11-2. Its elements will be designated x_{ij}. In addition, the tableau contains a matrix of m rows and 2 columns; the latter are designated $j(i)$ and d_i, respectively. The $j(i)$ column contains m integers which fulfill the condition

$$1 \leq j(i) \leq n + m \tag{11.36}$$

and each integer occurs at most once. The m numbers in the d_i column fulfill the relation

$$d_i = c_{j(i)} \tag{11.37}$$

Table 11-2
Simplex Tableau

i \ j	1	$\cdots$	$n + m$	0
1	x_{11}		$x_{1,n+m}$	x_{10}
.				
.				
.				
m				
$m + 1$				
$m + 2$	$x_{m+2,1}$		$x_{m+2,n+m}$	$x_{m+2,0}$

$j(i)$	d_i

In addition, the following relations are required to hold:

$$x_{m+1,j} = \sum_{i=1}^{m} d_i x_{ij} \qquad (j = 0, \cdots, n + m) \qquad (11.38)$$

and

$$x_{m+2,j} = x_{m+1,j} - c_j \qquad (j = 0, \cdots, n + m) \qquad (11.39)$$

The simplex algorithm is a set of rules which serves to calculate an "improved" simplex tableau from a given tableau, provided that at least one of the numbers $x_{m+2,j}$ is negative. These rules are as follows:

1. Find the column $j = k$ in which

$$A = \min_{j} x_{m+2,j} \qquad (11.40)$$

occurs.

2. Find the row $i = r$ in which

$$B = \min_{i} \frac{x_{i0}}{x_{ik}} \qquad (x_{ik} > 0) \qquad (11.41)$$

occurs. As indicated, the minimization is only over the rows for which $x_{ik} > 0$.

3. Compute the elements x'_{ij} of the new tableau (with the exception of row $m + 1$) by the formula

$$x'_{ij} = \begin{cases} \dfrac{x_{ij}}{x_{ik}} & \text{for } i = r \\[2ex] x_{ij} - x_{rj}\dfrac{x_{ik}}{x_{rk}} & \text{for } i \neq r,\ i \neq m + 1 \end{cases} \qquad (11.42)$$

4. Replace $j(r)$ by k and $d_{j(r)}$ by d_k.
5. Calculate the elements

$$x'_{m+1,j} = \sum_{i=1}^{m} d_i x'_{ij} \qquad (11.43)$$

using the up-dated column d_i.

The calculation of row $m + 1$ (step 5) is often unnecessary in applications, but, by Eq. 11.39, it may serve as a check for row $m + 2$.

It can also be shown that

$$x'_{m+2,0} = x_{m+2,0} - Bx_{m+2,k} \qquad (11.44)$$

must hold.

Interpretation of the Simplex Tableau

Consider the linear programming problem of maximizing the function

$$z = \sum_{j=1}^{n} c_j x_j \qquad (11.45)$$

with respect to the variables $x_1, \cdots, x_n$ subject to the constraints

$$\sum_{j=1}^{n} a_{ij} x_j \le a_{i0} \qquad (i = 1, \cdots, m) \qquad (11.46)$$

and

$$x_j \ge 0 \qquad (j = 1, \cdots, n) \qquad (11.47)$$

where $m < n$, and the c_j and a_{ij} are given constants. (Problems of minimization may be transformed into problems of maximization by multiplying the objective function by -1; similarly, inequalities involving lower bounds can always be rewritten as inequalities involving upper bounds. Thus, the present formulation is no loss of generality.) It is customary to introduce m slack variables

$$x_{n+1}, \cdots, x_{n+m} \ge 0 \qquad (11.48)$$

which are used to transform the inequalities of Eq. 11.46 into equations. If we extend the definition of the matrix a_{ij} by attaching an m by m unit matrix

$$U = \begin{pmatrix} 1 & & 0 \\ & \ddots & \\ 0 & & 1 \end{pmatrix} \qquad (11.49)$$

at the right-hand side, we can then rewrite the restrictions of the problem as

$$\sum_{j=1}^{n+m} a_{ij} x_j = a_{i0} \qquad (i = 1, \cdots, m) \qquad (11.50)$$

and

$$x_j \ge 0 \qquad (j = 1, \cdots, n + m) \qquad (11.51)$$

The values of $x_{n+1}, \cdots, x_{n+m}$ are defined by Eq. 11.50 for each admissible set of values $x_1, \cdots, x_n$. If we also extend the definition of the coefficients c_j by introducing

$$c_{n+1} = c_{n+2} = \cdots = c_{n+m} = c_0 = 0 \qquad (11.52)$$

we can then rewrite the objective function as

$$z = \sum_{j=1}^{n+m} c_j x_j \qquad (11.53)$$

We now have a problem in $n + m$ variables. It is well known that the optimal solution will contain only m nonzero variables. The simplex technique is an iterative procedure which only utilizes solutions with m nonzero variables. [A set of values x_j ($j = 1, \cdots,$ $n + m$) is called a solution if and only if it satisfies all constraints of the problem.]

We can now interpret the simplex tableau (Table 11-2) in terms of an approximate solution of the linear programming problem in $n + m$ variables. The integers $j(i)$ indicate which m variables are nonzero in the solution in question; the d_i column gives the coefficients of these variables in the objective function; $x_{10}, \cdots, x_{m0}$ are the numerical values of the nonzero variables; $x_{m+2,0}$ (as well as $x_{m+1,0}$) measures the value of the objective function z corresponding to the solution in question. In the next iteration, variable $j(r)$ (see Eq. 11.41) is replaced by variable k, that is, x_k will be nonzero and $x_{j(r)}$ will be zero. All other nonzero variables will remain in the solution. The elements $x_{m+2,j}$ ($j = 1, \cdots, n + m$) measure the cost (in terms of the objective function) which would be incurred if variable j were increased by one unit. In particular, a negative cost element $x_{m+2,j}$ means that the objective function could be *increased*. If all elements are nonnegative, the solution is optimal.

Solving the Linear Programming Problem

The linear programming problem stated in the previous section may now be solved by the simplex algorithm if an initial simplex tableau is given. The tableau given in Table 11-3 may be used as the initial tableau. We have used the abbreviations

$$x_{m+1,j} = z_j \qquad (11.54)$$

$$x_{m+2,j} = z_j - c_j \qquad (j = 0, \cdots, n + m) \qquad (11.55)$$

The first m rows of the tableau consist of the generalized coefficient matrix a_{ij} given by the restrictions. The solution corresponding to this tableau is

$$x_1 \quad = 0$$
$$\cdot$$
$$\cdot$$
$$\cdot$$
$$x_n \quad = 0$$
$$x_{n+1} = a_{10}$$
$$\cdot$$
$$\cdot$$
$$x_{n+m} = a_{m0}$$

The nonzero variables (the slack variables) $n + 1, \cdots, n + m$ are indicated in the $j(i)$ column; their cost coefficients d_i are zero. The two remaining rows of the tableau are easily calculated by Eqs. 11.42–11.43.

Table 11-3
Initial Simplex Tableau

$\diagdown \ j$ $i \ \diagdown$	$1 \ \cdots \ n$	$n + 1 \cdots n + m$	0		$j(i)$	d_i
1		$1 \qquad 0$	a_{10}		$n + 1$	0
$\cdot$		$\cdot$	$\cdot$		$\cdot$	$\cdot$
$\cdot$	a_{ij}	$\cdot$	$\cdot$		$\cdot$	$\cdot$
$\cdot$		$\cdot$	$\cdot$		$\cdot$	$\cdot$
m		$0 \qquad 1$	a_{m0}		$n + m$	0
z_j	$0 \ \cdots \ 0$	$0 \ \cdots \ 0$	0			
$z_j - c_j$	$-c_1 \cdots -c_n$	$0 \ \cdots \ 0$	0			

In summary, the following steps lead to the solution of the general linear programming problem:

1. If necessary, rewrite the problem so that the objective function is to be maximized, the variables are nonnegative, and all inequality constraints involve upper bounds of the linear functions in question.

2. Set up the initial simplex tableau given in Table 11-3.

3. By the simplex algorithm, construct further tableaus until all elements of the last row are nonnegative.

4. From the last tableau, read off the optimal solution: the $j(i)$ column identifies the nonzero variables, the column $j = 0$ gives the values of these variables and the value of the objective function.

THE ASSIGNMENT PROBLEM

The assignment problem is a special (degenerate) case of the transportation problem and may be stated as follows. Given an n by n matrix with positive elements, select n independent elements in such a way that the sum of the selected elements is a minimum. A set of n elements is said to be independent if there is exactly one element in each row and each column. If the rows and columns represent two sets of objects each of which contains n members, then a set of independent cells may be interpreted as a way of forming n pairs between these sets or, briefly, as an "assignment." If we further interpret the elements of the matrix as costs, the problem becomes one of finding the assignment with minimum total cost.

By the following set of rules, a sequence of transformed matrices is derived from the original matrix. After each step, the transformed matrix should be examined for occurrence of a set of n independent zeros. If such a set exists, an optimal solution has been reached, and the following steps need not be carried out. The optimal assignment is given by the cells in which the n independent zeros occur.

1. In each column, subtract the smallest element of the column from all elements of the column. (After this step, each column contains at least one zero.)

2. In each row, subtract the smallest element of the row from all elements of the row. (After this step, each row and column contain at least one zero.)

3. Find a minimal set of lines (covering rows and columns) by which all zeros can be covered. Subtract the smallest element of the non-covered submatrix from all elements of the noncovered submatrix. Add the same element to all elements which lie at intersections (if any) of lines.

4. Repeat steps 1, 2, and 3 until a solution is reached.

chapter 12
An Illustrative Case Study

In this chapter we give a numerical illustration of the application of inventory concepts set forth in the main body of this book. The material is based on a case study of a retail store conducted under the direction of the author. For various reasons some changes and simplifications in the data and the results of the actual study were made. However, all essential points have been preserved.

One of the purposes of the study was to explore the feasibility and economics of scientific inventory control in a retail store. The store under study carries about 5000 items. It almost goes without saying that no inventory records or sales records are kept on an item level. As is the case in most retail stores, the manager or stock clerk periodically inspects the physical stock, makes his subjective forecast of requirements by item, intuitively decides on the ordering quantity, and writes it down in the order book. As in all scientific inventory studies, it was essential to gain some insight into the demand pattern on an item level, its behavior in time, and the possibility or impossibility of forecasting it with sufficient accuracy to be useful in scientific ordering rules. Thus, the first phase of the study consisted in an extensive program of observation and measurement. From a list of all items carried by the store, a sample of about 150 items was selected at random. For each of these items, the stock on hand was measured daily by a physical count. At the same time, new arrivals into stock and orders placed were recorded. The data collection also included remarks on promotions, specials, advertising, and other factors of interest. The program was continued for ten weeks. From the data about daily stock status and arrivals into stock, daily sales by item could be inferred. Sales may not exactly equal demand since there is the possibility of some unobserved shortages between observations. But sales seemed to be the best feasible approximation of demand.

For each item in the sample, the time average of the (positive) dollar inventory was calculated. Items were ranked in decreasing order of sales during the period of observation. Let us define the rank x of a given item as the fraction of all items in the sample that have sales greater than or equal to the sales of the item under consideration. Thus,

$$0 \leq x \leq 1 \tag{12.1}$$

Furthermore, let the function

$$y = \alpha(x) \tag{12.2}$$

designate the fraction of the combined sales of all sample items that is contributed by items with rank less than or equal to x. Similarly, let the function

$$y = \beta(x) \tag{12.3}$$

designate the fraction of the combined (average) dollar inventory of all sample items that is contributed by items with rank less than or equal to x. By definition,

$$0 \leq y \leq 1 \tag{12.4}$$

and

$$\alpha(0) = \beta(0) = 0$$
$$\alpha(1) = \beta(1) = 1 \tag{12.5}$$

The functions $\alpha(x)$ and $\beta(x)$ were determined from the sample data and are shown in Fig. 12-1. As one would expect, the sales buildup is "faster" than the inventory buildup. The function $\beta(x)$ reflects the present informal inventory control.

The notion of rank x can be extended to the whole system comprising all items in the store. It was assumed that the functions $\alpha(x)$ and $\beta(x)$ derived from the sample were representative of the whole system. Thus, letting

I_0 = average inventory investment in the system under present procedures

S_0 = total stores sales per unit time

$I(x)$ = average inventory investment contributed by items with rank less than or equal to x (under present procedures)

$S(x)$ = sales per unit time contributed by items with rank less than or equal to x

we have the following relations:

$$S(x) = S_0 \, \alpha(x) \tag{12.6}$$

$$I(x) = I_0 \, \beta(x) \tag{12.7}$$

The quantities S_0 and I_0 can be obtained from records kept by the store.

Having gained some insight into the demand pattern of individual items and the inventory performance under the present control scheme, we can turn to the critical questions of forecasting and of scientific

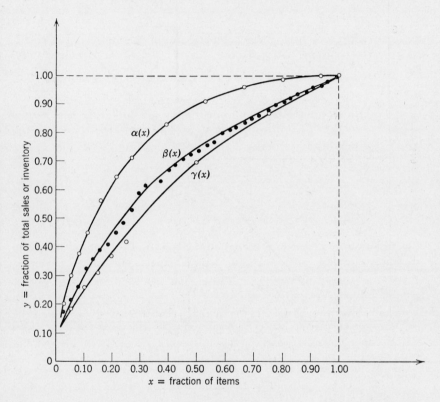

Fig. 12-1. $\alpha(x)$ = *sales;* $\beta(x)$ = *present inventory;* $\gamma(x)$ = *proposed inventory.*

ordering decisions. Ordering decisions will be made with the same frequency as in the present system, say weekly. Assume that orders are placed on Mondays and delivered on Wednesdays. Hence, we will be interested in predicting the demand for an item for a "forecasting interval" of one week and two days. Having learned something about the standard deviation of the forecasting error, we shall make ordering decisions in such a way that the forecast (i.e., expected) inventory level at the end of the next forecasting interval is no less than a specified number of standard deviations.   Forecasts will be based on historical information only.

Let $r_n{}^*$ be the forecast prepared for a given item on the preceding Monday, and let r_n be the corresponding actual sales.   On the follow-

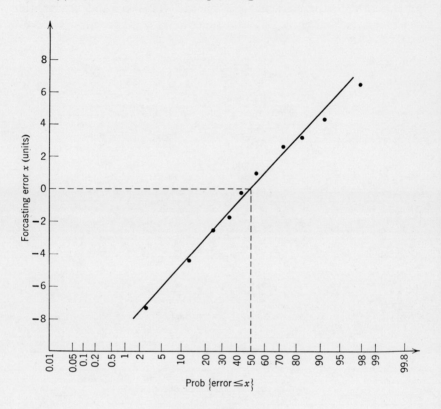

Fig. 12-2. One item.

ing Monday, the next forecast is calculated by the exponential smoothing formula

$$r^*_{n+1} = 0.1r_n + 0.9r_n{}^* \tag{12.8}$$

Given the sales data r_n and the forecaster Eq. 12.8, we can generate simulated forecasts for a certain test period and study the probability distribution of the forecasting error.   Figure 12-2 shows the result for a typical item.   The forecasting error (in physical units) and its cumulative probability of occurrence have been plotted on probability paper.   The graph shows that the error distribution is fairly close to a normal distribution with mean zero (see 50% point). We have an unbiased forecast. It seems desirable to have a simple method of estimating and adjusting the standard deviation σ of the error distribution. Figure 12-3 shows a plot of standard deviations for a sample of items as observed during the test period. The standard deviations are plotted (on log-log paper) as a function of average sales per fore-

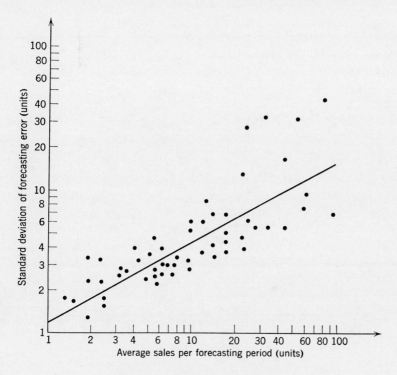

Fig. 12-3. One point per item.

casting period; each point corresponds to one item. A linear relationship appears to be a good approximation to the data. This result suggests the following formula for estimating σ as a function of the forecast r_n^*:

$$\log \sigma = a \log r_n^* + b \qquad (12.9)$$

where the constants a and b are determined from the data exhibited by Fig. 12-3. In summary, demand will be treated as normally distributed with mean r_n^* and standard deviation σ where these quantities have been determined by Eqs. 12.8 and 12.9.

Next, we turn to the ordering rules.   Let A be the stock level of a given item at ordering time, and let q be the ordering quantity.   The expected inventory level at the end of the forecasting period is $A + q - r_n^*$.   If we wish to avoid shortages with a confidence of at least 0.98, we must choose q so that

$$A + q - r_n^* \geq \lambda \sigma \qquad (12.10)$$

where λ is the appropriate number of standard deviations determined from a table of the normal distribution.   We, therefore, choose a reorder point of

$$P = r_n^* + \lambda \sigma \qquad (12.11)$$

and a reorder quantity* of

$$q = (r_n^* + \lambda \sigma - A)^+ \qquad (12.12)$$

Note that both quantities are continuously adjusted on the basis of the latest forecast.   A computer was programmed to simulate the retrospective application of the ordering rule Eq. 12.12 over the entire ten-week period for which data had been collected.†   The computer printed out the average inventory level for each item as well as the occurrences of stockouts.   From these results, the new inventory buildup curve $\gamma(x)$ can be constructed (Fig. 12-1).   Now let us suppose that the simulation has yielded an acceptable level of actual stockouts and an inventory reduction of 20%.   In terms of the whole system this means that implementation of the scientific rules would reduce inventory investment from I_0 to $0.80 I_0$.

Nothing has been said as yet about the cost of the new procedures. Whether or not the new control scheme can be implemented economically, and for how many items, depends on this cost.   At this stage, we must be specific about implementation.   It was assumed that at ordering time the stock clerk would record stock on hand (by item) on a machine-readable media such as a tape or a mark-sense card, and that this could be done at no increase in cost of labor and supplies.   The recorded data are then sent to a computer service center for processing.   Sufficient inventory history and ordering history are stored at the center so that the computer can infer sales rates

---

* For simplicity's sake, we omit considerations of minimum ordering quantities.

† Ideally, there should be no overlap between the test period for the forecaster and the test period for the ordering rule.   The small amount of data forced a compromise in this study.

and calculate forecasts and ordering quantities.   Ordering quantities are printed out, and the inventory records are updated (by item).* The order list is then processed through the usual channels at no increase in cost.   Thus, the only additional cost is the service charge of the computing center.   A more detailed analysis showed that the (weekly) computing cost was a linear function $cn + d$ of the number n of items included in the new control scheme.   (The coefficients c and d can be estimated by programming considerations.)   If N is the total number of items in the system, then

$$x = \frac{n}{N} \tag{12.13}$$

is the percentage of items included in the new control scheme.   By analogy with Eq. 12.7, the total inventory investment in the system may be written

$$I = 0.80 I_0 \gamma(x) + I_0[1 - \beta(x)] \tag{12.14}$$

Equivalently, the inventory reduction may be written as

$$I_0 - I = I_0[\beta(x) - 0.80\gamma(x)]$$
$$= I_0 s(x) \tag{12.15}$$

with an obvious definition of the quantity $s(x)$ which measures the inventory reduction as a fraction of the original inventory I_0.   The annual net savings $S(x)$ are given by the difference of the savings in inventory carrying cost and the cost of computation.   Assuming a 20% carrying charge, we have annual savings of

$$S(x) = 0.20 I_0[\beta(x) - 0.80\gamma(x)] - 52(cNx + d) \tag{12.16}$$

This relation may be used to determine the optimal fraction $\hat{x}$ of items to be controlled; $\hat{x}$ is defined as the value of x that maximizes $S(x)$. We now make the following numerical assumptions which deviate somewhat from the real case:

$$I_0 = 100{,}000 \text{ dollars}$$
$$cN = 40 \text{ dollars/week}$$
$$= 2080 \text{ dollars/year}$$
$$d = 0$$

* Adjustments must be made for discrepancies between quantities ordered and quantities received.   This problem is not discussed here.

The functions $\beta(x)$ and $\gamma(x)$ are given by Fig. 12-1. We can now evaluate the function $S(x)$ as shown in Table 12-1. A graphical representation of the results (Fig. 12-4) shows that the function $S(x)$ has a relatively sharp maximum and that about 30% of the items should be controlled by scientific rules ($\hat{x} \approx .30$).

Table 12-1
Calculation of Savings as a Function of the Percentage of Items Under Scientific Control

x	$\beta(x)$	$\gamma(x)$	$0.80\gamma(x)$	$s(x)$	$0.20I_0s(x)$	$52cNx$	$S(x)$
0	0	0	0	0	0	0	0
0.05	0.20	0.19	0.15	0.05	1,000	104	896
0.10	0.30	0.26	0.21	0.09	1,800	208	1,592
0.15	0.37	0.31	0.25	0.12	2,400	312	2,088
0.20	0.45	0.37	0.30	0.15	3,000	416	2,584
0.25	0.51	0.42	0.34	0.17	3,400	520	2,880
0.50	0.74	0.70	0.56	0.18	3,600	1,040	2,560
0.75	0.89	0.87	0.70	0.19	3,800	1,560	2,240
1.00	1.00	1.00	0.80	0.20	4,000	2,080	1,920

A few comments are in order. It was clear from the beginning of the study that no greater savings could be expected than a few thousand dollars per year ($4000 for a 20% carrying charge, a 20% inventory reduction, and a total inventory of $100,000). It may seem to the reader that these savings are insignificant and that a detailed study was not warranted on the basis of such preliminary calculations. However, the importance of the savings must be judged in light of the very low profit margins in retailing. A few thousand dollars often represent something of the order of 10% of the annual gross profit of a sizable store. Hence, it seemed worth while to investigate in detail whether these savings were indeed obtainable. In the case of a chain operating many stores, the magnitude of savings, if significant, can, of course, be considerable. Furthermore, the 20% carrying charge is probably conservative. We have not given a derivation of this figure. In addition to the opportunity cost of capital tied up in merchandise inventories, one has to consider the opportunity cost of space as another major item. Freed display space could be used to earn extra profit from additional lines of merchandise. The difficult subject of a possible interaction between the displayed inventory of a given item and the sales of that item is beyond the scope of this chapter.

The preceding analysis is confined to "staple items." Nothing has been said about "exceptions handling" of items on promotions, specials, etc.,* and the necessary "smoothing" of sales history when such items are put back on the regular list. Also, nothing has been said about special events affecting *all* items, for example, bad weather, holidays, etc. The final word about the merits of the scientific system cannot

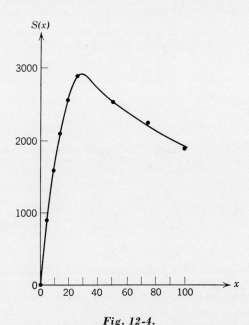

Fig. 12-4.

be spoken until exceptions handling has been integrated into it, and the relative importance of exceptions has been studied. In any event, it would be highly advisable to implement the scientific system for a small sample of items on a test basis before a large-scale implementation is made. It is clear that the order list printed out by the computer must be reviewed and edited by the responsible decision maker, say, the store manager, at least until sufficient experience is gained and confidence in the new system is established. This may create some timing problems especially when the store is located at some distance from the computing center.

May these few selected points serve as a general warning to the reader: dealing with a practical, empirical situation in a scientific manner may be vastly more complicated than may appear from this brief account.

* These items were deleted from the sample.

Bibliography of Inventory Theory
and Its Applications

This bibliography was compiled from the following sources. The journals *Operations Research*, up to and including Vol. 9, No. 1 (Jan.–Feb. 1961), *Management Science*, up to and including Vol. 7, No. 2 (Jan. 1961), and *Naval Research Logistics Quarterly*, up to and including Vol. 7, No. 3 (Sept. 1960) were screened systematically for relevant articles. Volumes 1–6 of *Naval Research Logistics Quarterly* were covered by reference to the subject index published in Vol. 6, No. 4 (Dec. 1959). Articles published in other journals were included as reported in the "Periodicals" section of *Operations Research*. In particular, this should cover most of the relevant publications in *Operational Research Quarterly*, from Vol. 5, No. 3 (Sept. 1954) through Vol. 11, No. 2 (Mar. 1960). The collections of papers in the *Proceedings of the First International Conference on Operational Research* and in *Operations Research for Management*, Vols. I and II, by McCloskey et al., were also screened.

The second major source were existing bibliographies. Specifically the bibliography in *Studies in the Mathematical Theory of Inventory and Production* by Arrow et. al., the bibliography by Gourary et. al., published in *Naval Research Logistics Quarterly*, Vol. 3, No. 4 (Dec. 1960), and Whitin's bibliography in *The Theory of Inventory Management* are mentioned. In screening these bibliographies, the following criteria were applied. Publications written from the viewpoint of economic theory as well as publications in the nontechnical business literature were excluded. Most of the Whitin bibliography falls into these categories. As a rule, abstracts, research memoranda, reports, logistics papers, and the like were also excluded. It was felt that the still relevant portions of these writings have found their way to the technical journals. This excluded about two-thirds of the "Technical Publications" listed in the Gourary bibliography. Further omissions were: strongly overlapping publications by the same author(s) and publications dealing with mathematical and statistical techniques as such, although these techniques are used in inventory theory. The titles which remained after screening showed considerable overlap with the bibliography already compiled directly from the journals. Thus, only about ten additional titles each were contributed by the three bibliographies.

In addition, a number of books and articles from other sources have been included. Each title in this bibliography also appears in at least one of the classified bibliographies in the main body of this book. References in the text always refer to the next classified bibliography.

1. Abrams, I. J., *Contributions to the Stochastic Theory of Inventory*, Dissertation, Berkeley: University of California, 1957.
2. Ackoff, R. L., "Production and Inventory Control in a Chemical Process," *Operations Research*, **3**, No. 3 (Aug. 1955), 319–338.
3. Allen, S. G. "Redistribution of Total Stock Over Several User Locations," *Naval Research Logistics Quarterly*, **5**, No. 4 (Dec. 1958), 337–346.
4. Antosiewiez, H., Hoffman, A., "A Remark on the Smoothing Problem," *Management Science*, **1**, No. 1 (Oct. 1954), 92–95.
5. Arnoff, E. L., Chambers, J. C., "On the Determination of Optimum Reserve Generating Capacity in an Electric Utility System," *Operations Research*, **4**, No. 4 (Aug. 1956), 468–479.
6. Arnoff, E. L., Kania, E. B., Small Day, E., "An Integrated Process Control System at the Cummins Engine Company," *Operations Research*, **6**, No. 4 (July–Aug. 1958), 467–497.
7. Arrow, K. J., Harris, Th., Marschak, J., "Optimal Inventory Policy," *Econometrica*, **19**, No. 3 (July 1951), 250–272.
8. Arrow, K. J., Karlin, S., Scarf, H., *Studies in the Mathematical Theory of Inventory and Production*, Stanford, California: Stanford University Press, 1958.
9. Atwater, T. V. V., Jr., "The Theory of Inventory Management—A Review," *Naval Research Logistics Quarterly*, **1**, No. 4 (Dec. 1954), 295–300.
10. Barber, J. H., *Economic Control of Inventory*, New York: Codex Book Co., 1925.
11. Barnett, H. H., "Initial Provisioning with Confidence," *Operations Research*, **9**, No. 1 (Jan.–Feb. 1961), 127–128.
12. Baumol, W. J., Wolfe, Ph., "A Warehouse Location Problem," *Operations Research*, **6**, No. 2 (Mar.–Apr. 1958), 252–263.
13. Beale, E. M. L., Morton, G., Land, A. H., "Solution of a Purchase-Storage Programme," *Operational Research Quarterly*, **9**, No. 3 (Sept. 1958).
14. Beckman, M. J., Bobkoski, F., "Airline Demand: An Analysis of Some Frequency Distributions," *Naval Research Logistics Quarterly*, **5**, No. 1 (Mar. 1958), 43–52.
15. Beckman, M. J., "An Inventory Model for Repair Parts—Approximations in the Case of Variable Delivery Time," *Operations Research*, **7**, No. 2 (Mar.–Apr. 1959), 256–258.
16. Beckman, M., Muth, R., "An Inventory Policy for a Case of Lagged Delivery," *Management Science*, **2**, No. 2 (Jan. 1956), 145–155.
17. Beckman, M. J., "An Inventory Policy for Repair Parts," *Naval Research Logistics Quarterly*, **6**, No. 3 (Sept. 1959), 209–220.

18. Bellman, R., *Dynamic Programming*, Princeton, New Jersey: Princeton University Press, 1957.

19. Bellman, R., "On a Dynamic Programming Approach to the Caterer Problem—I," *Management Science*, **3**, No. 3 (Apr. 1957), 270–278.

20. Bellman, R., "Dynamic Programming and the Smoothing Problem," *Management Science*, **3**, No. 1 (Oct. 1956), 111–113.

21. Bellman, R., "On the Theory of Dynamic Programming—A Warehousing Problem," *Management Science*, **2**, No. 3 (Apr. 1956), 272–275.

22. Bellman, R., Glicksberg, I., Gross, O. "On the Optimal Inventory Equation," *Management Science*, **2**, No. 1 (Oct. 1955), 83–104.

23. Bishop, G. T., "On a Problem of Production Scheduling," *Operations Research*, **5**, No. 1 (Feb. 1957), 97–103.

24. Bonini, C. P., "Decision Rules for Buffer Inventories," *Management Science*, **4**, No. 4 (July 1958), 457–471.

25. Bowman, E. H., Fetter, R. B., *Analysis for Production Management*, Homewood, Illinois: Richard D. Irwin, 1957.

26. Bowman, E. H., "Production Scheduling by the Transportation Method of Linear Programming," *Operations Research*, **4**, No. 1 (Feb. 1956), 100–103.

27. Brown, Robert G., *Statistical Forecasting for Inventory Control*, New York: McGraw-Hill Book Company, 1959.

28. Brown, W. M., "Measuring Physical Inventories," *Journal of the American Statistical Association*, **43** (Sept. 1948), 377–390.

29. Bryan, J. G., Wadsworth, G. P., Whitin, T. M., "A Multi-Stage Inventory Model," *Naval Research Logistics Quarterly*, **2**, Nos. 1 and 2 (Mar.–June 1955), 25–38.

30. Busby, J. C., "Comments on the Morgenstern Model," *Naval Research Logistics Quarterly*, **2**, No. 4 (Dec. 1955), 225–236.

31. Canning, Sisson and Associates, *EDP Idea Finder, Data Processing Digest 1957 · 1958 · 1959*, Los Angeles, California: Canning, Sisson and Associates, Inc., 1960.

32. Case Institute of Technology, *Proceedings of the Conference on Operations Research in Production and Inventory Control* (Jan. 1954).

33. Chambers, J. C., Bond, A. F., Leake, J. H., "Optimum Lot Sizes for Parts Used in Aircraft Production," *Operations Research*, **6**, No. 3 (May–June 1958), 385–398.

34. Charnes, A., Cooper, W. W., Symonds, G. H., "Cost Horizons and Certainty Equivalents: An Approach to Stochastic Programming of Heating Oil," *Management Science*, **4**, No. 3 (Apr. 1958), 235–263.

35. Charnes, A., Cooper, W. W., Mellon, B., "A Model for Optimizing Production by Reference to Cost Surrogates," *Econometrica*, **23**, No. 3 (July 1955), 307–323.

36. Churchman, C. W., Ackoff, R. L., Arnoff, E. L., *Introduction to Operations Research*, New York: John Wiley & Sons, 1957.

37. Clark, A. J., Scarf, H., "Optimal Policies for a Multi-Echelon Inventory Problem," *Management Science*, **6**, No. 4 (July 1960), 475–490.

38. Clark, Charles E., and Rowe, Alan J., "Inventory Policies and Related Numerical Approximations," *Journal of Industrial Engineering*, **12**, No. 1 (Jan.–Feb. 1960).

39. Clark, C. E., "Mathematical Analysis of an Inventory Case," *Operations Research*, **5**, No. 5 (Oct. 1957), 627–643.

40. Clark, W. V. A., Jr., Richie, W. E., "Economic-Lot Size and Inventory Control," *NACA Bulletin*, **34**, No. 6 (Feb. 1953), 772–782.
41. Collcutt, R. H., Banburry, J., Massey, R. G., Ward, R. A., "A Method of Fixing Desirable Stock Levels, and of Stock Control," *Operational Research Quarterly*, **10**, No. 2 (June 1959).
42. Culbertson, R. W., Holt, Ch. C., "Production Control and Inventory Control Practices and Problems as Evidenced by a Survey of Eleven American Companies," *Middle Atlantic Conference Transactions, American Society for Quality Control*, 1956.
43. Dannerstedt, G., "Production Scheduling for an Arbitrary Number of Periods Given the Sales Forecast in the Form of a Probability Distribution," *Operations Research*, **3**, No. 3 (Aug. 1955), 300–318.
44. Danskin, J. M., "Mathematical Treatment of a Stockpiling Problem," *Naval Research Logistics Quarterly*, **2**, Nos. 1 and 2 (Mar.–June 1955), 99–110.
45. Dantzig, G. B., Ferguson, A. R., "The Allocation of Aircraft to Routes— An Example of Linear Programming Under Uncertain Demand," *Management Science*, **3**, No. 1 (Oct. 1956), 45–73.
46. Dantzig, G. B., "Linear Programming Under Uncertainty," *Management Science*, **1**, No. 3–4 (Apr.–July 1955), 197–206.
47. Dantzig, G., Johnson, S., "A Production Smoothing Problem," *Proceedings of the Second Symposium on Linear Programming*, Washington, D.C., (Jan. 1955).
48. Davis, R. H., "Optimal Inventory Control Decision Rules for a Large Supply System," *Operations Research*, **7**, No. 6 (Nov.–Dec. 1959), 764–782.
49. Day, L. W., "Production Control by Electronics," *Systems*, **19**, No. 4 (July– Aug. 1955), 22–23.
50. De Carlo, C. R., "Application of Electronic Computing Machines to Operations Research Problems," *Operations Research*, **2**, No. 3 (Aug. 1954), 348.
51. DeCarlo, C. R., "The Use of Automatic and Semi-Automatic Processing Equipment in Production and Inventory Control," *Proceedings of the Conference on Operations Research in Production and Inventory Control*, Case Institute of Technology, 1954.
52. Denicoff, M., Fennel, J. P., Solomon, H., "Summary of a Method for Determining the Military Worth of Spare Parts," *Naval Research Logistics Quarterly*, **7**, No. 3 (Sept. 1960), 221–234.
53. Derman, C., Klein, M., "Inventory Depletion Management," *Management Science*, **4**, No. 4 (July 1958), 450–456.
54. Derman, C., Klein, M., "A Note on the Optimal Depletion of Inventory," *Management Science*, **5**, No. 2 (Jan. 1959), 210–213.
55. Derman, C., "A Simple Allocation Problem," *Management Science*, **5**, No. 4 (July 1959), 453–459.
56. Dillon, J. D., "Geographical Distribution of Production in Multiple Plant Operations," *Management Science*, **2**, No. 4 (July 1956), 353–365.
57. Dreyfus, St. E., "An Analytic Solution of the Warehouse Problem," *Management Science*, **4**, No. 1 (Oct. 1957), 99–104.
58. Dreyfus, S. E., "Computational Aspects of Dynamic Programming," *Operations Research*, **5**, No. 3 (June 1957), 409–415.
59. Dvoretzky, A., Kiefer, J., Wolfowitz, J., "The Inventory Problem," *Econometrica*, **20**, No. 2 (Apr. 1952), 187–222; *ibid.*, No. 3 (July 1952), 450–466.

60. Dvoretzky, A., Kiefer, J., Wolfowitz, J., "On the Optimal Character of the (S, s)-Policy in Inventory Theory," *Econometrica*, **21**, No. 4 (Oct. 1953), 586–596.

61. Eagle, A. R., "Distribution of Seasonal Inventory of the Hawaiian Pineapple Company," *Operations Research*, **5**, No. 3 (June 1957), 382–396.

62. Eastman, W. L., "A Note on the Multi-Commodity Warehouse Problem," *Management Science*, **5**, No. 3 (Apr. 1959), 327–331.

63. Eilon, Samuel, "Economic Batch-Size Determination for Multi-Product Scheduling," *Operational Research Quarterly*, **9**, No. 4 (Dec. 1958), 217–227.

64. Eilon, Samuel, "A Note on the Optimal Range," *Management Science*, **7**, No. 1 (Oct. 1960), 56–61.

65. English, J. A., Jerome, E. A., "Statistical Methods for Determining Requirements of Dental Materials," *Naval Research Logistics Quarterly*, **1**, No. 3 (Sept. 1954), 191–199.

66. Evans, G. W., "A Transportation and Production Model," *Naval Research Logistics Quarterly*, **5**, No. 2 (June 1958), 137–154.

67. Fabian, T., Fisher, J. L., Sasieni, M. W., Yardeni, A., "Purchasing Raw Material on a Fluctuating Market," *Operations Research*, **7**, No. 1 (Jan.–Feb. 1959), 107–122.

68. Feeney, G. J., "A Basis for Strategic Decisions on Inventory Control Operations," *Management Science*, **2**, No. 1 (Oct. 1955), 69–82.

69. Feeney, G. J., "The Empty Boxcar Distribution Problem," *Proceedings of the First International Conference on Operational Research*, Bristol, England: John Wright & Sons, 1958, pp. 250–263.

70. Finch, P. D., "Note on a Stock Model," *Operational Research Quarterly*, **9**, No. 1 (Mar. 1958).

71. Flagle, C. D., "Queuing Theory and Cost Concepts Applied to a Problem in Inventory Control," in *Operations Research for Management*, Vol. II, J. F. McCloskey and J. M. Coppinger (eds.), Baltimore: The Johns Hopkins Press, 1956.

72. Foster, F. G., "A Unified Theory for Stock, Storage, and Queue Control," *Operational Research Quarterly* (Sept. 1959).

73. Freeman, R. J., "Ss Inventory Policy with Variable Delivery Time," *Management Science*, **3**, No. 4 (July 1957), 431–434.

74. Friedman, L., "A Competitive Bidding Strategy," *Operations Research*, **4**, No. 1 (Feb. 1956), 104–112.

75. Gaddum, J. W., Hoffman, A. J., Sokolowsky, D., "On the Solution of the Caterer Problem," *Naval Research Logistics Quarterly*, **1**, No. 3 (Sept. 1954), 223–229.

76. Gainen, Leon, "Inventory Control—Exploiting the Electronic Data Processor in the Air Force," *Journal of Industrial Engineering*, **11**, No. 1 (Jan.–Feb. 1959).

77. Galliher, H. P., Morse, Ph. M., Simond, M., "Dynamics of Two Classes of Continuous–Review Inventory Systems," *Operations Research*, **7**, No. 3 (May–June 1959), 362–384.

78. Gani, J., "Problems in the Probability Theory of Storage Systems," *Journal of the Royal Statistical Society*, **19** Series B (1957).

79. Garrett, J. H., "Characteristics of Usage of Supply Items Aboard Naval Ships and the Significance to Supply Management," *Naval Research Logistics Quarterly*, **5**, No. 4 (Dec. 1958), 287–306.

80. Gaver, D. P., Jr., "On Base-Stock Level Inventory Control," *Operations Research*, **7**, No. 6 (Nov.–Dec. 1959), 689–703.

81. Gaver, D. P., Jr., "Renewal-Theoretic Analysis of a Two-Bin Inventory Control Policy," *Naval Research Logistics Quarterly*, **6**, No. 2 (June 1959), 141–164.

82. Geisler, M. A., Karr, H. W., "The Design of Military Supply Tables for Spare Parts," *Operations Research*, **4**, No. 4 (Aug. 1956), 431–442.

83. Geisler, M. A., "A First Experiment in Logistics System Simulation," *Naval Research Logistics Quarterly*, **7**, No. 1 (Mar. 1960), 21–44.

84. Geisler, M. A., "The Simulation of a Large-Scale Military Activity," *Management Science*, **5**, No. 4 (July 1959), 359–368.

85. Geisler, M. A., "Some Principles for a Data-Processing System in Logistics," *Naval Research Logistics Quarterly*, **5**, No. 2 (June 1958), 95–105.

86. Gessford, J., "Scheduling the Use of Water Power," *Management Science*, **5**, No. 2 (Jan. 1959), 179–191.

87. Giffler, B., "Determining an Optimum Reject Allowance," *Naval Research Logistics Quarterly*, **7**, No. 2 (June 1960), 201–206.

88. Gluss, B., "Cost of Incorrect Data in Optimal Inventory Computations," *Management Science*, **6**, No. 4 (July 1960), 491–497.

89. Gluss, B., "An Optimal Inventory Solution for Some Specific Demand Distribution," *Naval Research Logistics Quarterly*, **7**, No. 1 (Mar. 1960), 45–48.

90. Gordon, M. J., Taylor, W. J., "The Condition for Lot Size Production," *Journal of the American Statistical Association*, **51** (Dec. 1956), 627–636.

91. Gourary, M., Lewis, R., Neeland, F., "An Inventory Control Bibliography," *Naval Research Logistics Quarterly*, **3**, No. 4 (Dec. 1956), 295–304.

92. Gourary, M. H., "An Optimum Allowance List Model," *Naval Research Logistics Quarterly*, **3**, No. 3 (Sept. 1956), 177–191.

93. Gourary, M. H., "A Simple Rule for the Consolidation of Allowance Lists," *Naval Research Logistics Quarterly*, **5**, No. 1 (Mar. 1958), 1–6.

94. Grassi, R. C., Gradwohl, A. J., "Obsolescence and Economic-Lot Size," *Journal of Industrial Engineering*, **11**, No. 5 (Sept.–Oct. 1959).

95. Greenwood, J. A., "Issue Priority: Last In First Out (LIFO) vs First In First Out (FIFO) as a Method of Issuing Items from Supply Storage," *Naval Research Logistics Quarterly*, **2**, No. 4 (Dec. 1955), 251–268.

96. Hadley, G., Whitin, T. M., "An Optimal Final Inventory Model," *Management Science*, **7**, No. 2 (Jan. 1961), 179–183.

97. Hadley, G., Whitin, T. M., "Replenishment Times, Service Times, and the Independence Assumption," *Operations Research*, **9**, No. 1 (Jan.–Feb. 1961), 132.

98. Hanssmann, F., Rivett, B. H. P., "Competitive Bidding," *Operational Research Quarterly*, **10**, No. 1 (Mar. 1959), 49–55.

99. Hanssmann, F., "Determination of Optimal Capacities of Service for Facilities With a Linear Measure of Inefficiency," *Operations Research*, **5**, No. 5 (Oct. 1957), 713–717.

100. Hanssmann, F., Hess, S. W., "A Linear Programming Approach to Production and Employment Scheduling," *Management Technology*, Monograph of the Institute of Management Sciences (Jan. 1960), 46–51.

101. Hanssmann, F., "Optimal Inventory Location and Control in Production and Distribution Networks," *Operations Research*, **7**, No. 4 (July–Aug. 1959), 483–498.

102. Harling, J., Bramson, M. J., "Level of Protection Afforded by Stocks (Inven-

tories) in a Manufacturing Industry," *Proceedings of the First International Conference on Operational Research*, Bristol, England: John Wright & Sons, 1958, pp. 372–389.

103. Harper, W. F., McGinnity, W. J., "A Completely Mechanized Material Control System," *NACA Bulletin*, **31**, No. 11 (July 1950), 1371–1377.

104. Henn, C. L., Jr., "Multinational Logistics in the Nuclear Age," *Naval Research Logistics Quarterly*, **4**, No. 2 (June 1957), 117–129.

105. Hertz, D. B., Schaffir, K. H., "A Forecasting Method for Management of Seasonal Style-Goods Inventories," *Operations Research*, **8**, No. 1 (Jan.–Feb. 1960), 45–52.

106. Hetter, F. L., "Navy Stratification and Fractionation for Improvement of Inventory Management," *Naval Research Logistics Quarterly*, **1**, No. 2 (June 1954), 75–78.

107. Heumann, H., Nobis E., "Bestimmung des durchschnittlichen und des wirtschaftlichen Materialverbrauches von Kunststoff bei Kabel- und Leitungsisolierungen," *Metrika*, **2**, No. 3 (1959), 230–238.

108. Heyvaert, A. C., Hurt, A., "Inventory Management of Slow-Moving Parts," *Operations Research*, **4**, No. 5 (Oct. 1956), 572–580.

109. Hoffman, A. J., Jacobs, W., "Smooth Patterns of Production," *Management Science*, **1**, No. 1 (Oct. 1954), 86–91.

110. Hollingshead, E. F., "An Application of Statistical Techniques to Management of Overseas Supply Operations," *Naval Research Logistics Quarterly*, **1**, No. 2 (June 1954), 82–89.

111. Holt, C. C., Modigliani, F., Muth, J. F., "Derivation of a Linear Decision Rule for Production and Employment Scheduling," *Management Science*, **2**, No. 2 (Jan. 1956), 159–177; Holt, C. C., Modigliani, F., Simon, H. A., "Linear Decision Rule for Production and Employment Scheduling," *Ibid.,*, **2**, No. 1 (Oct. 1955), 1–30.

112. Holt, C. C., Simon, H. A., "Optimal Decision Rules for Production and Inventory Control," *Proceedings of the Conference on Operations Research in Production and Inventory Control*, Cleveland, Ohio: Case Institute of Technology, 1954, pp. 73–89.

113. Horne, R. C., "Developing an Engineering Productivity Standard," *Naval Research Logistics Quarterly*, **1**, No. 3 (Sept. 1954), 203–206.

114. Hu, T. C., Prager, W., "Network Analysis of Production Smoothing," *Naval Research Logistics Quarterly*, **6**, No. 1 (Mar. 1959), 17–24.

115. Hugli, W. C., Jr., "Production Planning Through Inventory Control," *Management Technology*, **1**, No. 2 (Dec. 1960), 59–65.

116. Hurni, M., "The Use of Operations Research in Inventory Control," *Proceedings of the Conference on Operations Research*, New York: Society for Advancement of Management (Jan. 1954).

117. Hurst, F. V., Jr., "Evaluating the Adequacy of Airport Parking Lots," *Operations Research*, **3**, No. 4 (Nov. 1955), 522–535.

118. Isaac, E. J., "Note on Selection of Capital Equipment with Uncertain Delivery Date," *Operations Research*, **4**, No. 3 (June 1956), 354–356.

119. Jackson, R. R. P., "A Stock Model," *Operational Research Quarterly*, **7**, No. 4 (Dec. 1956).

120. Jewel, W. S., "Warehousing and Distribution of a Seasonal Product," *Naval Research Logistics Quarterly*, **4**, No. 1 (Mar. 1957), 29–34.

121. Johnson, S. M., "Sequential Production Planning Over Time at Minimum Cost," *Management Science*, **3**, No. 4 (July 1957), 435–437.

122. Karlin, S., "Dynamic Inventory Policy with Varying Stochastic Demands," *Management Science,* **6,** No. 3 (Apr. 1960), 231–258.

123. Karlin, S., "The Structure of Dynamic Programming Models," *Naval Research Logistics Quarterly,* **2** (1955), 285–294.

124. Karr, H. W., Geisler, M. A., "A Fruitful Application of Static Marginal Analysis," *Management Science,* **2,** No. 4 (July 1956), 313–326.

125. Karr, H. W., "A Method of Estimating Spare Parts Essentiality," *Naval Research Logistics Quarterly,* **5,** No. 1 (Mar. 1958), 29–42.

126. Karreman, H. F., "Programming the Supply of a Strategic Material—Part I. A Nonstochastic Model," *Naval Research Logistics Quarterly,* **7,** No. 3 (Sept. 1960), 261–280.

127. Karush, W., "On a Class of Minimum Cost Problems," *Management Science,* **4,** No. 2 (Jan. 1958), 136–155.

128. Karush, W., "A Queuing Model for an Inventory Problem," *Operations Research,* **5,** No. 5 (Oct. 1957), 693–703.

129. Karush, W., Vazsonyi, A., "Mathematical Programming and Employment Scheduling," *Naval Research Logistics Quarterly,* **4,** No. 4 (Dec. 1957), 297–320.

130. Karush, W., Vazsonyi, A., "Mathematical Programming and Service Scheduling," *Management Science,* **3,** No. 2 (Jan. 1957), 140–148.

131. Kawata, T., "Standing Time of a Freight Car in a Marshalling Yard," *Proceedings of the First International Conference on Operational Research,* Bristol England: John Wright & Sons, 1958, pp. 243–250.

132. Kellerer, H., "Lagerumschlag und Lagerdauer in Handelsbetrieben," *Archiv fuer Mathematische Wirtschafts- und Sozialforschung,* **VI** (1940), 120–130.

133. Kendall, D. G., "Some Problems in the Theory of Dams," *Journal of the Royal Statistical Society,* **19** Series B (1957).

134. Klein, M., Rosenberg, L., "Deterioration of Inventory and Equipment," *Naval Research Logistics Quarterly,* **7,** No. 1 (Mar. 1960), 49–62.

135. Klein, M., "Some Production Planning Problems," *Naval Research Logistics Quarterly,* **4,** No. 4 (Dec. 1957), 269–286.

136. Koenigsberg, E., "Production Lines and Internal Storage—A Review," *Management Science,* **5,** No. 4 (July 1959), 410–433.

137. Koopmans, T. C., "Water Storage Policy in a Simplified Hydroelectric System," in *Proceedings of the First International Conference on Operational Research,* Bristol, England: John Wright & Sons, 1958, pp. 193–227.

138. Laderman, J., Littauer, S. B., Weiss, L., "The Inventory Problem," *Journal of the American Statistical Association,* **48,** No. 264 (Dec. 1953), 717–732.

139. Levary, G., "A Pocket-Sized Case Study in Operations Research Concerning Inventory Markdown," *Operations Research,* **4,** No. 6 (Dec. 1956), 738–739.

140. Levinson, H. C., "Experiences in Commercial Operations Research," *Operations Research,* **1,** No. 4 (Aug. 1953), 220–239.

141. Levitan, R. E., "The Optimum Reject Allowance Program," *Management Science,* **6,** No. 2 (Jan. 1960), 172–186.

142. Levy, J., "Further Notes on the Loss Resulting from the Use of Incorrect Data in Computing an Optimal Inventory Policy," *Naval Research Logistics Quarterly,* **6,** No. 1 (Mar. 1959), 25–32.

143. Levy, J., "Loss Resulting from the Use of Incorrect Data in Computing an Optimal Inventory Policy," *Naval Research Logistics Quarterly,* **5,** No. 1 (Mar. 1958), 75–82.

144. Levy, J., "Optimal Inventory Policy When Demand is Increasing," *Operations Research*, **8**, No. 6 (Nov.–Dec. 1960), 861–863.

145. Lieberman, G. J., "Lifo Versus Fifo in Inventory Depletion Management," *Management Science*, **5**, No. 1 (Oct. 1958), 102–105.

146. Little, J. D. C., "The Use of Storage Water in a Hydroelectric System," *Operations Research*, **3**, No. 2 (May 1955), 187–197.

147. Llewellyn, R. W., "Order Sizes for Job Lot Manufacturing," *Journal of Industrial Engineering*, **11**, No. 3 (May–June 1959).

148. Lynch, C. F., "Notes on Applied Analytical Logistics in the Navy," *Naval Research Logistics Quarterly*, **1**, No. 2 (June 1954), 90–102.

149. Macdonald, N., "A Big Inventory Problem and the IBM 702," *Computers and Automation*, **4**, No. 9 (Sept. 1955), 6–12, 38.

150. Magee, J. F., *Production Planning and Inventory Control*, New York: McGraw-Hill, 1958.

151. Manne, A. S., "A Note on the Modigliani-Hohn Production Smoothing Model," *Management Science*, **3**, No. 4 (July 1957), 371–379.

152. Manne, A. S., "Programming of Economic-Lot Sizes," *Management Science*, **4**, No. 2 (Jan. 1958), 115–135.

153. Mansfield, E., Wein, H. H., "A Model for the Location of a Railroad Classification Yard," *Management Science*, **4**, No. 3 (Apr. 1958), 292–313.

154. Marshall, B. O., Jr., Boggess, W. P. II, "The Practical Calculation of Reorder Points," *Operations Research*, **5**, No. 4 (Aug. 1957), 513–517.

155. McDowell, Ian, "The Economical Planning Period for Engineering Works," *Operations Research*, **8**, No. 4 (July–Aug. 1960), 533–542.

156. McShane, R. E., "Science and Logistics," *Naval Research Logistics Quarterly*, **2**, Nos. 1 and 2 (Mar.–June 1955), 1–7.

157. Meade, R., Jr., Fischer, C. A., "Mobile Logistics Support in the 'Passage to Freedom' Operation," *Naval Research Logistics Quarterly*, **1**, No. 4 (Dec. 1954), 258–264.

158. Mellon, W. G., "A Selected, Descriptive Bibliography of References on Priority Systems on Related, Nonprice Allocators," *Naval Research Logistics Quarterly*, **5**, No. 1 (Mar. 1958), 17–27.

159. Mickey, M. R., "A Method for Determining Supply Quantity for the Case of Poisson Distribution of Demand," *Naval Research Logistics Quarterly*, **6**, No. 4 (Dec. 1959), 265–272.

160. Mills, E. S., "Expectations and Undesired Inventory," *Management Science*, **4**, No. 1 (Oct. 1957), 105–109.

161. Mills, E. S. "A Note on the Asymptotic Behavior of an Optimal Procurement Policy," *Management Science*, **5**, No. 2 (Jan. 1959), 204–209.

162. Mills, E. S., McClain, H. G., "A Study of Optimum Assembly Runs," *Operations Research*, **9**, No. 1 (Jan.–Feb. 1961), 30–38.

163. Mills, E. S., "The Theory of Inventory Decisions," *Econometrica*, **25**, No. 2 (Apr. 1957), 222–238.

164. Minas, J. G., Mitten, L. G., "The Hub Operation Scheduling Problem," *Operations Research*, **6**, No. 3 (May–June 1958), 329–345.

165. Mitchell, H. F., "Electronic Computers in Inventory Control," *Proceedings of the Conference on Operations Research in Production and Inventory Control*, Cleveland, Ohio: Case Institute of Technology, 1954.

166. Modigliani, F., Muth, J. F., "Optimum Lot Size Under Uncertainty and Joint Costs," *ONR Research Memorandum*, Nos. 6 and 21.

167. Modigliani, F., Hohn, F. E., "Production Planning Over Time and the Nature of the Expectation and Planning Horizon," *Econometrica*, 23, No. 1 (Jan. 1955), 46–66.

168. Moran, P. A. P., "A Probability Theory of a Dam with a Continuous Release," *The Quarterly Journal of Mathematics*, VII (1956), 130–137.

169. Moran, P. A. P., *The Theory of Storage*, John Wiley & Sons, New York: 1960.

170. Morgenstern, O., "Consistency Problems in the Military Supply System," *Naval Research Logistics Quarterly*, 1, No. 4 (Dec. 1954), 265–281.

171. Morin, F., "Note on an Inventory Problem Discussed by Modigliani and Hohn," *Econometrica*, 23, No. 4 (Oct. 1955), 447–450.

172. Morris, W. T., "Inventorying for Unknown Demand," *Journal of Industrial Engineering*, 11, No. 4 (July–Aug. 1959).

173. Morse, P. M., *Queues, Inventories, and Maintenance*, New York: John Wiley & Sons, 1958.

174. Morse, Ph. M., "Solutions of a Class of Discrete-Time Inventory Problems," *Operations Research*, 7, No. 1 (Jan.–Feb. 1959), 67–78.

175. Naddor, E., "Elements of Inventory Systems," in *Operations Research and Systems Engineering*, C. D. Flagle, W. H. Huggins, R. H. Roy (eds.), The Johns Hopkins Press, 1960, pp. 175–220.

176. Naddor, E., Saltzman, S., "Optimal Reorder Periods for an Inventory System with Variable Costs of Ordering," *Operations Research*, 6, No. 5 (Sept.–Oct. 1958), 676–685.

177. Naddor, E., "Some Models of Inventory and an Application," *Management Science*, 2, No. 4 (July 1956), 299–312.

178. Okun, B., "Design, Test, and Evaluation of an Experimental Flyaway Kit," *Naval Research Logistics Quarterly*, 7, No. 2 (June 1960), 109–136.

179. Oliver, R. M., "The Design and Error Analysis of a Sampled-Data Production and Inventory Control System," *Proceedings of the First International Conference on Operational Research*, Bristol, England: John Wright & Sons, 1958, pp. 228–242.

180. Page, E. S., Muris, S., "The Effect of Departures from Assumption When Manufacturing to a Specification," *Operations Research*, 5, No. 1 (Feb. 1957), 68–74.

181. Paradiso, L. J., "Significance of Inventories in the Current Economic Situation," *Journal of the American Statistical Association*, 43 (Sept. 1948), 361–376.

182. Pessemier, E. A., "The Management of Grocery Inventories in Supermarkets," *Economic and Business Studies Bulletin No. 32*, Pullman, Washington State University, 1960.

183. Petersen, J. W., Geisler, M. A., "The Costs of Alternative Air Base Stocking and Requisitioning Policies," *Naval Research Logistics Quarterly*, 2, Nos. 1 and 2 (Mar.–June 1955), 69–82.

184. Petersen, J. W., Steger, W. A., "Design Change Impacts on Airframe Parts Inventories," *Naval Research Logistics Quarterly*, 5, No. 3 (Sept. 1958), 241–256.

185. Pinkham, R., "An Approach to Linear Inventory-Production Rules," *Operations Research*, 6, No. 2 (Mar.–Apr. 1958), 185–189.

186. Prager, W., "On the Caterer Problem," *Management Science*, 3, No. 1 (Oct. 1955), 15–23.

187. Radell, N. J., "An Operations Research Application in Retailing," *Retail Control*, 28, No. 10 (June 1960), 33–49.

188. Reiter, St., "A Note on Surrogates for Uncertain Decision Problems," *Econometrica*, **25**, No. 2 (Apr. 1957), 339–345.

189. Rinehart, R. F., "Effects and Causes of Discrepancies in Supply Operations," *Operations Research*, **8**, No. 4 (July–Aug. 1960), 543–564.

190. Rogers, J., "A Computational Approach to the Economic-Lot Scheduling Problem," *Management Science*, **4**, No. 3 (Apr. 1958), 264–291.

191. Rosenblatt, M., "An Inventory Problem," *Econometrica*, **22**, No. 2 (Apr. 1954), 244–247.

192. Russell, M. E., "A UNIVAC System of Material Control," *Computers and Automation*, **4**, No. 4 (Apr. 1955), 15.

193. Sadowski, W., "A Few Remarks on the Assortment Problem," *Management Science*, **6**, No. 1 (Oct. 1959), 13–24.

194. Salveson, M. E., "A Problem in Optimal Machine Loading," *Management Science*, **2**, No. 3 (Apr. 1956), 232–260.

195. Saposnik, R., Smith, V. L., "Allocation of a Resource to Alternative Probabilistic Demands: Transport-Equipment Pool Assignments," *Naval Research Logistics Quarterly*, **6**, No. 3 (Sept. 1959), 193–207.

196. Sasieni, M., "Dynamic Programming and Inventory Problems," *Operational Research Quarterly*, **11**, Nos. 1–2 (Mar.–June 1960).

197. Savage, I. R., "Cycling," *Naval Research Logistics Quarterly*, **3**, No. 3 (Sept. 1956), 163–175.

198. Schaefer, Ch. G., "Electronic Brain Manages Sperry Inventory," *Aeronautical Purchasing* (Sept. 1958), 19–21.

199. Schild, A., "On Inventory, Production, and Employment Scheduling," *Management Science*, **5**, No. 2 (Jan. 1959), 157–168.

200. Schneider, E., "Absatz, Produktion und Lagerhaltung bei einfacher Produktion," *Archiv fuer mathematische Wirtschafts- und Sozialforschung*, **4**, No. 1 (1938).

201. Schupack, M. B., "Economic-Lot Sizes with Seasonal Demand," *Operations Research*, **7**, No. 1 (Jan.–Feb. 1959), 45–57.

202. Shaunty, J. A., Hare, V. C., Jr., "An Airline Provisioning Problem," *Management Technology*, **1**, No. 2 (Dec. 1960), 66–84.

203. Sherman, S., "Comment on Smooth Patterns of Production," *Management Science*, **1**, No. 3–4 (Apr.–July 1955), 271.

204. Simon, H. A., "On the Application of Servomechanism Theory in the Study of Production Control," *Econometrica*, **20**, No. 2 (Apr. 1952), 247–268.

205. Simon, H. A., Holt, C. C., "The Control of Inventory and Production Rates— A Survey," *Operations Research*, **2**, No. 3 (Aug. 1954), 289–301.

206. Simon, H. A., "Dynamic Programming Under Uncertainty with a Quadratic Criterion Function," *Econometrica*, **24**, No. 1 (Jan. 1956), 74–81.

207. Simpson, J. R., "A Formula for Decisions on Retention or Disposal of Excess Stock," *Naval Research Logistics Quarterly*, **2**, No. 3 (Sept. 1955), 145–156.

208. Simpson, K. F., Jr., "In-Process Inventories," *Operations Research*, **6**, No. 6 (Nov.–Dec. 1958), 863–873.

209. Simpson, K. F., Jr., "A Theory of Allocation of Stocks to Warehouses," *Operations Research*, **7**, No. 6 (Nov.–Dec. 1959), 797–805.

210. Solomon, H., Denicoff, M., "Simulations of Alternative Allowance List Policies," *Naval Research Logistics Quarterly*, **7**, No. 2 (June 1960), 137–150.

211. Solomon, M. J., "Optimum Operation of a Complex Activity Under Con-

ditions of Uncertainty," *Operations Research*, **2**, No. 4 (Nov. 1954), 419–432.

212. Solomon, M. J., "A Scientific Method for Establishing Reorder Points," *Naval Logistics Quarterly*, **1**, No. 4 (Sept. 1954), 289–294.

213. Solomon, M. J., "The Use of an Economic-Lot Range in Scheduling Production," *Management Science*, **5**, No. 4 (July 1959), 434–442.

214. Steers, N. I., Jr., "A Past System of Inventory Control," *NACA Bulletin*, **33**, No. 6 (Feb. 1952), 753–760.

215. Sussams, J. E., "The Surplus Stock Formula," *Operational Research Quarterly*, **8**, No. 3 (Sept. 1957).

216. Sutherland, W. H., "Graphical Selection of Military Supply Tables," *Operations Research*, **6**, No. 5 (Sept.–Oct. 1958), 775–777.

217. Suzuki, G., "Procurement and Allocation of Naval Electronic Equipments," *Naval Research Logistics Quarterly*, **4**, No. 1 (Mar. 1957), 1–7.

218. Theil, H., "A Note on Certainty Equivalence in Dynamic Planning," *Econometrica*, **25**, No. 2 (Apr. 1957), 346–349.

219. Vassian, H. J., "Application of Discrete Variable Servo Theory to Inventory Control," *Operations Research*, **3**, No. 3 (Aug. 1955), 272–282.

220. Vazsonyi, A., "Comments on a Paper by Karush," *Operations Research*, **8**, No. 3 (May–June 1960), 418–420.

221. Vazsonyi, A., "Economic-Lot-Size Formulas in Manufacturing," *Operations Research*, **5**, No. 1 (Feb. 1957), 28–44.

222. Vazsonyi, A., "Operations Research in Production Control—A Progress Report," *Operations Research*, **4**, No. 1 (Feb. 1956), 19–32.

223. Vazsonyi, A., *Scientific Programming in Business and Industry*, New York: John Wiley & Sons, 1958.

224. Vazsonyi, A., "The Use of Mathematics in Production and Inventory Control: I. Theory of Parts Listing. II. Theory of Scheduling," *Management Science*, **1**, No. 1 (Oct. 1954), 70–85; *ibid.*, Nos. 3 and 4 (Apr.–July 1955), 207–223.

225. Ventura, E., "Sur l'utilisation des intégrales de contour dans les problèmes de stocks et de délais d'attente," *Management Science*, **6**, No. 4 (July 1960), 423–443.

226. Wagner, H. M., Whitin, T. M., "Dynamic Problems in the Theory of the Firm," *Naval Research Logistics Quarterly*, **5**, No. 1 (Mar. 1958), 53–74.

227. Wagner, H. M., Whitin, T. M., "Dynamic Version of the Economic-Lot-Size Model," *Management Science*, **5**, No. 1 (Oct. 1958), 89–96.

228. Wagner, H. M., "A Postscript to 'Dynamic Problems in the Theory of the Firm,'" *Naval Research Logistics Quarterly*, **7**, No. 1 (Mar. 1960), 7–12.

229. Watkins, H. R. W., "The Cost of Rejecting Optimum Production Runs," *Operational Research Quarterly*, **8**, No. 4 (Dec. 1957).

230. Whitin, T. M., "Erich Schneider's Inventory Control Analysis," *Operations Research*, **2**, No. 3 (Aug. 1954), 329–334.

231. Whitin, T. M., "Inventory Control and Price Theory," *Management Science*, **2**, No. 1 (Oct. 1955), 61–68.

232. Whitin, T. M., "Inventory Control Research: A Survey," *Management Science*, **1** (1954–1955), 32.

233. Whitin, T. M., "On the Span of Central Direction," *Naval Research Logistics Quarterly*, **1**, No. 1 (Mar. 1954), 16–24.

234. Whitin, T. M., *The Theory of Inventory Management*, Princeton, New Jersey: Princeton University Press, 1953.

235. Whitin, T. M., Youngs, J. W. T., "A Method for Calculating Optimal Inventory Levels and Delivery Time," *Naval Research Logistics Quarterly*, **2**, No. 3 (Sept. 1955), 157–174.

236. Wilson, A. H., Finn, W. R., "Improvise or Plan?," *Naval Research Logistics Quarterly*, **4**, No. 4 (Dec. 1957), 263–267.

237. Winters, P. R., "Forecasting Sales by Exponentially Weighted Moving Averages," *Management Science*, **6**, No. 3 (Apr. 1960), 324–342.

238. Young, W. M., "Priorities in the Naval Supply System," *Naval Research Logistics Quarterly*, **1**, No. 1 (Mar. 1954), 16–24.

239. Youngs, J. W. T., Geisler, M. A., Brown, B. B., *The Prediction of Demand for Aircraft Spare Parts Using the Method of Conditional Probabilities*, Santa Monica, California: Rand Corporation (Research Memorandum RM-1413), Jan. 1955.

240. Youngs, J. W. T., Geisler, M. A., Mirkovich, A. R., *Confidence Intervals for Poisson Parameters in Logistics Research*, Santa Monica, California: Rand Corporation (Research Memorandum RM-1357), Sept. 1954.

Index

Boldface page numbers indicate longer sections where subject is treated in more detail or repeatedly referred to.

DATE DUE